Domestic Rabbits
&
Their Histories

• Breeds of the World •

By

BOB D. WHITMAN

For additional copies or more information, please contact the author at:
website = **http://www.rarebitsandpieces.com**
e-mail = **rarebits@ev1.net**

ISBN 1-58597-275-4

Library of Congress Control Number: 2004095299

A division of Squire Publishers, Inc.
4500 College Blvd.
Leawood, KS 66211
1/888/888/7696
www.leatherspublishing.com

ACKNOWLEDGEMENTS

The author would like to especially give a big THANK YOU to the following people and organizations, who have assisted to make this book become a reality, for without you, I don't believe that it would have been at all possible and certainly not so quickly:

UNITED STATES — Ingeborg Whitman, Clint Whitman, Scott Whitman, Eddie Patten, Shaun Richardson, Carla Clifton, Mark Berhens, Glen Carr, American Rabbit Breeders Association, Inc., Oren Reynolds, ARBA's *Domestic Rabbits,* ARBA's Hall of Fame Library, Cindy Wickizer, Carrol Hooks, Barbi Brown, Bert Binks, Jack Binks, Sharon Odegar, Dick Gehr, Kathleen Blair, Loretta Ann Bowman, Tonna Thomas, Frank Zaloudek, Sue Turner, Doug King, Linda Thompson, Kathy Gustafson, Betty Chu, Candy Haenszel, Edna Shaler, *Field & Stream,* Leslie Ardison, Linda Telega, Alan Platt, Claudia Sweley, Dr. Steven D. Lukefahr, Mollie Eulitt and Margaret Dalke of Leathers Publishing, and Warren Loose.

ALGERIA — Nacera Zerrouki.

AUSTRALIA — Margaret Levin and Warren Hill.

AUSTRIA — Marina Caldwell and Reinhard Danninger.

BELGIUM — Reginald Deyaert, Het Belgisch Raskonijn vzw and Yolanda Bortels.

CZECHOSLOVAKIA — Lenka Kadeoabkova.

DENMARK — Sofie Lundus, Anton Dam Nielsen and Gerner Rasmussen.

ENGLAND — Judy Le Marchant, Patricia Gaskin, *Fur & Feather* and Staff, Peter Smith, British Rabbit Council, Jo Jalland, Veronica Mayhew, North East Lincolnshire Council, John Wilson and Museum of Natural History, London.

FRANCE — Pierre Periquet, Jean-Claude Periquet, Jacques Czsechan, Dr. Francois Lebas and Federation Francaise de Cuniculture.

GERMANY — Zentralverband Deutscher Rassekaninchenzuecher.

HUNGARY — Professor Zsolt Szendro.

NEW ZEALAND — Sitereh Schouten, Chris Schouten, Beverley McCulloch, Michael Trotter, Nick Torr, Wayne Costello, Dr. Karen Nicoll, Michael Willis and Pauline Taylor.

SCOTLAND — Miss Meg Brown.

SWEDEN — Mirjam Gille

SWITZERLAND — Ursula Glauser and Schweizerischer Rassenkaninchenzucht Verband.

And last, but not least, the World-Wide Web!

DEDICATION

Ingeborg Whitman.

Oren Reynolds.

Meg Brown.

Sitereh Schouten.

Rabbit Show winners at the Crystal Palace, 1872.

DEDICATION

It gives me great pleasure to be able to dedicate this book to four very special people — without them, I don't believe that this book would have ever become a reality. Their guidance, encouragement, support and mentor hood, kept me going through the entire process.

INGEBORG WHITMAN — My mother, who bought me my first rabbit in 1960, when I was six. I suppose I came by my love of rabbits honestly, as her father kept rabbits in Germany, for meat and wool, she being the chosen one to cut the green foods for the rabbits in the nearby fields. She always encouraged me in most all my life's projects and has been a wonderful ear throughout the entire process of writing this book in our daily conversations.

OREN REYNOLDS — My American mentor. When you're a kid and you hear of these great people and then are finally able to meet them, you're in awe. Such was the case with Oren Reynolds whom I first met in early 1969. He was a great rabbit person then and still remains so today — after all, I am speaking of "Mr. ARBA." Oren has dedicated his life to the betterment of our organization and the industry, and at 98 years young is the world's oldest active rabbit judge ever.

MEG BROWN — My international mentor. When I was searching for English Lops, I was put in contact with Meg Brown of Scotland in 1971. She sent over a pair of French and English Lops as a gift. It was Meg who stirred my interest in rabbit histories, when she helped me with a senior high school thesis, "History of Rabbit Raising in England," which caused me to catch the book collecting fever that continues to-day. No doubt the greatest woman of rabbits who has ever lived.

SITEREH SCHOUTEN — Sitereh shipped my first Enderby Island rabbits in 2003, and greatly assisted my research to prove that the rabbits did not evolve from the Champagne D'Argent, which had previously been so well documented. A great friendship has been forged between Texas and New Zealand, and she encouraged me to write a book on the amazing rabbits of Enderby Island. Well, that book hasn't happened yet, but this one did!

FOREWORD

Bob Whitman's lifetime passion has been collecting historical information on domestic rabbits and the people instrumental in their development. His research references the origins and evolution of rabbit breeds around the world. Each breed and the people who helped to promote them are carefully documented in his book. *Domestic Rabbits & Their Histories* is a valuable resource for information which has existed in other publications, but has not previously been collected into one volume. This new book dispels some of the common myths about the origins of breeds of rabbits. Almost three-quarters of the illustrations and pictures in the book have not been seen in over seven decades or more and have never been collected together in one book. With this documentation, Bob creates a picture of how, why and where rabbit breeds have evolved. While some breeds of rabbits have become extinct, others have evolved, and a few have stayed the same.

Bob Whitman began raising rabbits at an early age when his mother gave his brother and him their first pet rabbits. That little rabbit, Snow White, scoured and died within two days and Bob adopted his brother's rabbit. As a fourth grader, he took this now 12-pound rabbit to school for show and tell. One of the assignments given by his teacher was library research on determining the breed of rabbit and its care. That small assignment was the catalyst for a lifetime of interest. Across the railroad tracks from where he lived was an elderly man who had rows of rabbits in cages. Bob remembers being fascinated with all of those rabbits and wanting to know more about all of them.

Bob began collecting stories and memorabilia from some of the founders of early American rabbit clubs. He gathered those stories and kept that history either in the original publications or with pictures and written notes. When other individuals started asking him if he had research material on early origins of rabbit topics, he decided to compile the information into this reference. Not only has he been interested in the research of these rabbits, but he also tries to preserve and breed some of the rarest breeds available in various parts of the world.

My earliest memories are of Bob as a teenager in 1969 at the Calgary, Alberta, Canada ARBA Convention. He would follow the founders of the American Rabbit Breeders Association, asking them questions. Bob later told me that they would tell him to go and play with some of the youth his own age just to get some peace from his steady stream of questions. Reverend Wayne Willmann, past ARBA president, and James Blyth, past Secretary of the association, took the time to show him some of the early records and papers of the association. While still a teenager, he had tried to start an archive for the association. I do not know if Bob recorded all of the stories that he heard, but the words of some of those individuals echo in this book.

Interest in rabbits continued to remain strong in Bob's world. He has been a member of the American Rabbit Breeders Association since 1968. Bob Whitman can be remembered as the 1970 American Rabbit Breeders Association Rabbit King, and was the person who introduced the Blanc de Hotot into the ARBA standard in 1979. Throughout his life he continued to collect rabbit information and memorabilia from his travels all over the world. He boasts that there is not an empty wall in his house — they are all filled with pictures, prints and drawings of rabbits.

As you read the history of the Enderby Island rabbits, imagine sailing with the early rabbits on the ship that was to deposit them on unknown shores. The plan to make a food source for castaways turned into an epic journey of discovery. While other writers might have focused on the adventures of the ship, Bob chose to focus on the introduction and influence that these rabbits had on the environment. He also chose to focus on preserving this part of history by preserving the animals themselves.

Domestic Rabbits & Their Histories is **the** reference for those interested in the evolution of rabbits throughout history.

—*Cindy Wickizer*
American Rabbit Breeders Association
President and ARBA Hall of Fame Member

CONTENTS

 HAPTER I

RABBIT BREEDS OF YESTERYEAR
AND NOW EXTINCT

Each and every day species, whether flora or fauna, become extinct somewhere in the world, but mostly in our tropical rainforest, due in most part to habitat destruction. It is no different with our various breeds of domestic livestock. Did you know that in the last one hundred years, just over one thousand breeds of livestock have been reported to have become extinct? Studies by various rare breed conservation organizations have reported that domestic breeds are vanishing at the alarming rate of two per week throughout the world. In grave danger are many poultry breeds: chickens, ducks, geese and turkeys, followed by sheep, goats and swine. Our domestic breeds of rabbits are rather the lucky ones as, being the lovable creatures they are, they have found a huge following throughout the world.

In the United States, we have the American Rabbit Breeders Association, with 30,000-plus members, and most all European countries have strong memberships in their national rabbit organization to keep all the breeds alive and in reasonably good numbers. Certainly some breeds have larger followings than others, but still, with over 180 different rabbit breeds worldwide, there is certainly a type rabbit to suit everyone's fancy.

Serious rabbit keeping, on the exhibition level, has been around just over 150 years, with the first rabbit club being formed in England in 1840. As other breeds were developed, so did the interest of man in keeping rabbits for pleasure and profit. When one considers all the breeds of rabbits today, there aren't many that have realized the unlucky title of "Extinct." Because of the plasticity of the domestic rabbit, most extinct breeds can be recreated, if one is willing to dedicate themselves to such a project.

Several extinct breeds have already been recreated, especially in England, over the past thirty years.

From the list of extinct breeds, one can easily see that some breeds died out, because of a preferred change in weight classification: Giant Blanc de Hotot, Giant Blue Beveren, Heavy Weight Belgian Hare, etc., while some gave their genes to create varieties of popular breeds we have today, such as the Standard Rex. Other breeds just simply died out due to breeder preferences. I'm quite certain that this listing of extinct breeds is by no means complete, and I would be delighted to hear from anyone who may offer additional documentation of other rabbit breeds from throughout the world.

Alaska Red Fox — USA
Andalusian — France
Adoldro — Holland
Beaver — UK
Belgian Giant (Red Giants) — Belgium and USA
Black Siberian Hare — USA
Blanc de l'Oural — France
Blanc de Chauny — France
Blue Imperial — UK and USA
Blue Squirrel — USA
Brabancon Blues — Various
Bronze Sable — UK
Chifox — UK
German Rabbit — Germany
Giant Blanc de Hotot — France
Giant Blue Beveren
Golden Fawn — USA
Gouda — USA
Heavy Weight Belgian Hare — USA
Heavy Weight Havana — USA
Hooded (Russian Rabbit) — Russia
Husumer — Germany
Land Kanichen — Germany
Little Gray Swiss — Switzerland
Lotharinger Risen — Germany
Lorain — USA and UK

Kai Gai — USA
Mini Dwarf — France
Nubian — UK
Old English Red — UK
One Eared — UK
Patagonian — Europe and UK
Piruvian — USA
Prussian — UK
Rex Breeds
    Beveren Rex — USA
    Blue Vienna Rex — USA
    Chinchilla
        American Chinchilla Rex — USA
        Giant Chinchilla Rex — USA
        Standard Chinchilla Rex — USA
    Flemish Giant Rex — USA
    Havana Rex — USA
    Heavyweight Havana Rex — USA
    Himalayan Rex — USA
    Lilac Rex — USA
    New Zealand Rex — USA
    Polish Rex — USA
    Sable Rex — USA
    Silver Marten Rex — USA
Rouennais (Bulldog) — France
Sherman's Long Hair — USA
Sherman's Short Hair — USA
Siberian (Moscow Rabbit) — Russia
Silver Black Giant — USA
Silver Glavcot — UK
Sitka — UK
Swan Rabbit — UK
Trent — USA
Wachtebeke — Belgium
White Alaska — USA and UK
White Blue Eyed Riverias — USA
White of Teruren — Belgium

ALASKA RED FOX

alter B. Garland, of North Canton, Ohio, developed the Alaska Red Fox, during the late 1920s (see Silver Fox). Walter Garland created the Silver Fox which had been recognized as a breed in 1925, and there is very little doubt that his Silver Fox were in the genetic makeup of his new creation, as the standard for the breed called for either silvering or white hairs to be evenly distributed throughout the body, including the head, ears and legs. The color was to be a reddish tan over the top of the back and carried as far down the side as possible into a slate blue on lower sides and belly, which would tell use that the breed was not actually a red, but a tortoise shell. The fur also was just as his Silver Fox breed, to stand straight up when stroked from rump to head. Weight were 9 pounds for bucks and does at 10 pounds. Havanas could have easily played a roll in the breeds development, as Garland kept both the standard Havana, as well as the Heavyweight Havanas. Alaska Rex Fox were given a working standard by the Standards Committee of the American Rabbit and Cavy Breeders Association, Inc. during the St. Louis, Missouri Convention of October 9th to 13th, 1931. This breed was never officially recognized in America and has long ago become extinct.

ANDALUSIAN

ndalusians were the largest rabbits known (surely the French had heard about the Flemish Giants) in the middle of the 1800s, being a native of Spain. They were brought into France, mainly in the area of Paris and were known as the "Ram Rabbit," because of their heads being very large, and its forehead quite rounded. Ears were also large and hanging in the same fashion as the Half-Lop of the same era. The fur is said to have been smooth and lustrous and was a russet gray color (Agouti). Good specimens of the breed weighed in at 12 to 20 pounds.

The Andalusian breed was only a rabbit for the wealthy of the time, as breeding stock was extremely expensive. Those that were fortunate enough to own the Andalusians were quite reluctant to sell any of their stock, other than for very high prices. At eight to ten weeks old, the breed weighed as much as the normal breeds at maturity. The breed has long been extinct, except in the fact that this breed was also used to create the French Lop.

APOLDRO

Apoldros are a product of the Netherlands, created by Mr. C.H. Cornelissen de Beer, using Chinchilla and Havanas to create the breed in the early 1920s. The breed is now extinct

BEAVER

eavers were brought into England from France by a Mrs. Lacy-Hulbert; large brown rabbits were at the time called Castorex (note it is spelled with one "r"), by the French. It was probable that the Castorex had a common origin with the Havanas, but had been bred up in size for the restaurant trade. Brown rabbits were extremely popular in Britain at this time. Lacy-Hulberts' association with rabbits was extremely short lived, having relinquished her rabbit-breeding activities that same year and gave two does to Mr. Fairfoul, who after trying several matings, found one that he considered right. Fairfoul, showed these to Mrs. Lacy-Hulbert, who christened the breed as Beavers. These animals were shown at the Crystal Palace Show in 1924, and the *Daily Mail* commented that they greatly resembled the real Beaver. Mr. Fairfoul advertised his Beavers, but they were met with only a limited popularity. The Beavers were adopted by the British Fur Rabbit Society and given a standard in 1928. These nine-pound large Havana colored rabbits are now long ago extinct.

BELGIAN GIANT

elgian Giants are, of course, from Belgium, where they were being bred in the early 1900s, reported to be a cross of the Belgian Hare and Flemish Giant. Before the First World War, they were also found in France, where they were known as the "Red Giants," with a standard weight of 17 and 18 pounds. These rabbits were brought to America in July 1900 by a Mr. Fred H. Dewey, of Princess Anne, Maryland, formerly of Westfied, Massachusetts. Dewey writes of these large animals, "These Giants I had were red, varying from somewhat light to a rich maroon shade, the dark families keeping dark; however, as types were very well fixed by careful fanciers ... These hares were magnificent, noble animals, beautiful in color and huge in body; their heads were large and round like cats; ears were deeply and sharply laced and the ticking was wonderfully fine and neat. When they laid out on their sides, they looked like great dogs." Fred Dewey originally wrote of these Giants as a form of Giant Belgian Hares in August of 1900, upon returning to the America with these animals (see Belgian Hare). These massive rabbits are now extinct, but could well have been introduced into Flemish Giants in those early years, but that we will never know.

BLACK SIBERIAN HARE

lack Siberian Hares were known both in the United States and Europe. Actually on American soil the breed came in from Canada, where they were developed. Europeans could not pinpoint the origin of the breed, with conflicting claims that they came from the Alaska breed, while others said they were the product of Black Russians which were exhibited at the Jardin d'Acclimatation in Paris during the 1880s. Other claims place the breed's ancestors as the Sitka rabbit, developed in England. We do know, however, that it is not related to the extinct Siberian, which was a wool breed with Himalayan markings.

Charles S. Gibbons, writing on the breed in 1920, states, "Why the National Breeders & Fanciers Association of America, Inc., should include the Black Siberian in its new standard is something we are all interested in at the present time. To begin with, this writer has fought this breed or (of) rabbits from the start, because it was first started with a fake cur and a lot of fake propaganda that was very misleading to an unsuspecting public, and did a great amount of harm. On the first literature sent out by the Black Siberian breeders, we saw poor old African Chief, the famous old Belgian Hare buck, all dyed black and showing the public the type of rabbits they were breeding. The description was entirely different from the cut, for they described a giant rabbit and not one with hare type at all. The writer has enjoyed some very interesting correspondence along the lines of the Black Siberian Hare, standard with both Mr. Bradley of Victoria, B.C. and Mr. Evans of Wyoming, Ontario (Canada), both registrars and officers of our organization."

Black Siberian Hare, circa 1924.

Black Siberian Hares were recognized in America in 1924. Canadians were buying loads of Black Flemish Giants from the Americans. The early Black Siberian Hares that were shipped back to the United States were basically underweight Flemish in the early days, but later importations, greatly improved. The breed had more distinctive lines, much finer in bone and a racier build which was suggestive of the Belgian Hare. Fur quality was also greatly improved, which leads one to believe that Belgian Hares had been introduced into the genetic makeup. Black Siberian Hares were not to weigh over 9 pounds in the bucks and not over 10 pounds for the does. The coat was to be sparking jet black. The breed became extinct by the mid-1930s and dropped from the standards. The breed is also extinct in Europe, where it never appeared to be very popular.

BLANC A L'OURAL

France is the native home of the Blanc A L'Oural, which was developed at the beginning of the twentieth century by a M. Petrequin. This large white rabbit with red eyes is now extinct, having been mentioned for the last time in the 1927 Book of Standards in France. The fur was dense and lustrous, and the breed weighed in at 4 to 5 kg or 9 to 11 lbs.

BLANC DE CHAUNY

Little is known of the now extinct breed from France called the Blanc de Chauny. It was a large white rabbit with a dark eye, not pink, and was mostly bred for the fur industry, as the fur took readily to dyeing and printing. The breed was largely kept in the North

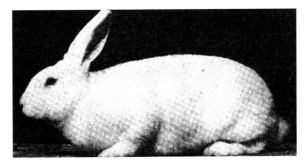

Blanc de Chauny of France.
Photo courtesy Meg Brown, Scotland.

East and Champagne region of France and believed to have been bred from the Champagne de Argent.

BLUE IMPERIAL

 ngland is the native home of the Blue Imperial, which was developed by Miss Mabel Illingworth, beginning in 1896. It should be noted that this young woman is the first female to ever develop a breed of rabbit anywhere in the world, and during her time was considered the greatest woman rabbit fancier ever. For many years Miss Illingworth would not divulge the secrets of how the Imperial was developed, but once the breed was firmly established in Britain, she released the methods in the mid-1920s.

In 1896, she mated a Blue English Lop to a Sooty Fawn (Tortoiseshell) English Lop. The young from their progeny was bred to a White Angora to see what

Miss Mabel Illingworth with Blue Imperial, circa 1905.

hidden color would be revealed. This method of introducing white had long been used by breeders as a means of discovering from the color of the ensuing young the dominant colors behind them. In the second generation appeared some self-blues of a beautiful dark shade with long erect ears. The blue does from this cross were mated to a heavily marked blue-fawn Dutch buck, and later a self-blue Dutch buck was used. Various other matings to improve the color would follow, until the desired specimen was obtained.

Mabel Illingworth exhibited the Blue Imperials for the first time at the famous Crystal Palace Show in London in 1903. They were thought by

Imported Blue Imperial buck to America, circa 1917.

some of the fanciers of the day to be nothing more than the Blue Beveren, which had just been imported into England.

A doe that appeared in the second year of experimenting was given the name of "Blue Pussie." This rabbit showed all the outstanding features that Illingworth wanted in the breed. Blue Pussie's color was considered the idea as was her type, and she was used extensively in the breeding program to fix the desired traits. The doe was named Blue Pussie, because it was due to the blue breeds of cats that Illingworth's mother raised, in which she conceived the idea of producing a blue rabbit. Blue Pussie had a rather remarkable history, raising her last litter when almost eight years old, and was over ten years old when she died.

The color of the Blue Imperial was a dark-slate blue, with a bright appearance and with a slight suggestion of purple. The type was rather mandoline, and were to be under seven pounds in weight; otherwise they were disqualified.

Mabel Illingworth shipped Blue Imperials to America about 1915, which were recognized by the National Pet Stock Association. The breed never quite caught on in America, due largely to the popular American Blue, which was a much larger animal. Blue Imperials were dropped from the standards by 1934. The breed has long become extinct in America, as well as in England.

BLUE SQUIRREL

This beautiful and uniquely colored Chinchilla was developed in America by Marcellus W. Meek. Blue Squirrels were appearing in litters of the American Chinchillas of an unimpeachable ancestry. The color was isolated and named by Meek in 1924, because of the color resemblance to the genuine Russian squirrel. There is a British and Dutch version simply called Squirrels, but these were much smaller than the Blue Squirrels of the United States. Mature bucks should weigh 9 pounds (4.08 kg) and does 10 pounds (4.53 kg). The Blue Squirrels have long been extinct.

BRABANCON BLUE

rabancon Blues were an imported breed to the United States and recognized by the National Breeders and Fanciers Association in 1920. It is a smaller version of the Blue Beveren. As to whether it was imported from Belgium or England, this is not known, but the Brabancon Blues reached England in 1915. The American standard for the breed is rather short and sweet: Color, rich brilliant slate blue, not pale or lavender. Shape body, compact, broad across back and loins, and slightly arched. Weight, 6 to 7 pounds." Now it should be noted that it was from the Brabancon that the Dutch rabbit breed evolved. The term Brabancon was originally used to designate the type of meat rabbit common to the province of Di Anvers, part of Limbourg and the northern Brabant in Belgium. Here this variety was highly esteemed as one of the best market breeds for the Ostend meat trade to England. From French, Belgian and Italian writers, we learn that it was standardized about 1894, which originated from a cross between Flemish Giants and the Dutch, and that it appeared in self-black, gray, blue and yellow body colors, with a small white blaze, narrow collar and narrow feet stops, which is our earliest Dutch rabbit. It is not difficult to trace the development of the self-blue Brabancon (the Belgian Merchtem rabbit), as well as the St. Nicholas Blue, from this common source. The self-colored Barbancon Blue was short-lived in America and has long been one of our extinct breeds.

BRONZE SABLE

The Bronze Sable was a popular breed during the first half of the 1940s, but would become extinct in Britain just after the Second World War. The breed was a tortoiseshell, with a dull orange saddle, with extensive black shading on the head, ears, feet, sides and stomach. The color of the saddle was highlighted by a rich red rufus color, given the rabbit the bronze coloration. The Bronze Sable was said to be medium to large in size.

CHIFOX

hifox are a British creation, which was begun by a Mr. O. Millsum, back in 1916. Millsum was breeding Beverens for commercial purposes when he came upon the idea of creating a breed with a long coat of fur that resembled the fur of the true Artic Fox. Millsum was one of the founders and president of the National Chinchilla Rabbit Club, and he said he had built the largest rabbitry in the British Isles for the breed, but resigned as president and sold his Westwood strain of Chinchillas to concentrate on his Chifox breeding program. Mr. Millsum was most secretive in his breeding program, but authorities believe that Chinchilla, Beveren, Silver Fox (Silver Martens) and Angora were all used in the breed's genetic makeup. After ten years of breeding, Millsum's goals were nearing fruition, as he had produced Chifox in white, blue, sable, silver, smoke, chinchilla gray and squirrel gray. Two pelts were shown to expert furriers in January 1928, and their remarks were that the fur was quite suitable for trimming of dresses, coats, evening cloaks, etc. The only fur of the time that came close to the Chifox was the Siberian Hare, known in

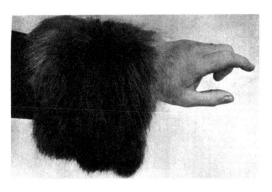

Cuff made of Chifox, circa 1927.

the trade as Foxaline. However, only the flank portions could be used effectively. The major drawback to this hare fur was the very poor wearing qualities, being paper-thin and brittle. Chifox were shown for the first time to the general public at the British Fur Rabbit Society Show, held at the Royal Horticultural Hall in Westminster, December 1928, to an amazing reception by both fanciers and the fur trade. The coat was to be approximately two and a half inches in length, and not at all woolly, nor did the coat have a tendency toward matting. Texture of the coat was like any normal fur rabbit. This beautiful rabbit is now extinct.

GERMAN RABBIT

ermany is the native home of this very old breed, which was first exposed in Chemnitz in 1855. The breed was created using the common rabbit population of the time which appeared in the very first rabbit standards issued in Germany under the name of Deutsches Kaninchen or German Rabbit. The breed was reported to be a rustic one, very prolific and rather small in size, weighing in at 2 to 2.5 kg or 4.5 to 5.5 lb. The German Rabbit was bred in all the known rabbit colors of the time. In order to improve the size of the breed, it was crossed with the Flemish Giant and renamed Neudeutsches Kaninchen or New German Rabbit, but this increase in size, weight, and even the new name could not save the breed, as foreign breeds of greater interest were being brought into Germany. Little by little the breed lapsed into extinction, but not before lending its blood to the development of the Gray Vienna.

GIANT BLANC DE HOTOT

Giant Blanc de Hotots are probably nothing more than a larger version of the Blanc de Hotot we know of today, which was created by Mrs. Eugenie Bernard of France from the Hotot en Auge region. When Bernhard showed her Hotots for the first time at the Paris International Show in 1920, they were called Geant (Giant) Blanc de Hotot (see Blanc de Hotot).

GIANT BLUE BEVEREN

iant Blue Beverens are obviously a product of Belgium, since that is the home of the original Beveren. However, I refer to it here as being a recognized breed in the United States, and was recognized by the National Breeders and Fanciers Association in 1920. The standard description given for the breed is rather short and sweet; similar in type to the above breed (Blue Beveren). Color clear, intense shade of lavender blue throughout. Size as large as possible, not under 7 pounds. Now it should be noted that the spelling of the breed used an "I" instead of an "E" to be Beverin. This breed was very short lived and long ago became extinct.

GOLDEN FAWN

Golden Fawns were created in America in the very early 1900s and are believed to have been nothing more than the buff-colored sports produced by the early Belgian Hares of the day. These buff sports were probably further mated to Flemish Giants of the time. Although Golden Fawns have been extinct for nearly a century, they were used to create the ever-popular Red New Zealands, America's first true breed of rabbit. The Golden Fawn was never recognized as a breed by the newly founded National Pet Stock Association, in 1910.

GOUDA

The Netherlands is the native home of the Gouda, which was bred in 1917 by a Mr. C.H. Spruty of Gouda, for which he named the breed. Spruty crossed Blue Beverens with Havanas, which produced black rabbits. Upon crossing these black offspring amongst themselves, he produced the first lilac-colored rabbit, which weighed 7 to 8 pounds or 3.17 to 3.6 kg. The Gouda arrived in America during the early 1920s and were recognized by the National Breeders and Fanciers Association in their 1924 book of standards. Oddly enough, when the Lilac breed was developed in England in 1922, it too was imported to the United States and both breeds were being shown. By 1930, the Gouda had become extinct, perhaps due to the slightly lighter color and the bit smaller size of the Lilac breed. The Gouda rabbit is now extinct world wide.

HEAVYWEIGHT BELGIAN HARE

elgian Hares of a larger form were the bright idea of the Americans, and could be found in this country at the end of the Belgian Hare boom period of early part of the 1900s. Although the Belgian Hare was first touted to be a fine meat animal with a delicate tasting flesh, it was by no means ideal. Therefore, a heavier Belgian Hare was being created for the meat markets. Both breeds of Belgian Hares were recognized by the National Pet Stock Association when it was founded on January 10th, 1910. The breed's weight was not to be under 9 pounds (see Belgian Hare). The Heavyweight Belgian Hares were dropped from the Standard of Perfection by 1939.

HEAVYWEIGHT HAVANA

Heavyweight Havanas made their appearance in American in the late 1920s and were given their own standard by the American Rabbit and Cavy Breeders Association in 1930. The breed was created to have a larger animal for the furriers of the day, and a larger carcass for the dinner table. One national specialty club sponsored what was then termed as the Standard Havana and the Heavyweight Havana (see Havana). The Heavyweight Havana, which was to weigh in at over 7 pounds, would last but twenty-five years, when it was dropped from the Book of Standards

HOODED RABBIT

The Hooded rabbit is without a doubt one of the most unique breeds of rabbits to vanish from the face of this earth. It is not said as to whether the

Hooded rabbit, circa 1791.
Courtesy The Natural History Museum, London.

breed is of domestic origin or a species, but I would be inclined to believe it is of domestic origin. A description of the breed appears in *Bewick's Quadrupeds* of 1791, and I quote, "With a double skin over the back, into which it can withdraw its head: another under the throat, in which it can place its fore feet: has small holes in the loose skin on the back, to admit light to the eyes; color of the body cinereous: head and ears brown." By chance that this rabbit was true, I contacted the British Museum, who kindly confirmed and sent a copy of the drawing for this book. Note in the drawing that the Hooded rabbit appears to have yet another very unique feature, webbed feet. This is almost a "Believe It or Not," but it is true, at least according to the book.

HUSUMER

usumers are a product of Germany and were created by Hermann Ziemer, who was also a well-known rabbit judge. His goal was actually to produce an all-white rabbit, but with a colored eye, other than red. Ziemer began to work with giant white rabbits; no doubt these were Flemish Giants and Dutch at the beginning of 1900. However, he had great difficulty getting the black spotting to disappear. Spots were often appearing on the nose, around the eyes and on the tail. After many matings, Hermann Ziemer rabbits were all white, with the ex-

Husumer drawing by Fiona Mackie.
Courtesy Meg Brown, Scotland.

14

ception of black eye circles and a black tail, and had blue eyes, which he would christen as the Husumer. During World War I (1914-1918), Ziemer was forced to give up his rabbit, which would become the extinction of the Husumer breed.

LAND KANINCHEN

Land Kaninchens are from Germany where spotted rabbits were known to exist from the middle of the 1800s. In the later part of the 19th century, in the region of Lorthringen, spotted rabbits were mated with French Lops and Flemish Giants, in order to produce a better meat

Land Kaninchen of Germany, circa 1900.

animal. This would give rise to a race called the Land Kaninchen, which weighed in at 4.5 to 5.5 kg or 10 to 12 pounds. The interesting feature of this breed was there was no butterfly marking to the nose; yet ears were colored, eye circles present, spine marking and cluster of spots on the haunches also present. Land Kaninchens soon spread throughout Germany and into other countries. It was from this breed that the Lorraine rabbit or Deutsche Riesenschecke (Great German Spotted) was developed (see Checkered Giant). This breed is extremely rare today, if not actually extinct. The last reference that this author has been able to locate on the Land Kaninchen is from 1943.

Land Kaninchen, circa 1907.

LITTLE GRAY SWISS

 witzerland is the native home to the Little Gray Swiss that was created by Charles Weber starting in 1918. Weber crossed a common wild agouti rabbit with the black guard hairs to a Silver

Gray buck. The doe produced four offspring, of which a pair of them were a light blue gray agouti coloration. Charles Weber set to fix this new color, and at seven months mated the brother and sister together. He would further cross mother with son, father and daughter, and brother to sister, which greatly improved the evenness of the pearling effect. The Little Gray Swiss is very close in

Little Grey Swiss.
Courtesy Meg Brown, Scotland.

appearance to the Perlfee which originated in Germany. However, it should be noted that the Perfees' genetic makeup included Havana, but Weber's creation did not. The Little Gray Swiss is a rather small rabbit at 5-1/2 lbs. and is rather cobby and rounded in all directions. The bone is not nearly as fine as in the Perlfee breed.

This rabbit is now extinct in Switzerland, having been merged with the Perlfee breed that we have today throughout Europe.

LORAIN

ery little is known of the Lorain rabbit, other than a British standard for the breed, which appears in an American book by Marcellus W. Meek, THE STANDARD OF PERFECTION FOR AMERICAN DOMESTIC RABBITS, 1928. The Lorain rabbit was to be large, all white, long coat of fur, and light pale blue eyes. It may well be one of the same of a breed known during the early 1920s as the White Blue Eyed Riveria. The name Lorain would certainly suggest that the rabbit is of French origin. However, no reference of this can be found in publications from that country. The breed obviously made little headway in America, and has long ago become extinct.

COLOR — Intense white, no creaminess or yellow tint in under coat
    or on neck, shoulders or ears 20
COAT — Long without any appearance of openness or wooliness

as in the Angora. Soft and very lustrous; dense undercoat 25
SIZE AND WEIGHT — A large rabbit of not less than (adults)
    8 pounds. The larger the better, without loss of type and quality. 10
HEAD — Not coarse or snipey, but distinctly long from set-on
    of ear to nose tip. Roman nose in profile. Bucks more massive
    in type, slight dewlap nose (does) permissible. Ears fairly long,
    well furred, without any tufts, not too broad and carried alertly.
    Eye a beautiful light blue is the ideal color, but many good
    specimens have the ruby eye showing the fire in a subdued light ... 15
BODY — Long without weakness, broad back, loins slightly arched,
    long, well-developed thighs, tail large and held tightly to croup
    — a solid rabbit 15
LEGS AND FEET — Fore legs straight and strong, hind legs long
    and well furred. Nails white 5
GENERAL APPEARANCE — A very handsome, active rabbit
    without Flemish Giant lumber. Should be shown in good
    condition 10
                                        Total = 100
FAULTS — Badly carried and hairless ears. Short or harsh coat. Under
    size.
DISQUALIFICATIONS — Pendant ears, bent legs, creamy or yellow tint
    of coat. Any colored markings.

LOTHARINGER RIESEN

Germany was the home of the Lotharinger Riesen rabbit. There is very
little known of this now extinct breed, other than being a very large rabbit,
which typically came in two different colors, brown and a blue gray. It was
widely kept in Ger-
many for its meat-pro-
ducing qualities, and
was believed to have
been a cross of Flem-
ish Giant and perhaps
the French Lop, and
the Lotharinger Riesen
typically always had
one ear which lopped.

Lotharinger Riesen, drawing by Fiona Mackie.
Courtesy Meg Brown, Scotland.

KAI GAI

Kai Gai is a breed which appeared in several advertisements in the United States during the early 1920s. The only mention as to the origin is found in Dr. F.L. Washburn's book, *The Rabbit Book, Belgian Hares Flemish Giants and Other Breeds,* 1920, and I quote, "The Kai Gai is said to be a cross between a blue and white Angora with the blood of other breeds added." The breed has long seen extinction in America.

MINI DWARF

From France comes this rather recent creation which was being developed in the 1970s. However, it has already become extinct in its native land. While the dwarfing gene can be a rather nightmare to many fanciers that keep the breed, just imagine a Mini Dwarf whose top weight was placed at 450 grams or 15.888 ounces, with ears not to exceed 1.77 inches. According to the creator of the breed, these animals were very fragile physically, they were prone to diseases, and the death rate to the newborn kits was extremely high. Little wonder these comments were made, as one can just breed down so small in any type of livestock. Of course, these Mini Dwarfs were strictly created by breeding the Netherland Dwarf down in size. Seeing the problems of such a tiny rabbit, the weight was elevated to a maximum of 800 grams, or 1.75 pounds; yet this increase was not enough to save the breed, since it is no longer seen.

NUBIAN

Very little is known of the extinct breed call the Nubian, which was recognized in England in the early 1920s. It was an-all black rabbit, with a compact body, broad across the back and loin section, with well-developed hindquarters. It was the deepest black of all the known black varieties at the time, and weight was not to exceed 6 pounds. Some people believe that the Nubian of England was actually the Alaska breed, which was developed in Germany. However, the Nubian was much smaller. It appeared to be quite a popular rabbit during its existence, winning awards regularly at the major British shows.

OLD ENGLISH RED

rior to 1916 when the New Zealand Red was first imported into the United Kingdom from America, there was a breed of rabbit call the Old English Red. Little has been written on this now long ago extinct breed. However, it had a standard and was recognized by the National Self-Coloured Rabbit Club.

ENGLISH STANDARD

COLOR — Rich red of tomato tinge (similar to the Red Cavy) carried well down sides and hindquarters; belly, under parts of tail and under jaw, white permissible, but preferably a paler shade of red than body. Free from ticking 35
SHAPE — Body compact and shapely, good broad loin with well-developed hindquarters and closely carried tail 20
HEAD — Bold, or medium length, no dewlap. Ears about 4-1/2 inches long, carried upright and free from lacing. Eyes hazel color, large, bright, round and bold 15
LEGS AND FEET — Clean and straight, medium bone, well-colored and free from white bars; reddish-brown toenails 5
COAT — Thick, soft and glossy, lying close to skin 10
WEIGHT — Six to 8 pounds 5
GENERAL APPEARANCE — Smart and alert; firm and hard in flesh .... <u>10</u>

Total = 100

Some experts claim that the Old English Red was nothing more that the Fauve de Bourgogne of France, while others believe it to have been developed from the old-time Belgian Hare, which for years threw self red sports. The breed was mainly used for meat and fur, rather than a show animal.

ONE EARED

England appears to be the native home of this "Unicorn of the Rabbit World" which was being bred true to form during the later part of the 18th century. I have been able to find next to nothing on this unusual rabbit, other that a small passage in Dr. John Sheail's book, *Rabbits and*

Their History, 1971. Sheail mentions that the one eared rabbit bred true, and the population slowly increased. However, little commercial value could be placed on such a rabbit, and that little notice was taken by the authors of the time. From all indications, it would appear that the One Eared rabbit was produced in the warrens of the day, and was probably of the wild agouti coloration. I have not been able to locate any further information on this most unusual mutation.

Two One Eared rabbits born in 1958.

As strange and unbelievable as this may seem, I was fortunate in finding a picture of a couple of One Eared rabbits in the February 1959 issue of the *National Rabbit Raiser Magazine.* Claude Holbrook of Evansville, Indiana, who raises rabbits for a hobby, got a surprise when he looked into a nest box recently. Two of the new litter had but one ear — right in the middle of their forehead." So as rare as the legendary Unicorn may be, so is the One Eared rabbit.

PATAGONIAN

atagonians did not come from the furthermost tip of South America as the name would imply, but are probably more closely associated with Belgium which seems to have been the land of the giant breeds. It was probably dubbed the Patagonian because of the tales of giants in Patagonia, and the name would be a bit more glamorous. This breed began to emerge in the mid-1800s, throughout Belgium, into France, then Germany and crossing the channel to the British Isles. U. Aldrovandi in his *De Quadrupedibus Digitatis,* of 1637 wrote that P. Valerianus, who died a very old man in 1558, had seen rabbits in Verona, Italy four times bigger than the normal rabbits. These "Giants" could well have been the nucleus of all our giant breeds.

The word Patagonia is of Spanish origin, which means "Big Foot." In the year 1520, when the explorer Fernando Magellan first saw the Tehuelche Indian tribe of Patagonia, they were said to have been wearing boots which had been stuffed with grass. The word "Pata" refers to the paw or foot of an animal, but this is rarely used in human context.

Patagonian rabbit, circa 1870.

Some early writings do list the Patagonians coming from the Patagonia region of South America and brought by early sailors to Europe, because there is a breed known as the Patagonian Rabbit or Hare. By chance, I contacted the Fundacion Patagonia Natural in Patagonia Madryn, Chubut, Argentina, which they gladly shared photos of the Patagonian Rabbit. This is not a rabbit at all, although their carriage and color resembles a Hare, with very short ears, and they hop like a kangaroo. That is about as close to a rabbit as this creature comes, which is actually one of the species of the family *Cavildas,* or Cavy. Locally they are called Maras, and spend their lives on the pampus, and are scientifically known as *Dolichotis patagonum.* Further research on rabbits in Patagonia turned up some very mongrel-looking gray rabbits, but hardly this breed of yesteryear.

Patagonians frequently tipped the scales at 16 to 18 pounds, but 12 to 14 was usually considered the average weight. Breeders were encouraged to discard any animals

Patagonian Rabbit or Hare of South America, a member of the Cavy family.

Patagonian rabbit, circa 1879.

weighing less than 10 pounds. The breed's frame was considered roomy and a trifle coarse, and the hip-bones stood out very prominently. Even in the peak of condition, though massive, the breed was hardly a handsome one. Ears were a bit long and very heavy, and hence they would hang down slightly at the tips, the appearance being somewhat like the letter V, with the tops slightly bent out. Oar-lopped Patagonians were rather commonplace. The fur was a kind of a dark iron-gray or steel, sometimes lighter than others, and typically the head, ears, feet and legs would be darker.

They were a great utility breed of the time for meat and fur. However, one unusual feature was that they rarely had more than four kits at birth, with the record of seven being noted only on one occasion. Does were said to be excellent mothers, provided they did not trample the young the first couple of days. The Patagonian was a calm and gentle natured rabbit.

PIRUVIAN

he Piruvian rabbit was created during the early 1940s, by a Mr. V.L. Jackson, of Piru, California, hence the name for the breed. Piruvians were strictly a commercial breed. Although Jackson did not appear to release the methods used to create the Piruvians, there is little doubt that New Zealand Whites, Californians and perhaps Giant Chinchilla or Flemish Giants were used. In all appearance a Piruvian looked just like a large Californian.

A Piruvian Producers Association had been founded with Allen C. Houseworth of Carmichael, California, serving as secretary and treasurer. The breed was becoming rather popular throughout California, with some herds numbering one hundred animals.

Piruvians were presented at the 1955 Columbus, Ohio ARBA Convention and Show, where they were approved for a first showing by the Standards Committee. It was during the California State Fair, held in Sacramento in 1956, that a negative side would show its face. In *The National Rabbit Raiser and Poultry Grower,* August 1956, appeared a guest editorial written by Allen Houseworth. "The Amazing Piruvian Situation — Judging the Peruvians." Near the end of the show all judges were assigned by Show Superintendent Tom Fairchild to judge the Piruvians. This was done to avoid criticism of any individual judge.

V.I. Jackson on left who originated the Piruvian, with Frank Wallace holding a doe of the breed.

Here, for the first time, a tenseness seemed to fill the air. History was being made. The show stopped as the crowd gathered to watch this special judging event. The judges, J. Cyril Lowit and George Baylis (Orlan Onkst having bowed out), were in a quandary over interpretation of the standard. They called in V.L. Jackson, originator of the Piruvian, to explain. With this clarification the judging went speedily ahead and the awards were made. A great show came to an end.

All appeared well and good — as show secretary I had put in months of work during evenings and every weekend. After listening to the judges point out strong and weak points, I came home with opened eyes, critically going through my Piruvian Rabbitry. I had the feeling that, after all, there is a place in one organization for fancy, and for commercial. I felt that truly my long hours of hard work had been well worthwhile.

Sniping from the rear — Then came the sad disillusionment. The "boys" got their pens out, and behind-the-back letters started to circulate. Two fine judges were being "put on the spot." The RUMOR was spread that the Northern Californian Rabbit Breeders Association would lose its ARBA charter — all for daring to have Piruvians shown and judged.

Good faith manifested — The Piruvians Producers Association has acted in good faith. We are coming to the crossroads. Will our association, along with another commercial producer organization, go one way, and a strictly "FANCY" ARBA go another? Or do we dare to show our rabbit in defiance of a small biased, unreasonable, but obviously powerful minority. What has happened to the American concept of sportsmanship?

Well, the judges did not lose their licenses, nor was the club charter canceled, as no rules were considered broken. In 1958, the ARBA conducted a census of breeds being raised in the United States and the number of breeders keeping them. The Piruvians showed only two fanciers at this time. It appears, while the breed had excellent commercial properties, they might have been too good. An eight-week-old Piruvian fryer would typically weigh from 6 to 7 pounds, which appeared to be much too large for the commercial processors, lacking uniformity of the fryers produced by New Zealand Whites and Californians. The Piruvian breed came extinct during the early 1960s.

PRUSSIAN

From the United Kingdom comes a rabbit with the name of Prussian. There has only been one mention of this breed found, which appeared in January 1858 in a publication called the *Cottage Gardener and Country Gentleman,* which speaks of a show held in Nottingham in the same month and year where four classes had been provided for rabbits, and P. Boulton writes: "The Prussian Rabbit — At the Nottingham Show, January 1858, a pair of rabbits were exhibited under this name. They were remarkably small in size, and beautiful in their proportions; they were both white, with pink eyes, their ears were very short, and carried erect. The heads of both buck and doe were rounder than in any other variety. They were timid creatures; so much so, indeed, that the noise and inspection of the visitors at the Show were sufficient to destroy one of this very interesting pair of rabbits. They are the only pair I have seen, or heard of; and I believe that they were imported, but whether directly from Prussia, or not, I was unable to ascertain."

Now as to whether these little white rabbits called Prussian were actually imported from what is now northern Germany or not, we shall never know, but I'm of the opinion that these could well be the beginning of our breed we call Polish.

BEVEREN REX

Beveren Rex are an American creation which was developed during the craze to put a Rex coat on nearly every breed of rabbit. The breed was officially recognized by the Beveren Club, until the American Rabbit and Cavy Breeders Association ruled that the National Rex Club would be their sponsor (See the Rex). The breed is no longer found in America.

BLUE VIENNA REX

An American original is the Blue Vienna Rex, which was given a Standard in 1944. The breed was created when Americans were going crazy trying to put a Rex coat on just about every breed of rabbit. The breed was sponsored by the National Rex Club. However, the breed is long ago extinct.

CHINCHILLA REX

Chinchilla Rex, which I write of here, is not a variety which I speak of, but three different breeds: American Chinchilla, Giant Chinchilla, and the Standard Chinchilla. The Chinchilla breed was all the rage in America after the boom of the Belgian Hare, until the Rex breed hit our country. Because the Chinchilla coloration so resembled their South American namesake, breeders were very quick to try and Rex our three Chinchilla breeds, because it truly would resemble those cute little wide creatures. All three Chinchilla breeds had standards in place by 1944 and came under the sponsorship of the National Rex Club. Their existence in this country was rather short-lived, but not before putting their stamp in the Chinchilla variety of the Standard Rex we have today.

FLEMISH GIANT REX

Flemish Giant Rex were created in the United States during the Rex rabbit craze, as breeders began to try and place Rex coats on many of the popular breeds of the time. In the case of Rexing the Flemish Giant, it was to produce a much larger pelt for the booming fur industry. The breed was recognized by the Flemish Club, until the National Rex Club took the breed under their wing (see the Rex breed). Flemish Giant Rex are long ago extinct, and to my knowledge cannot be found in any other country.

HAVANA REX

Havana Rex, in both the Standard Havana and the Heavyweight Havana, were recognized by the American Rabbit and Cavy Breeders Association, with a standard that dates back to 1932. The two breeds were first under the sponsorship of the National Havana Club, until 1935 when the National Rex Club took them under their leadership. Though the two breeds are long ago extinct, they did give rise to the Chocolate Rex we know today.

HIMALAYAN REX

This is not the variety Himalayan, but a rexed version of the breed, which had their own standard that dates back to 1944 by the American Rabbit and Cavy Breeders Association. The breed is, of course, extinct

LILAC REX

This is not the variety, but the Lilac breed with a Rex coated that was developed and recognized at one time in America. The Lilac Rex were recognized by the American Rabbit and Cavy Breeders Association in 1944, with their own standard, and were sponsored by the National Rex Club of the day. Though the breed is extinct, it did give rise to Lilac variety of our Standard Rex today

NEW ZEALAND REX

New Zealand Rex were quite popular in the United States where they were developed after the Rex breed was introduced to the American soil. New Zealand Rex were recognized in both the Red and White varieties. This breed certainly had far superior bodies than the original imported Rex rabbits, which many people would call "Wrecks." The breed was recognized by the fast-

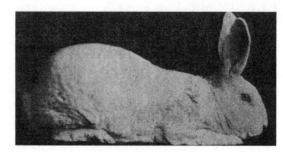

New Zealand Rex buck, circa 1930.

growing national club, called the American Federation of New Zealand Breeders, until 1935 when the breed was transferred to the Rex National Club (see the Rex breed). New Zealand Rex have been extinct for many years.

POLISH REX

Americans created the Polish Rex, and a standard was issued for the breed in 1944, with sponsorship of the breed by the National Rex Club of the day. Polish Rex were recognized in only the Ruby-Eyed White variety. The breeds existence was rather short-lived.

SABLE REX

Sable Rex is not a variety, but the Sable breed that has been created with a rex coat. The breed dates back to 1932 when it was issued a standard by the American Rabbit and Cavy Breeders Association. Sable Rex were first sponsored by the National Sable Club, until 1935, when it was ruled that the National Rex Club would cater to all breeds of Rex. Although the Sable Rex breed is extinct, it did give us the Sable variety of the Standard Rex we know today.

SILVER MARTEN REX

Rex coated Silver Martens were from America. The breed was recognized in both the Black and Blue varieties, with a standard for the Silver Marten Rex dating back to 1932. The Silver Marten Rex was under the sponsorship of the National Rex Club; they are long ago extinct.

ROUENNAIS

Rouennais is a very old French breed, also known as "Bulldog," because they had very square and broad heads like a Bulldog. It was in France during the early to mid-1800s. The breed weighed in at up to 14 pounds and came in two varieties: Light Fawn and Light Gray, but the Fawns were the most common color. They had rather long ears which were carried upright, but some carried the ears in the same fashion as the Half-Lop of the same era. France exported many of these rabbits to neighboring countries. Rouennais were often crossed with the Patagonian and were used in the genetic makeup of the French Lop. The breed has long been extinct.

SHERMAN'S LONG HAIR

From California comes this Sherman's Long Haired rabbit, which was produced prior to 1920 by a Mr. and Mrs. C.S. Sherman, of the Los Angeles Fur Farm in Culver City. Mrs. C.E. Sherman served on the board of the National Committee

Sherman's Long Hair, circa 1920.

The Shermans' Los Angeles Fur Farm, circa 1918.

on Rabbit Fur Industry, which had been established by the National Breeders and Fanciers Association in 1918. Other than a picture of the Sherman's Long Hair rabbit from F.L.

Washburn's book, *"The Rabbit Book Belgian Hares Flemish Giants and Other Breeds,"* 1920, and several ads for the breed, nothing has been located as to the genetic makeup of the breed. From looking at the picture, I would assume that Angora and either English Spots or Checkered Giants were originally used. The Shermans' Long Hair rabbit has been long extinct in the United States.

Right: Mrs. C.E. Sherman, circa 1919.

28

SHERMAN'S SHORT HAIR

Again from the rabbitry of Mr. and Mrs. C.S. Sherman, Los Angeles Fur Farm of Culver City, California, comes the Sherman's Short Hair rabbit breed, which was developed prior to 1920. Other than several advertisements in the guidebooks of the National Breeders and Fanciers Association, nothing is further known of the appearance or genetic makeup of this long ago extinct fur breed.

SIBERIAN

 iberians are known to us in two very distinct forms, far removed from one another in overall appearance and existence, since one is now extinct. Siberians came from the northern latitudes, namely Russia, and have been called the Moscow Rabbit, but this is not to be confused with the Hooded Rabbit, a long ago extinct breed which

Siberian Doe, circa 1924.

was also called by that name. Siberians were an Angora with dark brown colored points like the Himalayan breed. It was brought to England from both Russia and France in the mid-1800s. Charles Darwin wrote of the Siberian/Moscow rabbit in his *"The variation of animals and plants under domestication,"* 1868, "Two live rabbits were brought to me from Moscow, of about the size of the wild species, but with long fur, dif-

Siberian Buck, circa 1924.

29

ferent from that of the Angora. These Moscow rabbits had pink eyes and were snow-white, excepting the ears, two spots near the nose, the upper and under surface of the tail, and the hinder tarsi, which were blackish-brown. In short, they were colored nearly like the so-called Himalayan rabbits, presently to be described, and differed from them only in the character of their fur." There is little doubt that this breed could be easily recreated by pairing Angora and the darkest pointed Himalayan that could be found. Siberians are mentioned in the 1924 National Breeder and Fanciers Association of America Year Book and Standard. However, these would have to be the Black Siberian Hares, as the registration weights were listed at 10 lbs., and the Siberian that I write of here weighed in at 6 to 7 lbs. Siberians would become extinct in England in the late 1920s, no doubt due to the height of the Angora industry.

SILVER BLACK GIANT

Silver Black Giants date back to 1924 in America and were a recognized breed of the National Breeders and Fanciers Association. It was a rather large rabbit with bucks weighing 11 pounds and up, and the does at 12 pounds and over. The breed was probably nothing more that a Black Flemish Giant with loads of white hairs in the coat, as the standard called for white hairs to be evenly distributed over entire body, chest, head, feet, ears and tail with evenness of silver throughout. The hairs were not to be white tipped, and the breed is not to be confused with the Silver Fox of America. In fact, people were discouraged from crossing the two breeds together. By 1939, the weights of the Silver Black Giants were upped to 12 pounds and over for bucks, and over 14 pounds for does. Interest in the breed began to wane in the middle 1940s, and the breed was removed from the Book of Standards by 1950. Silver Black Giants are now extinct.

Silver Black Giant, circa 1924.

SILVER GLAVCOT

ngland is the original home of the Silver Glavcot, which was rather popular during the teens and twenties of the 20th century, but has since become extinct. This breed was also found in the United States during the 1920s, having been imported by Marcellus M. Meek in 1925, and became quite popular in the area of southern California. A Mr. M.L. Thayer of Los Angeles created an American version of the Silver Glavcot by crossing the American Blues to the Champagne D'Argents, then interbreeding the first generations. Thayer's Silver Glavcots were of a larger size and carried the mandolin type of the American breed, whereas the British version was very cobby in type. The English Silver Glavcot was created by O. Millsum and named by a Mr. Wesley T. Page. The Silver Glavcot was a dilute steel, a blue agouti, but with no agouti banding and had a colored stomach fur instead of white. The late geneticist Roy Robinson said the breed could be recreated by using a steel-

Silver Glavcot, from the Wippell Collection. Reproduced from a Fur & Feather colour plate first issued 4 January 1924.

colored rabbit as a male, and breed with Blue Beveren females. Then the steel offspring from the first crossing would need to be mated back to Blue Beveren. Silver Glavcots were a beautiful colored rabbit as painted by Wippell in the early 1920s for *Fur & Feather.* It appears that no one knows why the breed was given the name of Glavcot.

SITKA

 itkas originated in England by a Mrs. Violet D. Ker, who was the manager of the very powerful Fur Board of the time. Actually, Mrs. Ker called her creations Black Beverens when they were created in 1919. Violet Ker wrote in *Fur Producing Rabbits,* 1923, "The idea of establishing a breed of black rabbits that would serve the dual purpose of a really good table rabbit with a fine pelt, and would also be sufficiently symmetrical to take a high place among exhibition varieties, first occurred to me in early autumn of 1918. I had not long been breeding Beverens, and my first notion was to produce a black Beveren.

When about 18 months later I showed some of my blacks to one or two of the senior members of the Beveren Club, they were not so encouraging as I had hoped, and while criticizing the specimens pretty severely, also firmly vetoed the name. For the later I have since had cause to be grateful, because if my rabbits were not to be Beverens, that left me a free hand to develop them along the lines I thought best. To my mind, the Beveren is not an absolutely ideal table rabbit because, owing to its great size, it has a tendency to be a bit lanky during the growing stage and to require very heavy feeding to develop it to the fullest advantage.

There is no short cut to Sitka growing, as the rabbits are not the result of any first cross. The Beveren has, of course, entered largely into their composition, as it appeared to me the only rabbit that would give the length and quality of coat required. But the original maternal stock was of a com-

An American Sitka, circa 1924.

posite character. I had bought them without pedigrees and chosen them entirely on their face value, with the sole object of adding to the contents of my larder those lean days, and they were nothing more or less than good old motherly cross-breds. It was because two of them, when mated to a Beveren buck, gave decidedly good-looking self black youngsters, that I first decided to carry on and see what could be done toward fixing and improving the breed. Probably, if I had not been a mere novice in rabbit breeding, I should have discarded them in favor of does from some pure-bred pedigree strain. Equally probably, the descendants would not have turned out nearly so well. The results were just a sheer good-luck that sometimes attends the beginner, and certainly far beyond my deserts!

After being rejected by the Beveren Club as Black Beveren, Violet Ker named them for the Alaskan Sitka Fox. Those two mongrel does were a rather odd lot, one being an Agouti, said to have been a cross of Belgian Hare and Flemish Giant and the other doe a black and white spotted. The best offspring from these does were mated back to the Blue Beveren sire. The Beveren Club did finally accept Ker's black rabbits under the name of Sitka on February 24, 1922 and adopted a standard. Violet Ker's stud was quite small, so she was limited to the number of breeding stock she was able to supply to others. Sitkas became very popular as a fur breed, with large farms devoted to the breed.

Sitkas were imported into America in the early 1920s and given a standard by the National Breeders and Fanciers Association in 1924. This breed has now become extinct, not only in the U.S., but in the United Kingdom as well, with the Black Beveren taking the Sitkas' place.

SWAN

Swan rabbits have been extinct since about 1885, and there has been little recorded about this most usual breed. It is said to have come from the Isle of Man; at least that is where a couple of rabbit fanciers located stock to bring back to the British mainland.

Swan Rabbit drawing by Fiona Mackie.
Courtesy Meg Brown, Scotland.

The Swan rabbit was a massive creature, tipping the scales at 19 pounds when in prime condition, but very awkwardly built. The most amazing feature of this breed was that the ears were just about two inches long with the hollowed portions being directed to the front, instead of on the side. The color of this long forgotten breed was a tawny gray, and in its general characteristics greatly resembled that of the Patagonian breed. It is written that when you cross the Swan rabbit with the Patagonian, the progeny's ears would be of a much shorter length.

TRENT

I am at a total loss on the Trent rabbit breed, which has been mentioned only one time that I have been able to find any reference to, and that being during the Third Annual Convention of the National Breeders and Fanciers Association of America which was held in Cleveland, Ohio August 25th to 30th, 1919. It is listed with all the recognized breeds of the time, and was to be awarded a Championship certificate, provided there were at least five does shown. There is no other mention of this breed after this date; no standard has ever been located, nor a description of any sort.

WACHTEBEKE

This dual purpose rabbit was created in Belgium by Mr. M. Pulinchx in the later 1800s. The Wachtebeke rabbit is a rare color blending of the old Barbancon (forerunner of our Dutch breed) and Flemish Giant and weighed in at 8 to 10 lbs. The head and ears are blackish and the

Wachtebeke Rabbit, drawing by Fiona Mackie. Courtesy Meg Brown, Scotland.

black becomes more and more brown-gray toward the tail. It had white markings, with an even thin line collar around the neck and front of the throat. Front feet and legs carried white sock markings, just as the "New Style" Dutch rabbit of the late 1800s. It was known for its excellent mothering abilities and large litters, again just as Dutch are known for today. The breed has long been extinct.

WHITE ALASKA

hite Alaskas were originally from England, but were also to be found in the United States during the mid-1920s as reported by Marcellus W. Meek, in his *The Standard of Perfection for Domestic Rabbits,* 1928. Unfortunately, I have been able to find little of the breed, other than the official standard.

COLOR — Pure white 25
COAT — Thick, soft and glossy, lying lat to skin 20
WEIGHT - Not exceeding 6 pounds for adults 10
HEAD - EARS AND EYES — Head of medium length, broader in
    Bucks. Ears not exceeding 4 inches long, carried closely, and
    rounded at tips. Eyes red or blue and bright 10
BODY — Compact, broad across back and loin, the latter slightly
    arched, well-developed hindquarters, short tail carried close
    to body. No dewlap 20
LEGS AND FEET — Fairly fine in bone, straight, white or
    flesh-colored toenails 5
GENERAL APPEARANCE — Neat, smart and alert, clean and
    healthy, clean coat, firm and hard in flesh.................................... 10
                                                                 Total = 100

This is the only mention of this breed in America, and no reference has been found to date of the breed in any English writings. Of course, the White Alaska is long ago extinct.

WHITE BLUE EYED RIVERIAS

There is just about nothing known of this breed of rabbit. It is mentioned in the National Breeders and Fanciers of American Yearbook and Standard of 1924. Imported by E.W.C. Arnold of Babylon, Long Island, New York, who imported on a regular basis from England, France and Germany. It was obviously a white rabbit with blue eyes, perhaps the early White Beveren or White Vienna. Mr. Arnold also was the first to bring the Rhinelander to the United States.

WHITE OF TERVUREN

Belgium was the home to this now extinct breed of white rabbit. It is an old breed that appeared in the early 1900s, which had a standard until the mid-1920s. The White of Ter-vuren weighted up to 3.5 kg. and had a pronounced

White of Tervuren, circa 1928.
Courtesy Armand Vandenbroucke, Belgium.

mandoline type with blue eyes, but was quite different from the White Beveren.

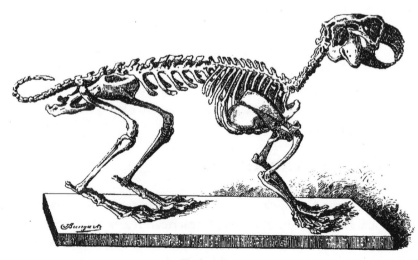

Extinction.

36

 HAPTER II

RABBIT BREEDS OF THE WORLD

To say that this is a complete list of all the rabbit breeds of the world would be false, as new ones are being developed all the time. Some which have been listed are breeds in the making, which are unique enough to be included in the list. If one takes the New Zealand of the United States and compares it with any other country, you will see a remarkably different rabbit, which in actual fact, could well be considered a different breed. The domestic rabbit is such a plastic species, as they can be shaped and molded through selective breeding over a course of years. Some breeds have been listed, not because they breed true to any particular color or pattern, but because they have adapted to the extremes of climate, and have evolved over many years, such as the Gotland, Bauscat, Brazilian, etc.

There are numerous definitions for just what exactly constitutes a breed, but one of the best is Quittet's: "A breed is a collection of individuals within a species which share a certain number of morphological and physiological characters which are passed on to their progeny as long as they breed among themselves."

It is unfortunate that little to no information could be found on some breeds of rabbits. It has been just nearly impossible to make contact with some countries in order to piece together some sort of historical matter in some breeds. These breeds have been listed below, yet have been noted.
+ Breeds with no information located.

Alaska — Europe
Altex — USA
American — USA
Angora Breeds
    Chinese Angora — China
    Dwarf Angora — Europe
    English Angora — USA
    French Angora — Various
    German Angora- Various
    Giant Angora — USA
    Mini English Angora — New Zealand
    Satin Angora — Various
Argente Breeds
    Bleu (Blue) — France
    Brun (Brown) — France
    Champagne — Various
    Clair — Belgium
    Crème — Various
    Noir (Black) — Holland
    Saint Hubert — France
Baladi — Egypt
Bauscat — Egypt
Beige — Europe
Belgian Hare — Various
Belgian Silver — Belgium
Beveren — Various
Blanc de Hotot — Various
Blanc de Popielno — Poland
Blanc de Vendee — France
Blue of Ham — Belgium
Bourbonnais Grey — France
Brazilian (Rustico) — Brazil
Britannia Petite (British Polish) — USA
British Giant — UK
Brown Chestnut of Lorraine — France
Caldes — Spain
Californian — Various
Carmagnole Grey — Italy

Chaudry — France
Checkered Giant — USA
Chinchilla Breeds
    American Chinchilla — USA
    Chinchilla Giganta — Various
    Giant Chinchilla — USA
    Standard Chinchilla — Various
Cinnamon — USA
Criollo — Mexico
Cuban Brown — Cuba
Czech Albin (White) — Czechoslovakia
Czech Spot — Czechoslovakia
Deilenaar — Various
Dutch — Various
Dwarf Hotot — Various
Dwarf Papillons — Germany
Dwarf Swiss Fox — Europe
Enderby Island — New Zealand
English Spot — Various
Fauve de Bourgogne — France
Fee de Marbourg (Marburger) — Germany
Flemish Giant — Various
Flemish Giant (British) — UK
Florida White — USA
Furless — USA
Gabali — Egypt
Geant Hongrois (Hungarian Giant) — Hungary
Giant Blanc du Bouscat — France
Giant Papillon — Europe
Gigante de Espana — Spain +
Giza White — Egypt
Goat — France
Golden Glavcot — UK
Gotland Rabbit — Sweden
Grey Pearl of Halle — Europe
Harlequin (Japanese) — Various
Havana — Various
Hermelin (German Polish) — Germany

Himalayan — Various
Holicsky Modry — Czechoslovakia +
Hulstlander — Holland
Ibicenco — Spain
Isabella — Sweden
Jamora — Europe
Japanese Giant White — Asia
Jersey Wooly — USA
Kabyle — Algeria
Kanel (Cinnamon) — Denmark
Klein Lotharinger (Dutch Papillon) — Holland
Large Himalayan (Russe) — France
Large Marten — Czechoslovakia +
Large Siamese — Czechoslovakia +
Large Silver — Europe
Lilac — Various
Lionhead — Various
Little Silver — Europe
Lop Breeds
    American Fuzzy Lop (Miniature Cashmere Lop — UK) — USA
    Cashmere Lop — UK
    Dwarf Rex Lop — France
    English Lop — Various
    French Lop — Various
    German Lop — UK
    Holland Lop (Dwarf of Europe)- Various
    Lionhead Lop — Various
    Meissener Lop — Various
    Mini Lop (Dwarf Lop — UK) — Various
    Mini Plush Lop — USA
    Royal Satin Lop — USA
    Velveteen Lop — USA
Lutino — Denmark
Lutterbach Ermine — France
Lux (Lynx) — Various
Magpie — Various
Maltese — Malta +
Marisk — Tjeckia +

Marten Sable — Various
Mecklenburger Scheck — Various
Mecklenburger Dwarf — Germany +
Mini Satin — USA
Moravian — Liberia +
Moravian White — Czeckhoslovakia
Moravien Blue — Czeckhoslovakia
Netherland Dwarf — Various
New Zealand — Various
Nil — Malta
Nitransky — Czechoslovakia +
Normand (Picard) — France
Orange — Sweden
Orestad — Sweden
Palomino — USA
Pani — Japan
Pannon White — Hungary
Perlfee — Various
Petit Papillon Tricolor — Switzerland
Pointed Beveren — UK
Polish — Various
Prat — Spain
Rex Breeds
    Astrex — UK
    Dwarf Rex — Germany
    Micro Rex — USA
    Mini Rex — Various
    Mini Satin Rex — Australia
    Opossum Rex — UK
    Standard Rex — Various
    Standard Satin Rex — UK
Rhinelander — Various
Rhoen — Various
Sable — Various
Sable de Vosges — France
Sachsengold (Saxon Gold) — Various
Sallander — Various
San Juan — USA

Satin — Various
Satin Dwarf — Germany
Schwarzgrannen — Various
Separator — Czeckhoslovakia
Siamese Sable — UK
Siberian — UK
Sichuan White — China
Silver — Various
Silver Fox — USA
Silver Marten (Silver Fox -UK) — USA
Smoke Pearl — UK
Spanish Giant — Spain
Squirrel — UK
St Nicholas Blue — Belgium
Stone (Steenkonijn) — Belgium
Stor Egern — Scandinavia
Stora (Large) Havana — Sweden
Sussex — UK
Svensk Pals — Sweden +
Swiss Fox — Various
Tadla — Morocco
Tan — Various
Tho Noi — Viet Nam
Thrianta — Various
Thuringer — Various
Tronder — Norway
Vienna — Various
Vienna White — Various
Vit Land (Hvid Land) — Denmark
Wiltshire — UK +
Wheaten — UK
White Dendermode (Blanc de Termode) — Belgium
Yellow Silver — Ghana +
Zemmouri — Morocco
Zemplinsky — Czechoslovakia +

ALASKA

he state of Alaska has nothing to do with the breed which bears its name, although it does appear rather odd that a totally black rabbit would be called Alaska to start with. Alaska rabbits are strictly of German origin, which began in 1900, and were created by Max Fischer, of Gotha, a rabbit judge, and another man by the name of Schmidt, from Langensalza. Their goal was to produce a breed that resembled the Alaskan Fox for the fur trade. By crossing Havanas, Dutch, Himalayans and Argentes, the two men had hoped to produce a black rabbit with much longer white hairs throughout the coat. Fischer and Schmidt never realized that goal, and instead settled for the jet black rabbit we have today, with the addition of self-black Papillons (Checkered Giants). These beautiful intensely colored black rabbits were first shown in 1907 and were quickly taken up by rabbit fanciers throughout Europe.

Alaska.
Photo courtesy Standard of Federation Francaise de Cuniculiculture, 1972, France.

Mr. Bert Reurs, of Ontario, Canada, imported the Alaska breed from his native Holland in the mid-1970s, when the ARBA accepted them to their book of standards. However, for some reason there would be little interest in the breed, especially after the late Lee Owen Stamm developed his Black variety of Havana. The Alaska breed was removed from the American standards in 1981.

ALTEX

he Altex rabbit is a commercial sire breed, and are an American creation, developed by Dr. Steven Lukefahr and his former graduate students, for the commercial meat rabbit industry. Because it is not a show breed, it is not a breed recognized by any national show rabbit governing body as a show animal. The project began in 1986, when a number of Californian, Champagne d'Argent and

Flemish Giant breeds were donated or purchased from a number of reputable fanciers and commercial establishments from various states and sent to Alabama A&M University at Huntsville. Flemish Giant bucks were mated with Californian and Champagne does to produce the first two F1 crossed lines. Bucks and does from these first line crosses were then mated together, which resulted in F2 population, consisting of breed fractions. Results were in the F2 rabbits, one-half Flemish Giant, one-quarter Californian, and one-quarter Champagne d'Argent. Dr. Lukefahr reported that there were many different coat colors

Dedicated to Dr. Steven Lukefahr, Texas.

in the F2 crosses, plus considerable variation in type, body size and rates of growth amongst the fryers. This blending of genes from the three breeds was then selected for rapid and efficient weight gains, high dress-out percentage and a high meat to bone ration in the males. Dr. Lukefahr reported that there were many different coat colors in the F2 crosses, plus considerable variation in type, body size and rates of growth amongst the fryers.

The F2 rabbits were then randomly separated into two genetic populations, selected and unselected, according to Dr. Lukefahr. This split was done to study the sire traits monitor genetic progress between selected and unselected lines for in each generation. While attention was not paid to color during the next five generations, the heaviest rabbits at 70 days were

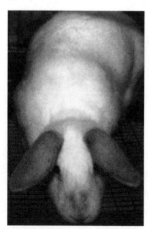

Altex. *Photo courtesy Dr. Steven Lukefahr.*

kept selected. There again Dr. Lukefahr reports that a total of 1,616 rabbits from 336 litters had been produced involved in this particular phase of the breeding program. Subsequent studies have shown that the dress-out rate and meat to bone ration is similar between Altex and commercial bred New Zealand White fryers.

In 1994, Dr. Lukefahr, accepted a faculty position at Texas A&M University, Kingsville, in 1994, and took with him with the best possible genetics from the unselected and unselected lines, which he would later cross together. It was here that the doctor named the breed Altex — Al for Alabama and, of course, Tex for Texas.

The breed is a Terminal Sire rabbit; that is, the Altex bucks are typically mated with commercial New Zealand Whites or commercial crossbred does, and never the other way around to produce fryers that, on average, go to market one week sooner than New Zealand White fryers, as this cross doesn't produce the high weight gains.

The Altex breed is typically 13 pounds in weight for both buck and does. It is an all-white rabbit with colored points as in the Californian breed. A research paper on the Altex breed was presented to the 6th World Rabbit Congress in Toulouse, France. This hybrid commercial sire breed (a purebred, not a hybrid or crossbred) should greatly improve profitability of the lives of people in developing countries meat rabbit production as a superior meat producer.

AMERICAN

he United States of America is the home to this old breed which was developed in Pasadena, California, by Lewis H. Salisbury, and recognized as a breed in March 1918 by the National Breeders and Fanciers Association of America. Lewis Salisbury was very secretive as to the breeds involved in creating the American, which was actually called the German Blue Vienna, but was quickly changed to American Blue because of World War I. Because of the mandolin shape of the breed, and that Blue Flemish Giants, Blue Viennas, Blue Beveren, and Blue Imperials were to be found in America at this time, it is quite likely that these breeds contributed to the race we know as American. It should be noted that Salisbury was a judge in the national organization and a member of the Standards Committee during this time period. The standard for the breed was written based on a single rabbit named "Pasadena Major," which was given registration number 5171 by the national association. The original standard for the breed was writ-

The famous Pasadena Major, whose exceptional quality the standard for the breed was written, ca. 1917.

45

Lewis H. Salisbury.

ten by Lewis Salisbury, Charles Gibson and John Fehr. The American Blue was judged for the first time ever in Los Angeles, California, by Charles S. Gibson. It was Gibson, along with several other men, who called a meeting together on January 10, 1910, at Gibson's home at 1045 West Warren Avenue in Detroit, Michigan, which gave birth to the National Pet Stock Association, the forerunner of the American Rabbit Breeders Association, Inc.

Salisbury's strain of American Blues were considered the best in the country, but for several years previous to 1917, other well-known breeders of the time; John Fehr of Indiana and Lewis Griffin of Colorado, were also centering their attention on blue rabbits, and specimens obtained by the various crosses were exchanged and intermingled. The poorer specimens were discarded, of course, and from pure breeding of the most promising animals gradually evolved the ideal type and deep blue color the variety is known for. When first exhibited, it is reported that many had poor color and were disqualified for brown patches and white hairs. The two most popular strains were Salisbury's Pasadena Strain and a strain developed in San Diego. The breed would get a great boost when a rabbit judge by the name of George Green, from Los Angles, California, became interested in the new and very popular breed, purchased animals from both strains and interbred them. This melting of the two different lines produced some of the finest American Blues of the day, and George Green was always winning with his animals.

The first standard for the breed that has been located dates to 1918, which appeared in *Rabbit Culture*, June 7, 1918:

American Blue

Shape	20
Color	25
Weight	10
Head	5
Eyes	5
Ears	5
Legs and Feet	20
Condition	10

Total = 100 Points

American Blues soon spread throughout the nation as a popular meat and fur animal. Furriers in 1920 were paying the unbelievable price of $2 for a good mature pelt, and a good pedigree doe of breeding age was bringing $25 and up, which was a hefty sum

American White doe bred by the author in 1974.

of the time, especially since the Belgian Hare bust, where hundreds and thousands of dollars were being spent on single animals.

The American White would follow in 1925, said to have been produced from white sports thrown by the American Blues, with White Flemish Giant blood added. The American rabbit never seemed to have been imported to other lands, which is understandable, as England and Europe had so many beautiful blue breeds.

Some people claim that the American was the first breed truly developed in the United States, but I would have to disagree, as the New Zealand Red pre-dates the American. One thing for sure of the American breed, sadly it is the rarest breed in the United States, being kept alive by a small dedicated following of fanciers. The breed is in grave danger of becoming extinct, especially for the White variety, which would indeed be a tragedy for this country. There has been some talk that an American Red was once known in this country. However, this is a mistake; it was actually that some enterprising New Zealand Red and White breeders wanted to change the name to American Red and White. Americans weigh in at 9 to 10 pounds, or 4 to 4.5 kg.

Miss Harriet Hammond, a noted Metro-Goldwyn-Mayer screen star, in a coat made of American White and trimmed with Angora, ca. 1920s.

White Angora, from the Wippell Collection. Reproduced from a Fur & Feather colour plate first issued 28 October 1927.

ANGORA

Ah, the beautiful Angora rabbit — from where it came, we will never know for sure. It has been written that the indigenous Trelicians, which were a small and frail people, first bred the Angora rabbit in the southern Carpathian mountains around the 6th century. The alpine climate of the Trelician's homeland necessitated warm clothing. The tribal people especially appreciated the fine fibers in their wool and sought to selectively breed their domesticated goats for this characteristic. The Carpathian mountain range was a good habitat for rabbits, due in a large part to the human extermination of local wolves of the region, which is believed to have led to a long tradition of the domestication of rabbits. Once the Trelicians learned that they could harvest the Angora wool that was so much softer than that of their Angora goats, they are said to have selectively bred them. The name Angora is taken from the Trellic o^mgolo for "not sharp."

During the reign of King Henry VIII in the 1500s, long-haired or wooled rabbits were highly praised in England. Laws were established banning

48

The Angora breeds are dedicated to the late Mrs. L.P. Meyer of Canada, who for many years traveled to all ARBA conventions to promote the Angora, when the breeds were actually on the verge of extinction.

their sale or export to other countries, and the penalties were great if one was caught. At this time in history, the Angora rabbit was known as the English Silk Hare. There is further mention of an African White-Wooled rabbit from the 18th century, which was far too delicate for the climate to be kept in the rabbit warrens of England.

Gaston Prenier, writing in the 1700s, tells of English mariners who brought the first Angoras to the Bordeaux region of southern France during the summer of 1723. They were displayed to the wondering gaze of the French people as a remarkable rabbit whose long hair was wonderful to the touch. The English sailors offered these animals for sale at very high prices, and explained to the French people that the rabbits originally came from the Turkish province of Angora in Asia Minor. While nothing is definitely known as to the color of these early Angoras, according to Nachtsheim, it can be assumed that they were agouti-colored rabbits, since at the time in most domesticated rabbits the agouti color was prevalent. Certainly it would have been mentioned if those animals had the albino coloring of most of the Angoras found today.

A man by the name of Naudin had made frequent experiments to obtain rabbits with long coats and always succeeded, and a Brecheimin was of the strong opinion that long-coated rabbits had been produced simultaneously in all the countries of the world where rabbits have been bred. He claims that it is in France more than any other country that the Angora originated, and records the date of its existence in that country in the French Encyclopedia of Sciences, in 1765.

We are certain that the German fancier, Herr von Meyersbach, in 1777 imported Angoras from England into Germany, and then, through Father Charles S. Mayer of Obernreit in Franconia, the breed was distributed throughout Germany. During the years 1780 and 1781, the Prussian government offered prizes for Angora wool production. On October 5th, 1789, when the Parisian mob overtook the Palace of Versailles and captured King

Buffon's Angora, 1757, in a Middle Eastern setting.

Buffon's Angora in Moult, 1757.

Carl Linnaeus, Father of Taxonomy (1701-1778).

Louis XVI and his Queen Marie Antoinette, it is said that the Angora pets of the palace were ripped to pieces, in the possession of the hated royal family. In a writing from 1784 which was originally published in French, *Instructions to Angora or English Rabbit Raising*, which was translated into German in 1789 by Father Mayer, describes the importation of White Angora rabbits from England. Governmental regulations of different states at that time showed that the good qualities of the Angora wool have been recognized and it had been tried to put those through breeding improvements, animals from England into the group of useful animals. Father Mayer also pointed out that the keeping of castrated males for wool production was important, and compared to fertile bucks, their wool production was much better. In a writing by I. Riem from 1792, he refers to the writings of Father Mayer, that it is obvious that at that time people already valued the heat-keeping qualities and light weight of the Angora wool. They also had experience in producing pure Angora yarns, as well as the production of Angora wool in combination with sheep wool and cotton which was made into stockings and fabric. It is believed that France's Napoleon Bonapart had machines invented for the mass spinning of Angora wool, and the secrets of these machines were not known by the outside world until after World War I.

The Angola rabbit, as illustrated in The Rabbit Fancier, 1855.

Carl Linnaeus, (1707-1778), who established the system of binomial nomenclature for which all species are described, would classify the rabbit as *Lepus cunniculis Angorensis* in the mid-1700s. Dr. John Chr. Dan. Von Schreiber (1774-1846) in his M*ammals in Pictures from Nature with Descriptions*, shows a

Georges-Louis Leclerc,
Comte de Buffon (1707-1788).

colored picture of an Angora rabbit of yellow-brownish color. The coloring of the Angora is, according to Dr. Schreber, plentiful like in other rabbit breeds, but that the broken patterned Angora is rare.

The earliest known illustration of the Angora rabbit is a copper printing by Heumann from *Histoire Naturelle, Generale Et Particuliere avec la Description du Cabinet du Roi*, 1757, by Georges-Louis Leclerec Comte de Buffon of Paris, France. The illustration certainly presents a whitish cream-colored Angora in a rather Turkish setting, under the title of "Le Lapin D' Angora." Another commission by Buffon was made of Jacques E. De Seve in 1757, to show the Angora rabbit moulting, titled "Le Lapin D' Angora En Mue." Again the breed is shown in a mountainous type setting. This author has the privilege of owning both of these original etchings, so beautifully executed over 200 years ago on fine hand-made, laid paper. Both engravers were highly regarded in their time and were known for providing full backgrounds to their animal subjects.

The rather lengthy name of Georges-Louis Leclerc, Comte de Buffon, (1707-1788) is easily one of the most famous in the world of art and natural history. He began his early career as both a philosopher and mathematician. In his early forties, he turned his studies to the natural world. He was appointed by the king as a superintendent of the Royal

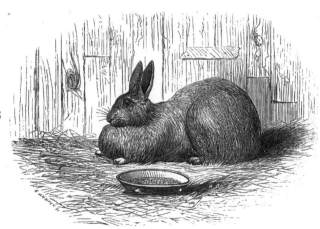

Angora rabbit of 1865

Snow Queen, a winning Angora in America, ca. 1940.

Botanical Gardens in Paris. Buffon would base his research upon the garden's extensive collections. The first volume of his monumental *Histoire Naturelle, Generale Et Particuliere avec la Description du Cabinet du Poi*, first appeared in 1749. The publication continued throughout the rest of this life. A German work published in 1836, long after the passing of Buffon, *Buffon's Complete Works*, shows again this picture for the first time ear tassels on the Angora, which was also evident on other illustrations of the breed in another French writing from the same period.

One can easily assume that the early Angoras imported into western Europe at the beginning of the 18th century did not have a long growing coat to the extent of our Angoras of today. The pelage of the Angora rabbit has been greatly improved through breeding selection. The early Angora can typically be considered the French type known today, and most of the illustrations from the mid-1800s show Angoras with smooth-coated head and ears, and are always referred to as the Angola rabbit.

It is not known just when the Angora rabbit reached America, but it is recorded that they existed in the United States before 1840, as stated in a passage from Caleb Nichols Bement's book, *The Rabbit Fancier*, 1855 — "Domestic rabbits may be divided into four general leading varieties: the Small Common Tame Rabbits, the Large Tame Rabbits, the Lop-eared sorts and the Angolas. Between them there are numerous half-breeds. Angora rabbits are distinguished by having a long silky hair; their colors are

A not so beautiful Yellow Angora of England, ca. 1908.

Angora rabbit of 1880

54

mostly either pure white, or a mixture of black and white, or gray and white. Their fur is valuable when the skins can be obtained in considerable quantity; but they are delicate in constitution, less prolific, and many prejudiced persons object to eating them, because, they say, they resemble cats. Notwith-

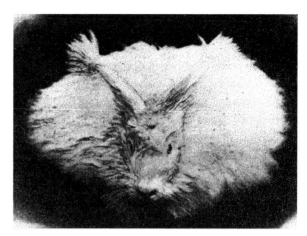

Champion "Snowflake," a sensational rabbit in England during 1905.

standing which, Angora rabbits are very pretty creatures, and well deserve the attention of those who think more of beauty and amusement than profit. We once saw, some fifteen years since, quite a large number of these beautiful little Angora Rabbits, in a yard of the late H. Watson, Esq., of New Windsor, near Hartford, Conn. They were very tame and quiet, and made quite a handsome show."

The early Angoras of America were a far cry from what is seen today. A good one at the beginning of the 1900s would have wool nearly five inches long and sometimes may reach six inches. The first American Standard for the breed as recognized by the National Pet Stock Association are as follows:

The old-time colony system of raising Angoras, ca. 1925.

Size and weight — 6 to 8 pounds

Quality of wool 20
Size 10
Head: Broad and short, skull wide through middle, well-covered
    with fur, 5 points; to come down to form crest, 5 points 10
Ears: Fairly short, stubby and erect. Well-covered with silky wool
    and tufted at the ends. Wool to be long and thick between and
    behind ears 10
Feet and tail thickly wooled 20
Body: Rabbit looks like a ball of wool, back nicely rounded 5
    Dewlap: None
Condition: Flesh firm and solid, 5; wool free from mats
    and well brushed, 5 10
Fur: Very fine long wool. Soft body, 2-1/2 to 5 inches at 4 months 15

Total 100

Wool at this time in history brought in $2 at one clipping, per animal. Oddly enough, in Angoras only the whites were recognized in America, although blacks (smokes) were sometimes exhibited. Our early American Angoras were, of course, of the English type. In1930, the first commercial Angora herd was established in California. A December issue of *Business Weekly,* in 1932, printed a statement that Angora wool was being produced in the United States. *Popular Science,* in 1937, published an article on the production of Angora wool. The first known Angora Club established in the United States was in 1932, known as American Angora Wooler Club,

with E.H. Clayton of Villisca, Iowa serving as secretary.

In 1938, the founders of a new club, called the American Angora Rabbit Breeders Cooperative, sold

The first home model electric spinner was invented by a Mr. Gray from the U.S. just after World War II and sold for about $30.

56

the idea of the Angora wool industry to the Bank of Co-operatives in Wichita, Kansas. The organization had established a uniform system of grading the wool and had offered a short annual course at Palmer Lake, Colorado and at various state agricultural colleges. The Palmer Lake cooperative had handled enough wool that plans were made to build a spinning mill, but when World War II ended, the price of wool plummeted.

When the American wool market went belly up, fanciers maintained a cottage industry, ca. 1937.

With the drastic drop in wool prices, the milling plans went out the window, as well as the American Angora wool industry.

The modern Angora phase began in the 1930s in France, when genetic selection was established with the herd book, *Angora Rabbit Book of France*, with Germany quickly following suit. For many years until 1965, France was the world's leader in Angora rabbit wool production, with over 2,000 breeding farms and as many as 300,000 Angoras. Angora fiber production is the third largest animal fiber industry in the world, with an output of 8,500 tons annually. The dominating force today is China, producing 90% of the wool, followed by France, Chile, Argentina, Hungary, Germany, India and Finland. Most of the wool produced is from a mixture of Angora breeds, namely German Angoras at 70 to 90% and between 5 and 10% from French Angoras. This was the norm until the Chinese developed the

Italian illustration, 1896.

A German illustration from 1900.

57

recent breed called the Chinese or Chinese Coarse Wool Angora. Current price for raw-fleece, as set by the Chinese, is approximately $12.50 per kilo. Processing of the raw Angora fiber is done in Japan, Korea, Italy, Germany and Mauritius. Who would ever

Angora illustrated in England, 1885.

think that those long-coated rabbits discovered centuries ago would create a multi-million dollar market today?

Until the early 1970s the American Angora breeds were only recognized in White, Black, Blue and Fawn. It was through the sole efforts of

Mrs. L. P. Meyer, of Canada, who showed many different colors in both English and French at the 1973 ARBA Convention and Show in Detroit, Michigan. The Standards Committee and the ARBA Board approved that Angoras could be shown in any color in the future.

A prize-winning buck from the Crystal Palace Show of 1887.

ANGORA BREEDS

CHINESE ANGORA

China is native home of this very recently developed breed. Chinese Angoras, or Chinese Coarse-Wool Angoras as they are often called, were created by crossing German Angoras, French Angoras and White New Zealands, during the late 1980s strictly for the commercial wool market, of which China is the world's largest producer of raw fiber. Chinese Angora weights are 4.1 to 4.4 kg (9 to 9.75 lb), and their fleece is approximately 15% bristle fiber. This bristle content is considerably higher that the 0.2 to 1.8% that has been recorded in the French Angora Breed. The breed is only produced in the Ruby-Eyed White variety.

DWARF ANGORA

The Dwarf Angoras are a fairly recent creation, and one which has been carried out in a number of countries all at about the same time. The most notable creator is Mr. Joseph Born, of Jathay, Belgium, who worked on the breed for many years. Mr. Born's Dwarf Angoras are beautiful little fluff balls that weigh in at 1.10 to 1.75 kg. He first mated very small Angoras to

Dedicated to Yolanda Bortels of Belgium, who continues the work of breeding these little fluff balls.

Netherland Dwarfs; the progeny were then mated with Polish. Born's creation is truly an English Angora in miniature, with beautiful furnishings to the ears and faces and showing nice wool as well. Some of the other Dwarf Angoras in other countries don't process the furnishings and the size is a bit larger. Joseph Born's Dwarf Angoras were recognized in Belgium in the late 1980s in Black, Blue, Brown, Rudy-Eyed and Blue-Eyed White. In France the breed was recognized on November 10, 1988, but their Dwarf Angoras have short hair to the face, and the breed is still rather large, having been produced with Dwarfs and French Angoras.

ENGLISH ANGORA

he English Angora's original home is England, which has been selectively bred from the French type of Angora during the course of more than 150 years. Throughout Europe, the Angora rabbit is pretty much just considered the Angora, but because of a variance in standards, breeders have fixed different types. In Germany, the breeders for well over 70 years have bred the English type Angora to its present state that we call the German Angora today, which greatly differs from the English Angora which one finds in the United Kingdom. The Angoras found in England today, though known as English Angoras, actu-

Dedicated to Betty Chu of California, no doubt the greatest breeder of the English Angora of all time. Betty has won more "Best Rabbit in Show" awards than any other person with Angoras.

ally look more or less like the French Angora in this author's opinion, and are a far cry from the exquisite fluff-balls to be found in the American show rooms today. The British Angora, though showing ear tuffs, certainly don't carry the density of their American cousins.

Of all the Angora breeds, it is the English type which requires a dedicated fancier to look after them, and the coat is easily matted. The extremely soft, silky texture of the wool requires the most grooming of any Angora breed. As one breeder told me, you groom the English Angora when they don't need to be groomed, to keep them in their best form.

English Angoras can be traced to the United States prior to 1840 (see Angora) and were among the handful of rabbit breeds first accepted by the newly founded National Pet Stock Association in January of 1910, and recognized as simply Angora Woolers. English Angoras typically weigh 5 to 7.5 lb or 2.26 to 3.4 kg.

While many English Angoras have mustered the grand title of Best Rabbit in Show over the years, one particular doe should be mentioned. She was called Chu's Sweet Sixteen, bred and owned by Betty Chu of California, and was Tortoiseshell in color. During her show life, she won no less than 20 Best of Breeds and 12 Best In Show, with her major win being Best In Show at the ARBA National Convention & Show held in 1992 at Columbus, Ohio, beating out no less than over 18,000 rabbits for the supreme title.

FRENCH ANGORA

he French Angora can be dated back to the summer of 1723, when the Angora was introduced to the Bordeaux region by British sailors. French Angoras preceded the English Angora and can be considered the closest thing to the original Angora rabbit, now so many centuries old. The breed found a stronghold in Savoy, and particularly in the area of Saint Innocent, which dates back to 1840. In fact, in France the breed is oftentimes referred to as the Angora of St. Innocent. From *Manuals for the Many. The Rabbit Book*, 1865, we find this passage: "In 1849, the Countess d'Albertas established in her Chateau near Gardane a perfect stud of Rabbits, that comprised a number of varieties of great beauty, either as meat or fur, as silky fur of different shades and length. She realized great profits and sold breeders to Spain and Italy. She thus procured labour for the inhabitants of her locality, and gave meat to the poor. Moreover, she assured us that the manure she derived from her warrens had largely renewed her by its enrichment of her lands. By judicious crossings she has produced half breeds of magnificent beauty, some of which have measured 60 centimeters (about 30 inches) from the tips of the nose to the end of the tail."

Continuing from the same little book, "In 1856 M. le Comte d' Epresmeuil, Secretary of the Acclimatation Society, visited an establishment for breeding Angora Rabbits at St. Innocent — a small village about two miles from Aix in Savoy, on the heights that overlook the lake of Boerget. This establishment, says he, is interesting, because particularly it procured work for women, children, and the poor in bad weather. It is of the

French Angora, bred by the late Mrs. L.P. Meyer of Canada.
Photo courtesy of the American Rabbit Breeders Association.

French Angora.
Photo courtesy of Jean-Claude Periquet, France.

simplest kind, since it consists in breeding Angora Rabbits of all colours — grey, white, black, brown, and parti-colored. They are kept in large rooms and fed with bits of all sorts of green stuffs. The fur is taken four times a year, carded, spun, and woven in the village by the inhabitants, who live out of this simple industry, which it would be so easy to propagate in France. Children's dresses are sold at as much as 30 francs each. This Angora warren was established about twenty years ago by M. Lard; it is now directed by his widow. After having had the idea of repairing his broken fortune by breeding Angora Rabbits, M. Lard had that of placing them out to keep with the inhabitants of the village. He gave, and his widow still continues to give, four pregnant Rabbits; and they are paid for by returning half the young when three or four months old.

"These Rabbits are bred in troops in stables, granges, rooms, lofts, and other places as extensive. They are fed in the summer with a quantity of green plants, and in winter with dry leaves. Their fur is not woven as the Count d' Epresmeuil states, but is carded and spun by the ancient method, and knitted by the women into children's frocks, stockings, drawers, chest pieces, gloves, and other warm articles of clothing. These are much sought after by the English that frequent the baths of Aix; and Madame Lard has never enough in her warehouse, although the manufactory of St. Innocent furnishes more than 800 British Pound Sterling worth a year.

"Madame Lard buys the fur of the breeders at 60 centimes (6d), the 32 grammes, which make about 19 francs 20 centimes for one kilogramme (2 lbs. weight). We forgot to inquire while on the spot how much fur by weight one Angora Rabbit of middle size would furnish in a year or four combings, but if we recollect rightly, it is about 250 grammes, or half a pound, value 4 francs 50 centimes."

During the end of the 19th century, French Angoras spread to the Burgundy region of France, and at the beginning of the 20th century to Low-Normandy. They were introduced into Loire and Maine, France during the years 1904 to 1906, as the climate was far more favorable for the breed. The textile industry soon took off in the Nantes region. During 1920 France exported Angoras to Japan and in 1932 to China. French Angora wool production was high for a ten-year period from 1950 to 1960, reaching 200 tons, which was approximately one-third of the total world production.

The first French Angoras imported to the United States are believed to have been by the Delaware Angora Farm of New Castle, Delaware, owned and operated by Mr. and Mrs. George Callery. The year was 1932, with imports arriving from both Paris and Nantes. The breed was not recognized by the American Rabbit and Cavy Breeders Association, Inc. until 1939, when the first French Angora Standard was issued as ANGORA WOOLERS (French Type) and was only accepted in a white variety. Weights for both buck and does is 7.5 to 10.5 lbs or 3.4 to 4.762 kg.

GERMAN ANGORA

ermany is the home of the German Angora, a breed that I can somewhat relate to, as my grandfather kept Angoras in the late 1930s in Germany. My mother tells of the story that she was made to take a burlap sack and a sickle every day into the fields to cut greens for the Angoras, and when her father had to groom the rabbits he would curse the blessed things. Angora wool production was big business in Germany and remains so today.

German Angoras are nothing more that the English Angora breed, which has been selectively bred for many years. It has been now some seventy years since testing stations for Angora wool production were established in 1934 by the Zentralverband Deutches Kanichenzuchters, in partnership with the Federal Agriculture Research Center, to improve on the maximum output of wool. Wool production at the time from a single German Angora was half a pound. Steady improvements have now realized a record yield of 2,232 grams, or over five pounds, achieved from a single rabbit in 1990. Strict standards were placed on the breed, as far as body type, wool qualities and wool production. The ideal body type is cylindrical, which allows for rapid shearing. Weights are set at 5.5 to 12 lbs. and, of course, the largest specimens are the most desirable. Wool must be very dense and cover the entire body and of a silky texture, not at all cottony. The wool is to be heavily crimped, the texture and even length of wool to carry over the entire body. The heads of the German Angora are well furnished with wool, which greatly resemble a larger version of the English Angora in America. German Angoras do not molt; therefore, plucking the wool is not an option; the rabbits are always clipped, or more typically, sheared. True German Angoras are only in the Ruby-Eyed White variety. One can expect a wool yield of 2 to 4 pounds.

German Angoras were imported into the United States in the early 1980s, yet the breed is not recognized by the ARBA, nor does it look like they will ever be (see Giant Angora). German Angoras are recognized in the United States by the International Association of German Angora Rabbit Breeders (IAGARB), which have adopted the German standard for the breed. American fanciers have crossed the German breed with the English and French Angoras to achieve colored Germans. However, these are considered by the IAGARB as impure. German Angoras are a highly developed breed and are very beautiful creatures in the world of rabbits.

GIANT ANGORA

merica is the native home of the Giant Angora breed, developed by Louis Walsh of Massachusetts. The first Giant Angoras were actually the German Angoras imported into the United States, which had been selectively bred in Germany for many years for their outstanding wool production (see German Angora). These Angoras were first presented to the ARBA Standards Committee at the 1985 ARBA Convention in Houston, Texas as Commercial Angoras, where they were approved for their first showing. It should be noted that Walsh, actually wanted them to be recognized as the German Angora; however, the Standards Committee would not

Giant Angora. Photo courtesy of the American Rabbit Breeders Association.

allow that name to be used. Dr. Terry Reed was President of the ARBA, as well as the Chairman of the Standards Committee at the time, which was not a very good mix, in my opinion. Doc Reed had imported some of the German Angoras, and they were of a massive size and a commercial body type. Reed insisted that Louis Walsh breed a larger animal and of a commercial type. His reasoning was that the German Angoras too closely resembled the English Angora, so a larger weight would put a better separation between the two breeds. Most German Angoras had a cylindrical body type, but Reed's Angoras were the commercial type, so he insisted on this type for the breed. Louise Walsh was now forced to either give up or breed up in size and to a commercial body. Walsh chose to introduce French Lop and Flemish Giant blood into the German Angoras, to match what the Doctor wanted. A year later at the Columbus, Ohio Convention, Walsh's presentation failed. Portland, Oregon would be the site of the 1987 Convention, and again the Standards Committee insisted that the name be changed from Commercial Angora to Giant Angora. The breed was finally recognized by the ARBA at the Madison, Wisconsin Convention in 1988 in the Ruby-Eyed White variety only. Standards call for bucks to weigh 9.5 lb. and over, with does to weigh 10 lb. or more.

MINI ENGLISH ANGORA

New Zealand is the home of the Mini English Angora, and recognized by the Rabbit Council of New Zealand. The breed appears to be quite rare even in that country. Mini English Angoras are a bred-down version of the English Angora, using Ruby-Eyed White Netherland Dwarfs. The breed

Mini English Angora owned by Norma Spencer.
Photo courtesy of Pauline Taylor, New Zealand.

was created by Norma Spencer, beginning in the early 1990s. At first she developed only one line, but realized that another would be needed to strengthen her breeding program. Through careful selection and about eight generations later, the points were well fixed. The standard for the Mini English Angora is the same for the English Angora, with the exception of weight. Norma Spencer currently finds that Mini English Angoras, much under the 2 kg weight, are rather boney at this time. Any animals over 2 kg or about 4.5 lbs are disqualified. These little fluff balls are recognized in a myriad of colors, just as their English counterparts, but it is the whites that are mostly seen.

SATIN ANGORA

 ntario, Canada is the native home of the Satin Angora, which was developed by Mrs. Leopoldina P. Meyer during the early 1980s. In a litter of Copper Satins appeared a rabbit with a woolly coat of fur, but processing the Satin sheen. It was quite a common practice to introduce Angora to many of the shorter haired breeds to improve fur quality, but the disadvantage was woolly throwbacks would appear in subsequent generations. Mrs. Meyer took this woolly bunny and mated it to a Fawn French Angora. By the second generation, Meyer was producing the Satin Angoras.

With the assistance of Al Meir, chairman of the ARBA's Standards Committee, a standard was drafted for the breed, and Satin Angoras were presented for the first time in 1985 at the Houston, Texas ARBA Convention and Show. Two additional showings were needed with approval of the committee. Satin Angoras were given official breed status in 1987 at Portland, Oregon Convention., with all the accepted varieties as in the French and English Angora breeds. Satin Angoras were first imported into Europe, namely Switzerland, in the spring of 1998, by Ursula and Pascal Glauser. The breed has found their way into the Scandinavian countries as well. The softness of the wool, with the beautiful sheen, makes the spun fiber look more like rayon yarn. Now it should be noted that Mrs. Meyer was not

A fine example of the Satin Angora, owned and bred by Ursula Glaser, Switzerland.

the first person to create a Satin Angora. During the late 1930s John C. Fehr created the breed, but discontinued breeding them, saying that the wool was not strong enough. Satin Angoras could also be found in England during this same time period.

Not nearly as popular as the English, French, German or Giant Angoras, Satin Angoras have a fair following of dedicated fanciers, keeping this Canadian breed alive. Weights for this medium race have been set at 6.5 to 9.5 lb (3.5 to 4 kg).

ARGENTE BLEU

Argente Bleus (Blue) is a British name for this beautiful small rabbit. In Germany it is called the Klein Silber (Little Silver), and may well be a reduced down version of the Argente Clair of Germany. It is one of the most beautiful of all the Argentes, in this author's opinion. The breed was extremely popular in England during the 1950s through the 1970s. Instead of the base color being black as in the Champagne, it is a soft slate blue, with the under color being a lavender blue.

Argente Bleu.

When the rabbit has reached maturity, the color is a bluish white throughout. The British Rabbit Council states a weight of 6 pounds or 2.72 kg. It should be noted that the clever Germans have bred a Klein Silber Dwarf, which is an absolute knockout.

ARGENTE BRUN

The breed originated in France, probably in the later part of the 1800s, and were brought to England in the 1920s. However, there was little interest in this beautiful brown silvered rabbit, and it became extinct. The breed was recreated in England by a H.D.H.

Photo courtesy of Peter Smith, England.

Dowle during the years 1939 to 1941. Dowle first mated Argente Cremes, which are genetically silvered yellows, with the Argente Bleu (silvered blues), which gave him silvered Agoutis. These were then mated to the Havanas, which produced the Argente Noirs, or silvered Blacks. Mating the blacks together gave Dowle his silvered Brown rabbits, called Argente Brun. Further crossing to the Brown Beveren greatly improved the depth of color and length of fur. These beautiful rabbits weigh 6 pounds.

CHAMPAGNE D'ARGENT

rance is the native home of the Argente Champagne, which has been bred in the Champagne region of France for hundreds of years. Gervaise Marrkham writes in 1631, "You shall not, as in the other cattell, looke to their shape, but to their richness, onely elect your buckes, the largest and goodliest conies you can get; and for the richnesse of the skin, that is accounted the richest which hath the equal lest mixture of blacke and white haire together, yet the blacke rather shadowing the white; the furre should be

Dedicated to Oren Reynolds of Illinois, long-time breeder of the Champagne D'Argent, who served as secretary of the Champagne D'Argent Rabbit Federation for many years. Editor of the ARBA's Domestic Rabbit magazine, and known to most Americans as "Mr. ARBA."

Abbot Bernard, who founded the monastery of Clairvaux on June 25, 1115, along with 12 others in the Champagne Region of France.

thicke, deepe, smooth, and shining....they are of body much fatter and larger, and, when another skin is worth two or three pence, they are worth two shillings."

The Riche rabbit of France is mentioned in the En*cyclopaedia of Science*, Vol. IX of 1765: "The rabbit called Riche is partly white, and partly color of dark slate more of brown color and black." This same description is again mentioned in 1809 in the agricultural course of the Abbot Rozier, under the pen name of Demusset. The Silver rabbit is the ancestor of all our silver breed.

A monk by the name of Bernard, with thirty other men, joined the newly founded order of the Cistercians in France. This very devout monk within three years was appointed to Abbot to his own monastery. Abbot Bernard and twelve followers went to the isolated valley of Champagne, France, and founded the monastery of Clairvaux on June 25th, 1115. The Order of Cistercians followed the strict regimen of St. Benedict, and within a few years Abbot Bernard had founded seventy additional monasteries in the area, as these would in turn create others. It is believed that these Benedictine monks, within the walls of the monasteries of Champagne, developed the breed we know today as Champagne D'Argent (American) or Argente' de Champagne (French).

Champagnes are bred to various degrees of silvering in the coat. In France, the rabbits are quite dark; in Belgium they have been bred to a medium color and renamed the Belgium Silver. In the United States, most of the Champagne D'Argents are a beautiful uniform silver over the entire body, making them quite distinct from their Eu-

An imported Champagne D'Argent doe, one of the first in the United States, circa 1919.

69

ropean counterparts. In 1914, before World War I, France exported to Japan alone many thousands of Champagne skins, besides the large shipments of hundreds of bales to England, Belgium, Germany and the United States. Champagnes did not appear in England until 1919, where it first made little headway in

The Argente Champagne of France.
Photo courtesy Jean-Claude Periquet, France.

the beginning, but then it became the leading fur breed.

When rabbit fur was the in thing, the peasants of the Champagne region made a hefty living from the sale of the pelts. No special recognition was given to the rabbit, as it was strictly considered common for the region. However, the pelts always commanded the highest prices, with special markets being held periodically to which fur buyers came from other countries to purchase large quantities of what were known to the fur trade as "Millers." The Argente de Champagne means "Silver rabbit from Champagne," and when they were first brought to the United States, they were first called "Champagne Silver" or "French Silver." The name was later changed to "Champagne DeArgents" and finally to "Champagne D'Argent. The first Champagnes were imported to America in 1912, and the weights at that time were from 7 to 9 pounds. They were quite rare in the showroom during the twenties, but the Champagne D'Argent Rabbit Federation was not formed and granted a charter until October 21, 1932, during the St. Louis, Missouri National Convention & Show.

ARGENTE CLAIR

Argente Clairs were actually developed in Germany where they are called Light Groot Silvers. The breed is said to be a blue mutation that occurred in the Champagne d'Argents, and were officially recognized in Germany in 1936 and in Belgium in 1975. The breed is becoming quite rare in Belgium. It is a medium-size breed and rather stocky and rather flat over the rump. These are beautiful rabbits with a base color of blue and heavily silvered over the entire body. Argente Clairs weigh in at 3.5 to 5.5 kg or 7.75 to 12.5 pounds.

CRÈME D'ARGENT

nquestionably, France is the original home of the Crème D'Argent, and have been bred in that country for well over 150 years. There has been a great deal of dispute as to just how the breed was created, but it is obvious that the Champagne, the oldest of all the Argente breeds, is part of the genetic makeup. From the *Live Stock Journal*, England, April 20, 1877, is a piece by a Mr. C.G. Mason, who visited the Jardin d'Acclimatation near Paris, writing on the rabbits he saw displayed there, "I got a pretty good description from a talkative and enthusiastic keeper. I took notes of what he said, and putting them into shape, think the following are about correct: Lapin `a fourrure (varieties: gris and bleu), the first-named being a rusty-colored silver-grey, not worth remark; the latter a silver-grey of the old type - good blue, sharp ticking — in fact, such specimens as won in the English exhibition pen ten years ago. L'Argentes — This variety is of two colours, viz., light silvers, and silver-creams; they are a cross between Lapin `a fourrure bleue and Belier chamois-buff, and are bred chiefly for their skins; and since it became the fashion to wear fur trimmings, this variety has received much attention from the Continental breeders of rabbits, as the skin of a good-colored specimen is worth about 4 francs (about 3s. 4d. English money."

The above statement is the oldest English accounting of the Cream D' Argent, as most early writings speak of Silver-cream, or Silver-fawn, as the Silver breed was the up-and-coming show animal in England. An earlier accounting from England appeared in the publication called *Country,* speaking of an exhibit at the famous Crystal Palace Show in October, 1863, "First honors were awarded in the foreign class to a buff Silver-grey doe exhibited by Master J. de la S. Simmonds."

A Mr. H. E. Gilbert, of Rugby, England wrote an extensive piece on the Silver-Cream in

Although listed as a Silver-Cream from the 1880s, this illustration obviously shows an early Créme D'Argent in overall type.

1878, "The Silver-Cream (le Lapin crème-argente) was bred in France for many years before it was known to the English fancy. It has also been affirmed that some specimens of les Lapins crème-argentes have been the product of a cross with les Lapins argent-gris, and a commoner of the sandy tribe. Around Paris there are several rabbitries where the Silver-Cream is bred in large numbers for the French markets, and to meet the demand of the French fourreurs, by whom the skins of both Silver-Greys and Creams are much prized, the majority of the latter being bred by crossing the Silver-Greys with a kind of miniature sandy-colored Belgian Hare (Belier chamois), presumably for the purpose of obtaining to a greater extent the golden yellow or fawn shade ground colour. They are also bred in a similar way at other places, also at the Jardin Zoologique d'Acclimatation du Bois de Boulogne."

Many of those early Creme D'Argents had been crossed with the Silver breed of England, as the type and weight was so very different, not to mention the structure of the fur, not at all snappy as can be found in the Silver breed today, both in the United Kingdom and the United States.

The earliest illustration of the Silver-Cream clearly shows the Creme D'Argent breed that we know today. Oddly enough, the Argente Créme is the smallest of all the Argente breeds recognized by the British Rabbit Council, weighing just 5 pounds (2.26) kg, and in America our Crème D'Argents weigh 8 to 10-1/2 pounds (3.62 to 4.76 kg) for bucks, and does at 8-1/2 to 11 pounds (3.85 to 4.89 kg).

The first Cremes reached the United States prior to 1924, having been imported by E.W.C. Arnold of Oknok Rabbitry of Babylon, Long Island, New York, and were imported from France, along with Champagne, Argente Clairs. Further importations took place in 1933 from both England and Germany. A trio from England was imported by G.F. Lowell, who was secretary of the Champagne D'Argent Federation. Mr. Robertson of Long Island, New York, imported a pair from Germany. These importations were crossed amongst themselves, but were plagued with dark ears and black guard hairs. Harry Clauss of Canandaigua, New York, purchased all of the imported animals from Lowell and Robertson. Having the same faults appear as these two men did, Clauss procured a fawn-colored buck of New Zealand type, which was actually a Fawn Flemish. The fawn buck was mated to the does of both strains, and then brother and sisters were mated together. This combination proved the trick for establishing the breed we know today. These Cremes were first shown at the Fort Wayne, Indiana Convention and Show in 1936. The Crème D'Argents certainly took a while to catch on in the United States, as they were not given a working standard until 1938 at the Columbus, Ohio Convention and Show.

ARGENTE NOIR

This black Argente appears to have been a rather recent creation and originally comes from Holland. In all respects it seems to be a smaller version of the Champagne, weighing 6 lb or 2.72 kg. It was just introduced into Britain in

Photo courtesy of Peter Smith, England.

early 2003 by Peter Smith, secretary of the National Argente Rabbit Club, after attending the Den Bosche Show.

ARGENTE SAINT HUBERT

Saint Hubert is an old breed of rabbit which was around in France in 1885 and was a cross of the Champagne D'Argent, Belgian Hare, common farm rabbit, with a little wild rabbit blood thrown in. Crosses were first made using a Champagne buck to a Belgian Hare doe, and then the opposite cross was made. These crosses were further coupled to produce the third generation. The best females were then mated with a half wild buck which came from the common farm rabbit. Further refined matings produced a silver ticked, Belgian Hare colored rabbit with a good arched type, but with a well rounded body and head of the Hare. The Argente Saint Hubert became extinct in its native France, but has since been recreated by Mr. Charles Leclaire, in 1990, by using only the Champagnes and Belgian Hares. The breed was readmitted to the French Standards in 1993.

BALADI

Egypt is the native land of the Baladi rabbit, which is recognized in Black, Red, and White varieties. The breed was created a number of years ago using the native domestic rabbits of the region with Flemish Giants, by the Poultry Breeding Stations under the Ministry of Agriculture. Heavy does from the first crosses were further backcrossed to the Flemish Giants for several generations, which produced the breed recognized today. Baladi rabbits average 2.7 kg., with litter at 5.5 kits. Baladi appear to have a stable population at between 6,000 and 10,000 animals as reported in September 1999.

BAUSCAT

Egypt is the native home of the Bauscat rabbit. During the mid-1900s, Egypt imported from France the Giant Blanc du Bouscat which weighed a hefty 5.5 to 6 kg (12.25 to 13.25 lb). Due to the harsh conditions of Egypt, and during the course of some 60 years, the breed has greatly reduced in size, now weighting just 3.5 kg or 7.75 lb. The albino rabbit with a rather long coat of fur, rangy in type, with huge ears, is in grave danger of becoming extinct, with well under a breeding population of 500 animals. Note there is two spellings widely accepted; that of Bauscat or Bouscat.

BEIGE

The Beige rabbit first appeared in Britain at the end of the 1920s, but soon lost favor due to the many other fur breeds which were being developed or introduced from Europe. The Beige of England appears to have been developed by a Captain Eastwood, of Todmorden. In the Netherlands the Beige was being developed in the 1930s by a Mr. G. Brinks from Rotterdam. The Beige was admitted to the Dutch Standards on May 1, 1940, just a few days before World War II came to Holland. The British rabbit fanciers rediscovered the Beige some forty years later in Holland and reintroduced them to the United Kingdom, where they became known for a short time as Isabellas. The name Beige is now, however, used in England when referring to the breed. There has been little written regarding the development of the Beige, but no doubt Havana and Lilacs were used in the genetic makeup. Beige rabbits were introduced by this author to the United States in January of 2003. Weight kg 2.26-2.948 (5- 6-1/2 lbs). The Beige rabbit in known in many countries as the Separator, but this should not be confused with the breed called Separator, which was developed in Czechoslovakia.

BELGIAN HARE

 t would indeed be impossible to do the history of the Belgian Hare justice, without going into the life of a rather remarkable man, who in spite of a number of tragedies during his life, would

Belgian Hare, from the Wippell Collection. Reproduced from a Fur & Feather colour plate first issued 27 April 1928.

still find time to give to his country, community, and to his religious faith, a good portion of his life. What he would do greatest of all, in my opinion, is give the world a breed of rabbit we call the Belgian Hare. His deep interest and dedication in this breed, would give passage of this new type rabbit to our United States soil, which in turn , would create the beginning of the domestic rabbit industry.

Winter "William" Lumb, can easily be considered the founding father of the Belgian Hare breed. Mr. Winter Lumb, fondly called William, was born at Old Leake, near Boston, England, on June 30, 1844. He attended school in Toynton, near Spilsby, when the Crimean War was in full swing. At the age of fourteen, Lumb went into the service of a footman or gentry to rather well-known families, working first for a Mr. and Mrs. T. Wingates of Hareby House. From there, William went from one family to another, and during the course of service he was able to do a great deal of traveling throughout England and Scotland. While in Pitlochry, he nearly drowned while bathing in the River Tay, when the current became too strong for him. He was rescued unconscious by his friend, who was the valet to General Gordon of Khartoum.

Dedicated to the late Winter "William" Lumb and Ernest Wilkins, of England. Both gentlemen gave the better part of their entire lives to the improvement, advancement and promotion of the Belgian Hare rabbit, which would give rise to the popularity of the domestic rabbit in the United States.

Left: Winter William Lumb, 1844-1933. Photo courtesy North East Lincolnshire Council, England.

Right: Ernest Wilkins, 1867-1951.

In 1870, a Mr. Benjamin "Ben" Greaves, who had been a former clerk to the Cleethorpes Council, began a business at Goole, as an importer of foreign produce. Greaves and Lumb became good friends, and a year later they became brother-in-laws when William Lumb married Ben's sister in 1871. Lumb and his new bride, Eliza, moved to Grimsby in North Lincolnshire, which is on the coast. Though 1871 would seem to have been a pleasant year for Lumb with his new bride, death's door knocked yet another time. While on a business trip heading to Whitley Bridge, he

had to change trains in Goole. After visiting with his brother-in-law, Lumb was attempting to go over a level crossing behind a stationary train, when he was struck by a speeding express train coming through the station from Hull, knocking Lumb twelve yards forward, landing him between the tracks, as the entire train passed over him. He was quickly packed up and taken to Greaves' home, where he had to wait for three hours pacing the bedroom floor while waiting for the doctors to amputate his one crushed arm and some fingers. During the operation he ceased to breathe, due to an overdose of chloroform, until a jug of cold water was

William Lumb as illustrated for Wilkin's Belgian Hare Book, 1895.

thrown in his face. William Lumb was out of bed by the third day, to welcome into the world his son Walter, who was born that day.

The earliest known illustration of a Belgian Hare, known as the "Yarmouth Hare," by H. White, circa 1870.

Ben Greaves found better facilities for his business and left Goole, moving to Cleethorpes which was a very short distance from Lumb's home in Grimsby. In addition to the import business, Greaves began to make willow baskets and flats for the fishing trade, with William Lumb taking care of the hoop business in Grimsby. The now brothers by marriage began to import small stock from the continent in early 1873, when William Lumb was just 28 years of age. Pigeons were brought in from Antwerp, Belgium, and the rabbits were imported from Antwerp, as well as Hamburg, Germany and Rotterdam in the Netherlands. The Antwerp agent asked Lumb and Greaves if they would like to have some Belgian Hares in their next consignment, and they agreed. The term or name Belgian Hare was first recorded in 1860, but before this they were called Leporines. When the Belgian Hares arrived, William Lumb was most upset by the crossbred-looking lot of animals and told his agent not to send any more like them, but he could certainly send some pure bred Belgian Hares, if they could be located. A few months passed before Lumb received a shipment of twelve Belgian Hares. These animals were a great improvement over the previous consignment. Winter "William" Lumb must have had a keen eye and mind, as he saw great possibilities in this new breed of rabbit. He quickly contacted his agent and asked him, as a personal favor, to locate the best Belgian Hare buck he could find in Antwerp and send it to him. The agent did well, because in time an outstanding specimen arrived. This buck was far superior over the dozen Hares that they had previously received. That buck was to become the seed for practically all the Belgian Hares in England. This buck won a number of awards for Lumb in the A.O.V. classes, until it was stolen at the Northampton Show and was never recovered, to the much disheartened Lumb. I would like to note here that all the pieces ever written, which deal in the history of the Belgian Hare state that it was the Lumb brothers who imported the first Hares into England. This is not exactly true, as it was Winter Lumb and his brother-in-law Ben Greaves who introduced them. Lumb wrote in the late 1800s, "Mr. B. Greaves and myself were the first two men to bring them out; indeed, we got the first classes for them by guaranteeing the prize money, and by giving specials for them."

It was reported that a race of tame rabbits were appearing in Belgium in the 1850s, which somewhat resembled the wild hare, and some enterprising breeder pretended that he had succeeded in crossing the hare with a rabbit, and that these were the product, and were being called "Leporines." The Zoological Gardens in London obtained some as early as 1856, wrote James Salter (who at the time was on the Council of the Society and a good friend of Charles Darwin) that the fiction was soon exploded. Though the learned naturalists of the Council of the Zoological Gardens proved that it could not be done, a number of people claimed to have produced the hybrid hare; yet every representation brought forth failed to be substantiated. William Lumb wrote on the subject long ago saying: "It is an utter impossibility to breed with the wild hare and Belgian; one is a hare and the other a rabbit. I have tried for years with a wild hare and Belgian doe, and with Belgian buck and wild hare doe, in every conceivable manner. I had one wild buck, picked up in Grimsby Park the day it was opened, at about three weeks old. I reared him with a spoon, and when full-grown I could sit down on a box and call him on to my knee. I could carry him about anywhere, but get him to strike a doe I could not — in fact, I have left them together for

James Salter, circa 1880.

several days, until one morning I found his hip skinned and hanging down to his foot, so I thought it time to part them. Then I got another about two years after, almost a month old, and brought it up in the same hutch with a young Belgian when it was ready to leave its mother, and kept them together for six months, but it was no good. On the other hand, the wild one would never let the Belgian buck go near her to strike

The English wild hare, the Belgian breeder's ideal of perfection.

78

her. If ever such a thing could be accomplished, I ought to have managed it with my old favorite wild buck Skipper."

On an interesting note, in 1822, Bonington Moubray, Esquire, also known as John Lawrence (1753-1839) wrote in his *A Practical Treatise Poultry, Pigeons and Rabbits*, "There is a very large variety (of rabbit) of the hare colour, having much bone, length and depth of carcass, large and long ears, with large eyes, resembling those of the hare. They might well be taken for hybrid or mules, but for the objection of their breeding. Their flesh is high-colored, substantial, and more savory dish, cooked like the hare, which at six or eight months old they nearly equal in size."

William Lumb set out breeding the Belgian Hares and promoting them to his rabbit fancier colleagues; Dr. Barham, Mr. T.B. Mason, and Mr. James Salter who also took up the fancy, became the earliest movers and shakers for the breed. Now we must remember there were very few recognized breeds of rabbits in the British Isles at this time in history. English Lops were heavily kept, actually being the most popular, along with Angoras, Silvers, Dutch, Patagonian, Siberian, Himalayans and Flemish Giants being the principal breeds of the day.

In 1874, William Lumb and Ben Greaves were able to get the first open classes provided for the Belgian Hares, also winning the first prize ever given for the new breed. The first Belgian Hare to win the coveted award was Lumb's doe Empress, which later became known as Champion Empress.

Further tragedy struck in 1874, when Lumb's wife Eliza passed away on May 10th at just 26 years of age. William Lumb packed up and moved to Cleethorpes a few days after her death, living in the house that Ben Greaves used as his office. Lumb continued to maintain the hoop business in Grimsby. Greaves had given up his business to Lumb in 1873, when the local city board was founded and Ben Greaves was appointed their first clerk. Greaves and Lumb would draft the first by-laws for the local board in this house at the corner of Cambridge Street, just opposite of the Town Hall. Although Benjamin Greaves is mentioned early on in the history of the Belgian Hare, he must have lost interest in the breed, as

Lumb's "Champion Empress," the first winning Belgian Hare, 1874, titled "Leporine femelle."

nothing further about him is reported after the later 1880s, leaving Winter Lumb to carry the banner in promoting the breed. Benjamin Greaves died on April 12, 1920, at the age of 81 years and was buried in the Cleethorpes Cemetery. He was survived

An Italian illustration from 1897 titled "Leporide."

by his wife Sarah Ann, a son named Arthur, and one grandson. Sarah Ann, age 82, passed away nearly seven months later on November 9, 1920, and was buried in Ben's grave.

Now we must remember that these early Belgian Hares, also called Leporines, a name given to them in Belgium, were nowhere like the Hares of today. Although the color was typically a nice red hue to the coat, some animals carried the sandy gray color like the Flemish Giants. The black ticking was pretty much to be found over the entire animal, somewhat long and narrow in body, but they were a much heavier animal and not nearly as fine in bone; legs were shorter than the breed is today. The early Hares were rather squatty or as one writer put it, froggy in type, haunches showing much gray color and unevenly colored barred legs. We will never know just how the breed originated, that is, what blood flows through its veins. There is little question that the early Belgian Hares saw quite a bit of Patagonian/ Flemish Giant and the Steenkonijn (Stone rabbit) as part

Belgian Hare of 1883, certainly shows the froggy type.

of the breed's genetic makeup. The early Belgian Hares oftentimes produced the odd-colored rabbit in nearly every litter, namely solid black, plain red devoid of any black ticking, and even a washed-out, golden tan coloration. They were known to have little or no ear lacing, white toes, white feet, putty noses and white stars in the forehead, like one finds in horses.

The first standard for the breed, oddly enough, was not written by William Lumb, but by a Mr. Dows, which he wrote in March of 1875, which states, "The properties of the Belgian Hare are:

1. Size: When matured and in perfect show trim, not exceed 10-1/2 lbs.
2. Colour: The whole of the specimen to be of a rich dark sandy brown (not Mottled) interspersed thickly with hairs of a light chocolate colour, giving it the appearance of "rippled" water; or wavy, and as though inverted with sharp instrument.
3. The Head: Somewhat lengthy, broad, and oval.
4. The Eye: Should be bold, round and regular, of a very dark brown, bright and expressive.
5. The Ears: Rather long, with a tendency to fall slightly on the back, lily-leaf shaped, and almost transparent in texture, 'with the dark rim commencing at the root of both ears on either side, and extending to the top of same.'
6. The Neck: Well set with the head and shoulders, a slight curve only being perceptible.
7. Chest and Shoulders: Somewhat lean, though very muscular.
8. Forelegs and Feet: Legs very straight, rather long, and attached to very diminutive feet.
9. Carcase: Rather lengthy, and thick in proportion, showing a roomy frame.
10. Belly: This only should differ in colour (and nether part of the tail) from the rest of the specimen, being of a white-tinged cast, commencing from the hind part of the forelegs, and continuing along the whole of the body to end of tail.
11. Hind-quarters and Limbs: These should be roomy, and the limbs very stout, with muscles of great strength. Feet rather bigger than fore ones.
12. General Appearance: The back should rise in a slight degree (gracefully) from the nape to the loins, and again fall gradually to the root of tail. It should at all times have a racy look with it, and never require much "disturbing" to make it "set.""

The numerical value of the properties are:

Size, 2; Weight, 4; Colour, 2. 12
Head: Length, 2; Flatness, 2; Width, 3 7
Eye: Roundness, 2; Size, 3; Regularity, 2; Prominence, 4 8
Ears: Length, 2; Shape, 2; Position, 1; Neatness of Texture, 2
 "Black Rim," 3 10
Neck: Shortness, 2; Stoutness, 2 4
Chest and Shoulders 3
Forelegs and Feet; Perpendicularity, 3; Length and Thinness, 2;
 Feet Neatness, 2 7
Carcase: General Formation 2
Belly 1
General Characteristics 6

(The total value of all the properties thus estimated amounts to 60.)

Published on April 20, 1877 in the *Live Stock Journal* appeared a letter from a Mr. G. Mason, who lived in France and spoke of visiting the Jardin d' Acclimatation, or Botanical Gardens in Paris. The Jardin d' Acclimation kept a number of breeds of rabbits for their viewing public, as well as sold rabbits for export. G. Mason writes of the Hares he saw and handled, "Lapin leporides `a poils ras is the variety that most nearly resembles what we are trying to breed in the Belgian Hares — viz., a good rich ground-golden body-colour, with plenty of dark rich ticking, ears erect and rather short, edged with black, small head, without dewlap, and of a lively appearance. My opinion is that many of our so-called Belgian Hares are a cross between this variety and the Angevin (a giant breed that was rather difficult to breed); hence the increased size, heavy dewlap, and shortness of ticking, so often seen in our show specimens. I have seen some good Belgians in my time, but never before have I seen such a grand collection at the Jardin d' Acclimatation."

Mason further writes of his visit, "There are many other kinds of Belgian Hares, the product, it would appear, of most careful crossing, and evidencing the fact that the French are even more careful on the matter of improvement of the breed than we are. There is the blanc, or white, variety. This is a very strange-looking animal. It is remarkably handsome, being very similar in make and in carriage of ear to our Belgian Hare, but the colour is pure snow-white, and is far superior even to the white of a prize Angora. The eyes, too, instead of being red, as would be supposed, are nothing of the sort, but are black; in exceptional cases being blue or brown. These breed pretty true to colour, and have been crossed with Silver-greys to get creams, but without signal success. The Belier noir, or black, is not so much to be prized, as black is not so calculated to show off the points of the Belgian as a lighter colour. In addition to these varieties, there is a species of grey Belgian Hare we consider far inferior to the average lot of English ones."

There is a short piece regarding Hares from the *Manuals for the Many — The Rabbit Book,* of 1877, "THE BELGIAN HARE-COLOURED. Large quantities of this Rabbit are imported, known and sold as French Hare-rabbits; but they are not hybrids as the name implies. They attain a large size, but are said not to be so fruitful as many other varieties; their ears are large, the head smaller than either of the before-mentioned varieties, and in colour they are very similar to a Hare." The two large rabbits that they are referring to are the Andalusian and the Rouennais or Bulldog of France.

During the Boston Show of 1880, William Lumb gathered up some twenty Hare breeders, and the first Belgian Hare Club was founded, named the Boston Belgian Hare Club. Lumb's standard was adopted as the first official standard for the breed. Lumb became the club's secretary, a position that he would hold for 21 years, with Dr. Barham being the club's first president. The standard was further revised in 1882 by Lumb and a Mr. J. Jennings, which was approved by the membership. During the next few years there would be a great deal of controversy regarding the Belgian Hare in the various fancy publications of the time. The controversy was all about the proper color and ticking. In *The Rabbit Keeper*, which was the forerunner of *Fur & Feather*, a Mr. J. H. Roberts' Belgian Hare standard appeared on July 12, 1888: "We hear an ex-hibitor that they should be this colour and that, and when asked to describe the colour it turns out to be either a rich amber or a sooty red, while others say it is a rich, deep red fawn, or it's very foxy, etc." Then the following week on July 19th Mr. James Rogers presented his standard for the breed and wrote, "There seems to be a slight difference of opinion on two points or characteristics of the Belgian Hare, viz., colour and ticking. In the standard drawn up by Mr. Jennings, and accepted almost to a man by the entire fancy, the colour is described as reddish brown ground colour. Now the question is — do we breeders, ex-

Dr. Herbert Barham, Maidstone, England, first president of the Belgian Hare Club.

hibitors and judges consider this the correct colour or the proper term for colour? If we want to imitate the English Hare, I for one say it is not. I have never seen a wild hare that could be called reddish brown in any part. Now the question is — shall we retain the reddish brown, or shall we alter it to rufus red shading to yellow, rather than brown or chocolate? Now a few words on ticking. The standard says, 'Ticking extended uniformly throughout and of a chocolate black,' and further on it says, ''Forefeet well colored and ticked.' Now a hare has no ticking along the sides or on the legs or feet. I venture to propose we adopt the rufus red colour, especially along the sides, on chest, legs and feet, and that the legs and feet be free from ticking, also that the ticking on back and loins be wavy." William Lumb insisted that the Belgian Hare standard should reflect that the breed be bred to look like the English wild hare in type and altered his standard in 1889, also reflecting on the rufus red color and the placement points of the ticking. Lumb submitted the newly revised standard at the annual meeting of the Belgian Hare Club, which was gladly approved and accepted, which would be the major turning point for the Belgian Hare throughout the world, even to this day. William Lumb was dubbed "King of the Belgians" by his fellow fanciers.

The official Belgian Hare Standard was rather short and sweet as it appeared in 1880:

Points of the Belgian Hare Rabbit

1. Richness of Colour .... 25 points
2. Ticking .... .20 Points
3. Shape .... .20 Points
4. Size .... 15 Points
5. Head................................... 5 Points
6. Ears — shape and lacing .. .10 Points
7. Eyes .... 5 Points

Total ... 100 Points

Trophy on left: The Belgian Hare Club's 25 Guinea Challenge Cup, won at the Crystal Palace by Mr. E. Wilkins.
Trophy on right: The Belgian Hare Club's first Ten Guinea Challenge Cup.

The year 1880 would be an important one, a national club had been formed, a breed standard in place, and Lumb would befriend a young 13-year-old boy named Ernest. Young Ernest Wilkins was visiting Grimsby with his father Landon. As they were passing Lumb's shop, the boy noticed some rabbits for sale in the store window. Young Ernest had a bit of money in his pocket, but his funds were not enough to make the purchase. Landon Wilkins noticed his son was visibly disappointed, and gave Ernest the rest of the needed money.

Belgian Hare rabbit, 1880.

Ernest Wilkins became the proud owner of a young Belgian Hare doe, and a friendship would be forged that would last a full fifty-three years until Lumb passed away. In fact, Lumb, penned a letter to his long-time friend just a few days before he died.

Ernest Wilkins, born July 20, 1867, along with his mentor and dear friend Winter "William" Lumb, did more to promote the Belgian Hares than anyone else during the later 19th century and first quarter of the 20th century. Both men kept Belgian Hares until the day they died. Ernest Wilkins first wrote his book on the breed in 1896, *The Book of the Belgian Hare.* The last revision he made was with the Fourth Edition in 1948. Of special note, the Third Edition, which appeared in 1900, of the nearly 2000 copies printed, most of them were sent to America at the peak of the "Belgian Hare Boom." This now little forty-seven page booklet is considered a classic and can still be purchased today from *Fur & Feather.*

James Salter wrote in *Poultry*, on February 12, 1885, from the viewpoint of a scientific naturalist, saying, "The breeding of fancy varieties of domestic animals has done much to interest and instruct men of science, and these efforts were thoroughly appreciated by my friend, Mr. Darwin. As regards rabbits, one curious result has been the pro-

Ernest Wilkins, circa 1890.

duction, by artificial selection, of a race which approaches in external configuration and colour the common hare of this country, *lepus timidus."*

The Belgian Hare Club grew by leaps and bounds, with Mr. J.E. Watmough, who was also the editor of the *Rabbit Keeper* which later became known in 1888 as *Fur & Feather.* Watmough had served as president for many years until writing Secretary Lumb in a letter dated October 7, 1901, asking to be replaced. At one time the club boasted over 700 members. Watmough, through his publication, greatly promoted the breed, urging both judges and breeders that the Belgian Hare ideal should be to a great extent an exact copy of the wild English Hare. The club later became known as National Belgian Hare Club and had cups and trophies valued at over $1,000 just after the turn into the 20th century. The Crystal Palace ten-guinea cup (trophy) was awarded for the first time in 1900, with Ernest Wilkins taking the prize.

Although I continue to refer to the wild English hare, it is actually called the Mountain Hare, scientific name, *Lepus timidus*, (*Lepus* = Hare and *timidus* = timid in Latin) described for science by Carl Linnaeus of Sweden (5/23/1707 to 1/10/1778) the Father of Taxonomy (describing species of plants and animals) in 1758. The Mountain Hare is recognized in sixteen subspecies. It is a widespread species and is extremely variable in color and size. Colors may be a dusky brown or pale gray in the mountainous regions and a rich rust-brown on the plains. They range in weight from 4-1/2 to 9 pounds. Carl Linnaeus would also describe the European Rabbit, *Oryctolagus cuniculus,* in 1758 from which all breeds of domestic rabbits evolved.

The first Belgian Hares reached the United States in 1888, when Mr. E.M. Hughes, of Albany, New York, a Scotchman by birth and a stonemason by trade, imported some from England. Shortly after this importation, an effort was organized to form the American Belgian Hare Association, with Mr. W. N. Richardson of Troy, New York, acting as secretary. The life of this organization was brief, with such a scattering of members it was extremely difficult to have a quorum to act upon business and was disbanded in a year. Three men in the persons of Hughes and Richardson along with a Mr. G. W. Felton of Barre, Massachusetts, are given the credit in founding the Belgian Hare fancy in America. Hughes and Felton were the original exhibitors, showing the Hares at poultry shows in mostly New York and Boston, while Mr. Richardson wrote about them through his publication known as *The Rabbit.* This publication greatly built interest in the new breed that would soon shake America and make the Belgian Hare a household name; the American rabbit industry was being born. Now it should be mentioned here that Belgian Hares were not the first rabbits ever imported from across the ocean. There are documented cases of Lop-eared rabbits (English Lops) being imported during the mid-19th century, as well as Angoras and Silvers.

In 1897 the second effort was organized to form a national club for the breed, thus the National Belgian Hare Club of America began, with headquarters in Denver, Colorado. Serving as secretary was the youthful, energetic and business-minded Mr. P.E. Crabtree. The new club took the standard given to them by Mr. Hughes, which was the same as used in England. However, they were confronted with difficulties, first with the true definition of "rich rufous red." Note that we spell it "rufus" which is considered incorrect. Then they came to the word ticking, which the standard said was to be "plentiful and rather wavy," but they didn't have a clue what the word ticking meant. Contact was made with Mr. Hughes, who referred them to Mr. J.I. Lawrence of Worcester, Mass. Lawrence was the owner of the winning first and second place bucks and does at the two Crystal Palace Shows in England for 1896 and 1897. Yet Lawrence could not give them the definitions they wanted and suggested that they write Ernest Wilkins of Hare Court in Wantage, England, as well as Mr. A.J. Kilby, and the firm of Styles & Howe, both of Banbury. Three replies came; Kilby and Styles & Howe combined with

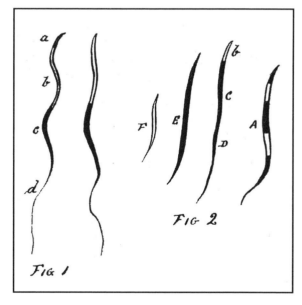

Fig. 1 — *Enlarged hairs from back of common hare (lepus timidus): (a) Black point. (b) Fawn ticking. (c) Black ground. (d) Slender stem.*

Fig. 2 — *(a) Enlarged hairs from Belgian hare rabbit. (b, c, d) The same as the hare. (e) Black ticking hair. (f) Fawn undergrowth.*

The Wilkins' Rabbitry illustrated in Fur & Feather, 1901.

Kilby serving as manager. Wilkins and Kilby both defined rufous red as "a cherry red with golden shade." The men enlightened the gentlemen on other points of the standard and learned what ticking was. These American fanciers became more and more interested, and Mr. A.W. Gilman of Denver decided to import a fine pair, which he did for $100. The buck he received was the famous Champion Yukon, and along with his mate they had an excellent lesson in proper color, ticking and type. Shortly after Gilman's importation, Mr. H.A. Stearns, of Salt Lake City, Utah imported a fine group of Belgians. Now that we are talking about dollars at this point in time, we must remember this was during a period when the a person would be paid on the average of just ten to fifteen cents per hour, or typically one dollar a day.

Leading American Hare fanciers considered that the British Standard was not explicit enough, so they took the disqualifications, arranged them in a paragraph and placed it at the top of the standard. Other than the disqualifications placed at the top of the standard, it is the same standard that Lumb wrote and was approved in 1889. Then they took the 100 points as the sum of perfection and devised a system by covering 29 specific requirements of the 100 points. The 29 specifics are then covered by a list of four requirements; size, shape, color and quality, on the various sections of the animal. P.E. Crabtree then designed a score card that would tabulate the 29 different requirements in accordance with the terms of the Standard of Perfection, which was approved and adopted by the national club. This was the birth of the first Rabbit Show Remark Card in America.

The American Belgian Hare Standard

DISQUALIFICATIONS — 1. Loped, or fallen ears. 2. White front feet or white bar or bars on same. 3. Decidedly wry front feet. 4. Wry tail. Note: A specimen should have the benefit of any doubt.

COLOR — Rich rufous red (not dark, smudgy color) carried well down sides and hindquarters, and as little white under jaws as possible 20

TICKING — Rather wavy appearance and plentiful 15

SHAPE — Body long , thin, well tucked up flank and well ribbed up; back slightly arched; loins well rounded, not choppy; head rather lengthy; muscular chest; tail straight, not screwed; altogether of a racy appearance 20

EARS — Five inches long, thin, well-laced on tips and as far down outside edges as possible; good color inside and outside and well set on 10

SIZE — Eight pounds 5

EYES — Hazel color, large, round, bright and bold 10

LEGS AND FEET — Fore feet and legs long, straight, slender, well colored and free from white bars; hind feet as well colored as possible 10

CONDITION — Not fat, but flesh firm like that of a racehorse, and good quality of fur 5

WITHOUT DEWLAP 5

TOTAL 100

Young energetic Ernest Wilkins was a businessman from day one, and dubbed the Belgian Hare as "The Business Rabbit of the World." Surely he knew something, as Belgian Hares were arriving in America at an alarming rate. Other countries, too, were seeking stock. Between 1899 and 1900, Wilkins shipped no less than 641 Hares to Canada, France, Belgium and the U.S., with most of the stock going to the latter destination. William Lumb had al-

Advert from Fur & Feather for the Sutton & Co. which shipped over 6,000 Belgian Hares to America in 1900.

ready shipped 133 Hares to America by 1900, when three weeks before the great show to be held at the Coliseum, in Chicago, Illinois, where he was scheduled to judge, the show committee decided it would be better to appoint an American judge, fearing Lumb might be partial to animals he sold. The shipping firm of Sutton & Company, with principal offices in London and Liverpool, announced in early 1901, "Over 6,000 Belgian Hares safely conveyed to the United States during 1900." The Belgian Hare boom was in full swing.

P.E. Crabree of Denver, Colorado, 1900.

Huge fortunes were being made, especially by P.E. Crabtree, and quite a few people went broke as well. Companies dealing with Belgian Hares were popping up all over the place, but mainly in California, Colorado and Missouri, with the east coast being a bit slow to jump in with both feet. The American Belgian Hare Institute was established by Mr. P. E. Crabtree in 1900, whereby you paid a fee of $15 to get a twenty-course lesson book which was 237 pages long. The course would last eight days and would be held anywhere in the country, provided that Crabtree had at least fifteen or more students. You got to keep your book and received a diploma if you passed. By 1901, nearly 100 people had taken Crabtree's instructions and graduated. Even Ernest Wilkins took Crabtree's course through the mail, and for his final exam, Crabtree had Wilkins score Hares that were being exported to America to see if he knew what he was doing. I found this a bit odd, considering just three years before Crabtree didn't have a clue what the proper color was for the Hares, nor did he know what ticking meant. By the time Wilkins took the course, he had been keeping Hares for twenty years. The National Association of Belgian Hare Judges, Inc. was founded, again with Crabtree as the official instructor. *The Belgian Hare World,* a monthly publication, was started in Boston, Mass., as well as the *Belgian Hare Gazette,* published six times a year also in Boston. The *Poultry and Belgian Hare Standard* was another magazine of 1900, from Kansas City,

Missouri which also published a book, *Standard Belgian Hare*, by M.D. Capps (1901, 151 pages). Hares and supplies could be secured from the New England Belgian Hare Company of Boston. They would even sell the animals scored by Crabtree, or design

The steamer Anchoria, bringing a shipment of Belgian Hares from England in 1900. The X at the bottom right is where the Hares were kept.

your Belgian Hare advertising for 15 cents per square inch. The company announced after May 1, 1901 they would prepay shipping charges for all orders of Belgian Hares over $35. Even *Field and Stream* magazine carried a Belgian Hare Department which was edited by no one else but P.E. Crabtree. The magazine started carrying rather lengthy columns of several pages on October 1, 1900, with the last feature appearing February 1, 1902.

One of the largest single shipments of Belgian Hares left Liverpool on September 7, 1900, on the steamer "Cymric" of the White Star Line (same company that would own the ill-fated Titanic) and landed in New York ten days later on the 17th. The Hares would reach their final destination at Northwestern Rabbitry, Woodstock, Illinois, on the 20th of September. The American Express Company took charge of the consignment of over 200 Hares in Liverpool, and even supplied a special train car to quickly steam them safely to their new Woodstock home upon reaching New York harbor. The rabbits were accompanied by Mr. C. F. Kingman, manager of the Northwestern Rabbitry, who went to England in early August to hand-select the best in the showrooms and the Hare Studs (rabbitries) of the countryside.

The so-called "Big Boom" of Belgian Hares would last but three years, from 1898 to 1901, with thousands of animals having been imported, mostly from England, but also from Belgium, France and Germany. The United States had more than their fair share of good quality Belgian Hares to work with, with the boom peaking in 1900. In 1901, $25 was considered to be a good price for a doe and $75 for a quality buck for those who wanted

Dumleton, an English Wild Hare, brought to America in 1900 by Crabtree to show as a comparison with the Belgian Hare.

to purchase a very high scoring animal for their breeding program. Lesser quality stock could be purchased for half of the forementioned prices. There were lots of Belgian Hares changing hands in America at $100 to $450 each for winning specimens, which were mostly brought in from England. The record setter was a buck, bred and finished as a Champion in England, called Champion Fashoda. This buck was born in early 1899, and won the Crystal Palace Cup, London, in November 1899, which would have given him the title as the Best Belgian Hare in all of England. Champion Fashoda was imported by Mr. C.W. Bowen, manager of the Northwestern Belgian Hare Co., with operations in Chicago and Minneapolis. Champion Fashoda was sold to a Dr. Burton C. Platt of Bonanza Rabbitry, with operations in Los Angeles and Philadelphia for the amazing sum of $5,000 in 1900. Dr. Platt at the time was president of the National Association of Belgian Hare Judges. Two sons of Champion Fashoda were imported March 28, 1900, with Fashoda King going to Rockledge Belgian Hare Company in Kansas City, MO and Emperor Fashoda staying with Bowen's Northwestern Belgian Hare Company. These bucks both sold for $1,500 each.

There is little doubt that California was the hot bed for Belgian Hare

England's famous Crystal Palace designed by Joseph Paxton, built in 1851 and burned to the ground in 1936.

activity in 1900, with southern California leading, especially Los Angeles County which boosted over 60,000 animals alone and growing rapidly. There was over six-hundred rabbitries, most carrying be-

The famous imported buck, Champion Fashoda, sold for $5,000 in 1900.

tween fifty and seventy-five head; many had over one-hundred animals, with some at the two-hundred mark and a few that had more than one-thousand Belgian Hares.

Emperor Fashoda.

The largest Belgian Hare operation in America at the time was said to be the Rockledge Rabbitry, at the corner of 49th and Main Streets, Kansas City, MO, which was approaching five-thousand head.

Millionaires even saw the money-making poten-tial of the ever popular Belgian Hare, in the persons of Morgan, Rockefeller, Guggenheim, Flagler and Dupont, to name but a few. One could well imag-ine the Hares these people could afford. New York's J. Pierpont Morgan, the famous financier, was the first to join the fancy. He instructed one of his foreign representatives to purchase a number of the finest specimens obtainable in England, and to also bring back an experienced English Bel-gian Hare breeder to accompany the stock and manage the Mor-gan Rabbitry. Will-iam Rockefeller of Standard Oil Com-pany fame had a large rabbitry built for his Hares at his Hudson

Fashoda King, son of Champion Fashoda, and his brother, Emperor Fashoda, both sold for $1,500.

Rockledge Rabbitry of Kansas City, MO, circa 1900.

River country estate. H. M. Flagler of the Flagler Railroad System had an extensive system of rabbitries built on his Florida estate.

It should be understood that not all of the Belgian Hares that were crossing the Atlantic were the super show quality animals, as many people were jumping on the bandwagon in England to raise rabbits for the booming American market. Some Hares were being crossed

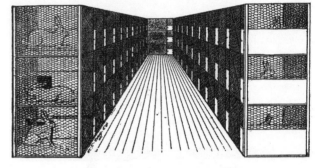
Illustration of the cage setup at the Rock Ledge Rabbitry.

with the Flemish Giants and the now extinct Patagonian rabbit. It appears that these animals were further mated to the true Belgian Hare and thus was born the Heavy Weight Belgian Hare and given its own standard. Dewlaps were permissible, and a weight of 11 pounds was called for. Animals would be judged first live and then judged again dressed. Americans thinking that this could procure better Hares also imported from Europe, especially Belgium, France and Germany, once again obtaining the larger Hares. Belgian Hares from Germany were always larger animals. Still to this day on the continent Belgian Hares are usually much stockier animals and larger in bone, but they do have some excellent color. The standard as it appeared in 1900 for judging dressed Heavy Weight Belgian Hares.

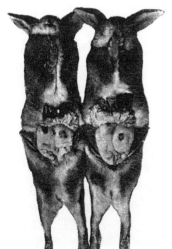
Properly dressed Belgian Hares for market, 1905.

Scale for Rating Fat Hares
Dressed Capons

Best portion of carcass, ham and loins .... 20 Points
Quality of flesh, size of bone considered .... 20 Points
Color of flesh, and fat .... 20 Points
Degree of fatness .... 10 Points
Weight.. 20 Points
Manner of dressing and preparing for shipment .... 10 Points

Total .... 100 Points

Mr. Fred H. Dewey, of Westfield, Mass., decided to go straight to Belgium in July 1900 to obtain what he believed was the true Belgian Hare. Dewey wrote on August 2, 1900, upon returning with his stock: "Am just back from the old country with a lot of genuine Belgian Hares from native land of the Belgium; had to go among the people and select them; their ideas and standard are unlike ours. If I had not been able to speak French, I could have done nothing. The natives eat the cats, train the dogs to haul wagons on the streets, and raise these hares for pets. Some of the women shed tears when the men sold them to me. They have diplomas framed on the walls of their houses and value them as family treasures. The animals that I have are all first prize winners, red in color, ticked and laced, good front feet, and when mature and fat will go from 13 to 16 pounds and more in weight. They are the genuine mammoth Belgian hare — rabbits. The preference and standard in Belgium is a darker shade, and the red was not easy to find. The people are genial and nice to meet. The well-educated speak both French and Flemish, but the common people use Flemish generally, which is unlike German or Dutch, but in spelling resembles those languages. I never saw such crops or such cultivation. And if I attempted to go into details, I should need many pages. One thing is certain, I could not have obtained such animals as I have now by sending for them." Again, this leads one to believe that the Belgian Hares are more of the Flemish Giant blood.

Kansas City, Missouri started the International Belgian Hare Registry Association, and southern California would start another national organization for the ever-popular Belgian Hare in 1899, and this was called the American Breeders of Belgian Hares, Inc., with offices at Room 104, Currier Block, Los Angeles, CA. This organization would have the distinction

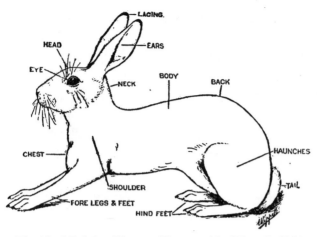

The ideal Belgian Hare as illustrated by Wippell, 1900.

of putting on the first national show for the breed called "Exposition, Mart and Feast," which was held in Hagard's Pavilion in Los Angeles on February 8 through 10, 1900. This exhibition would go down in the history books as being the largest single exhibition for a breed anywhere in the world at the time. There was a total of seventy classes provided for, with prizes varying from $2.50 to $100 in value, besides an array of specials of various sorts, offered by fanciers of the breed. The rules of this exhibition, or actually business venture which this show was, are somewhat different than we would find today in some respects.

Rules and Regulations Governing the American Breeders of Belgian Hares First Exhibition, Mart, and Feast
February 8-10, 1900

The Company wishes all Exhibitors to understand that this Exposition is a business affair and will be conducted on business principles. To this end, an Exhibitor may use any amount of his allotted space that he wishes as an office, for the transaction of any business that may be carried on by him.

A diagram of the floor space of the Pavilion, the Exposition building, may be seen at the office of the Corporation, Room 104, Currier Block, Los Angeles, California, where floor space for exhibits and booths may be engaged.

Mr. P.E. Crabtree, of Denver, Colorado, Official Judge of the "National Belgian Hare Club of America," will act as Judge of all specimens, judging the Belgian Hares, both standard bred and heavy weights, entered, by scoring, and all other classes of competitors, by comparison.

The judging will be done in public, and under the management of a Committee of prominent citizens of Southern California, who will be required to direct the presentation of the specimens in such a manner as will preclude any possibility of the Judge knowing whose animal is before him.

Numbers will be used to designate the exhibits, and these will not be placed until the award has been made.

The management is emphatically determined to obviate every possibility of dissension between the Exhibitors and the Judge, and all awards will be made upon pure merit.

The commencement of the judging will take place at nine o'clock, upon the opening day of the Exposition, February 8, and will be completed at the earliest moment possible.

All Premiums will be paid on the closing day of the Exposition, February 10.

All specimens competing for prizes must be in their places before nine o'clock on the morning of the 8th of February.

All animals admitted to the Exposition must be in good health.

No animals suffering from chronic ailments will be allowed to compete, and any animal that becomes sick after being entered must be removed at once to secluded quarters.

The supervision and examination of the health of the Hares will be in charge of a Committee, under the direction of Judge Crabtree and the Management.

Each Exhibitor will be required, on making entry of Hares, to make Affidavit before a Notary Public as to the correctness of his entries.

The Entrance Fee will be ten per cent of the amount of the purse, in each Class, and shall be paid at date of entry.

Exhibitors may rent and occupy space for the purpose of exhibiting stock that is for sale, in addition to their stock entered in competition, and will be allowed to make sales, and deliver Hares, except of those entered in

---

Official Score Card of the

National Belgian Hare Club

OWNER'S Name ....
Address ....
Date of birth—Mo.........., Day.........., Year.......
Specimens No.......... Name............................
Weight—Pounds................. Ounces..............
Denver, Colo., ...

CLASS		SIZE	SHAPE	COLOR	QUALITY
COLOR 20	Stray hairs....			4	
	Body			4	
	Sides			4	
	Hind quarter			4	
	Jaws			4	
TICKING 15					15
SYMMETRY 20	Body		4		
	Flank and rib		4		
	Back		4		
	Loins		4		
	Head		4		
EARS 10	Lacing			2	
	Otherwise....	2	2	2	2
EYES 10		2½	2½	2½	2½
LEGS AND FEET 10	Front	2	2	2	2
	Hind			2	
SIZE OF SPECIMEN 5		5			
CONDITION 5	Flesh				2½
	Fur				2½
NECK 5			5		
SCM OF COLUMN		11½	31½	45½	11½

Possible score, 100 Total vote.......... Score ....
Judge ....
.... President
.... Secretary

The National Belgian Hare Club score card, 1900.

97

competition, and refill the vacant places with other Hares, at any time, during the Exposition.

Exhibitors will be required to furnish their own cages for specimens, and these cages must be of uniform width and height; the cages must be two to two and a half feet wide, and twenty inches high, if two tiers of cages are used; but if only one tier is used it may be forty inches in height.

The length of the cage may be made to suit the space used by the Exhibitor. Tables to place the cages upon will be furnished by the Management, free of charge.

The construction, and arrangement, of the Office portions of the booths will be at the pleasure of the Exhibitor, and be complete by eight o'clock in the morning of the 8th February.

Not more than two tiers high of cages will be allowed.

Exhibitors will be required to furnish their own food, and to feed and water their own stock, and keep pens clean; the debris being carried away by the janitor. Sawdust, or Cut Straw, and Dry Earth, will be furnished by the Management, free.

At least five competitors must be entered in each Class, to fill out said Class, except where otherwise stated.

For Entry Blanks, enclose stamp or call upon the Secretary, or General Manager.

The score of an exhibit will determine the Winner, as in individual specimens.

The Exhibitor must provide lock, and retain key, to his cage, or cages, of Hares.

A Breeder is understood to be one who either breeds a Doe, owned by him at the time of mating; or purchases a Doe, and orders her bred, providing he is impressed of this fact before purchasing, and is also impressed as to what Buck she is bred to, and receives a Certificate of Breeding with the Doe.

An Auction Sale of Hares will take place, each day, during the Exposition, at 100 o'clock a.m., and 2 o'clock p.m. Specimens may be listed , with the Entry Clerk, on the day previous to the Sale, and a fee of ten per cent of the price realized from the Sale.

Exhibitors will be allowed to remove valuable Hares from the Showroom, after each night's exhibition, and return them on the following morning, not later than eight o'clock.

Exhibitors may begin the arrangement of their booths as early as Wednesday morning, February 7, and everything connected with the exhibit belonging to Exhibitors must be removed, from space occupied, not later than six o'clock in the morning February 12.

Exhibitors must not so arrange their business, and signs, as to obstruct the view of other booths, either in front or rear. Any reasonable arrangement will be permitted.

Entries of Hares will not be accepted later than 5th of February. Entries may be made by telegraph or by letter.

All due diligence and care will be exercised by the Management, to protect Exhibitors, and their specimens, in every practical manner.

Further than this the Management will not assume responsibility, in any sense.

A sufficient corps of assistants will be employed by the Management, both day and night, to render the best possible protection to Exhibitors.

Any ties occurring in Classes will be adjusted by dividing the premium equally between the number of Hares showing the same score in that Class, and a Certificate will be issued by the Company to the owner of each specimen, setting forth, in each case, the conditions of the award.

Exhibitors entering as many as three specimens for competition, or occupying purchased space at a cost exceeding Six Dollars, will be presented with a Season Ticket, admitting them to the Pavilion at all times during the Exposition.

Medals and Cups will be delivered to the winning competitors within sixty days of the close of the Exhibition, or earlier, if possible to get them made.

The Best In Show winner for this huge event was none other than that famous buck called Champion Fashoda. Judge Crabtree's comments about Fashoda, "When we come to the element of color we find that Fashoda possesses a rich, rose-gold under-color, together with beautiful, broadly defined and wavy ticking distributed to a nicety, giving to his coat a luster and depth of color equal to the tint of mahogany, extending from head to tail, from vertebrae all but to hocks, and nearly full depth of sides. A breadth of golden tan shades the sparkling ticking of the sides into the snowy white of his belly, and, under his jaws, blends with the brilliant flush of the rufus-red on his broad, splendidly arched breast. All of his feet are the indefinable coloring now the object of every fancier's efforts and the most difficult element to attain in the whole standard of perfection. This wonderful shade is really a new thing in nature. It resembles a mahogany, but has a brighter luster. It is like a wine color, but not so deep a shade. It might be called maroon, but is a little darker. Define it as you may, it gives a finish to the whole effect as yet rarely seen upon Belgians."

The Black Belgian Hares as mentioned earlier that would crop up in litters in the early days were beginning to at-

Early American Belgian Hare Pedigree. This doe was born January 4, 1900. Pedigree written February 18, 1901.

tract a great deal of interest. However, Crabtree was steadily putting them down as inferior. Crabtree wrote of them, "He who undertakes to establish an innovation, something new, should be an old and well tenacity of purpose, abnormally developed; otherwise he should drop the undertaking, if possible, just before he begins. Otherwise, the chances are that he will never become a fancier, where if he began with a well established variety, something that would breed reasonably true to requirements, and something for which there is a ready demand at reasonable prices he might become a power in the fancy and through his procedure make a financial success of the undertaking." These Black Belgian Hares would later become known and recognized as the Black Siberian Hare, and a standard was established for them by the National Breeders' and Fanciers' Association of America.

Crabtree also mentions the White Belgian Hare, saying, "I give awards on them as white rabbits, but not as white Belgians." Crabtree sort of changes his tune when he wrote in *Field & Stream* magazine April 1, 1901 issue: "Mr. August D. Arnold, the proprietor of the Keystone Rabbitry, whose advertisement appears elsewhere, owns a breed of hares

Furnessia, an imported Hare, was said to have been one of the finest Belgians in America in 1901.

that is considered very rare — the white Belgian. He showed a number of them at the Poultry and Pet Stock Show in Madison Square Garden, New York, where they created quite an interest."

By the year 1902, the American Belgian Hare Boom went bust, the United States was flooded with imported Hares, and the market began to bottom out, and Belgian Hare Clubs throughout the nation began to fold. The so-called dedicated American expert of the breed; P.E. Crabtree, wasn't too dedicated, as he was never heard of again after 1907.

Emblem of the Federated Belgian Hare Breeders of America, circa 1924.

It should be understood that the Belgian Hare was still the most popular breed of rabbit in America, up into the early 1920s, quickly followed by the Flemish Giant, New Zealand Red. The next national Club for the breed was founded before 1924 and called the Federated Belgian Breeders of America, with William J. Barnes, of Chicago, Illinois, serving as the first Secretary. Then in 1927 the former club was replaced with the National Belgian Hare Club of America, with P.E. Hawkins, of Kerrville, Texas, being the secretary.

Back to England, to the year 1933, in late January, William Lumb, wrote a letter to *Fur & Feather*, saying that he feels now he is very close to the very end of life's journey. He had not been able to give much time and attention to his beloved Belgian Hares, as he only has four Hares in his hutches and yet had never been without them for a full 59 years. Winter "William" Lumb passed away on Thursday, February 2, 1933, at his home called Hareby House, Thrunscoe Road, in Cleethorpes.

The Fancy's "Grand Old Man," Winter William Lumb, Published in Fur & Feather, January 1933.

He was buried at St. Peter's Church yard, surrounded by the stone and iron wall he was responsible for, and the eight tubular bells Lumb had commissioned and installed, which would chime the hymn that he had requested, "Jesus, Lover of my Soul." Thus the end of a great legend. It was almost as though the entire United Kingdom mourned Lumb's passing, as the National Belgian Hare Club disbanded that same year. A new national was founded in 1934, called the

Ernest Wilkins, from his obituary in Fur & Feather, 1951.

British Belgian Hare Club, which continues today.

The British Isles would mourn once again, when on Friday, November 2, 1951, it was announced that Ernest Wilkins died at his home, Hare Court in Wantage, at the age of 83. Wilkins bred his beloved Belgian Hares for no less than 71 years. This

Black Belgian Hare. *Photo courtesy Leo Vervecken, Belgium.*

would be the end of an era, as the two greatest men of the Belgian Hare breed were now gone.

Today the Belgian Hare is a rather rare breed throughout the world. It has been for nearly a century purely a fancy rabbit, maintained by very dedicated fanciers in keeping the breed alive. This author would say, "Once a Belgian Hare fancier, always one." It is a re-

Black and Tan Belgian Hare. *Photo courtesy Leo Vervecken, Belgium.*

markable rabbit to watch and breed. I only wish I had purchased some when I saw them in Calgary, Canada, in 1969 for the first time. The breed is wonderful, with such a remarkable history ... which began the Domestic Rabbit industry in United States at the turn of 20th century.

White Belgian Hare.
Photo courtesy John Chappell, England.

Fairly recent additions to the long standing since colored Belgian Hare are the self-Black, Rudy-eyed White and the exquisite Black and Tan Belgian Hare, which have been recognized in Belgium, Holland and Germany,

Winning Belgian Hare doe from the People's Palace, 1887.

these new varieties came about during the 1970s mostly through the efforts of Belgium breeders. Not far on the horizon is yet another variety, the self-Blue Belgium Hare.

Hillcourt Messenger, a Belgian Hare buck, as illustrated by Wippell, appeared on the cover of Fur & Feather, April 19, 1912.

103

BELGIAN SILVER

The Champagne de Argente is, of course, a breed which has its origins in France, and the Belgian Silver is actually one in the same breed. The breed had been renamed because of the amount of silvering the Flemish people have called for in their breeding programs. Therefore, in October of 1960 the Belgian Silver was officially recognized under that name by the national governing body, through the urging of Mr. A Van den Bossche, D. Lanneau, and J. Ronday. It was Ronday who presented the standard. With a European Standard now in place, it always takes the standard for the country in which the breed actually originated in, therefore France. The breed from Belgium could not possibly win when the European Standard was being used. The amount of silvering in the Belgian Silver is mid-way between dark and light, much like the ideal of the Silver Fox breed of America. Belgian Silvers weigh in at 4 to 5.5 kg or 9 to 12.25 lb.

Belgian Silver.
Photo coutesy Reginald Deyaert, Belgium.

BEVEREN

elgium is the native home of the Beveren, which originated about the year 1898 in the town of Beveren, which is in the Waas region of western Belgium. The original color was the blue, which came mostly from self Blue St. Nicholas (St. Niklaas), which was first reported in the year 1899. Typically the St. Nicholas Blue had a white blaze to the face, and often white boots or socks on the feet. Blue rabbits have been known for many years in this area of Flanders, the Flemish Giants from Ghent, Blue St. Nicholas from St. Niklaas, and Blue Beverens from Beveren. All three of these towns line up in a straight row with one another.

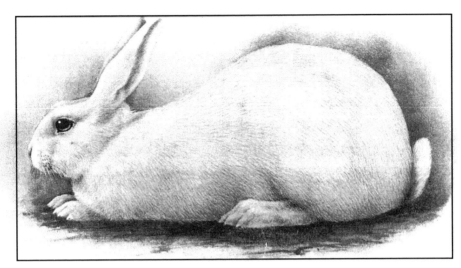

Blue Beveren, from the Wippell Collection.
Reproduced from a Fur & Feather colour plate issued 26 April 1929.

During those very early years, there were Beverens to be found in varying degrees of depth of color, but generally it was the lavender-blue that was preferred by the furriers of the day. Also, weight was a controversial issue, and two types would eventually emerge, the normal Beveren and the Giant Beveren.

The first Beverens to arrive in Britain were introduced by a Mrs. A.M. Martin, which she showed them for the first time at Norwich in 1905. These rabbits met with little favor from the judges, and she gave up her Blue Beverens. Years later, she wrote a letter to *Fur & Feather,* which was published on February 27, 1914, "In the first place the Vienna Blue is the oldest Continental blue rabbit known. They originally came from Austria but have been bred in France for nearly twenty years now.

"The Beveren Blue is a native of Belgium, and at the time when the Viennas were a known and recognized breed was only an ordinary blue and white rabbit. Some breeders in the vicinity of Beveren obtained some entirely blue specimens and in 1904 they first appeared at shows. Then in 1906 another blue and white variety also appeared in Belgium as St. Nicholas, and the breeders of this variety, obtaining some very fine specimens, tried to do away with the name Beveren Blue and adopt that of St. Nicholas for the Blue and White Belgian variety. Much discussion followed, and it was finally decided that the name Beveren should apply to the entirely blue variety, and St. Nicholas to the Blue with a white blaze on the front of the head.

Imported White Beveren doe, circa 1919.

"The Beveren Blue soon found its way into France and has since become so interbred with the Vienna Blue that at the present time it is almost impossible to determine to which variety a specimen belongs; many judges cannot distinguish between them and they are classed together at most shows abroad now."

While Mrs. Martin pretty much hit the nail on the head, so to speak, she was incorrect in the fact that the Blue Viennas were the oldest of the blue breeds.

Beverens were brought to the United States at the beginning of the second decade of the 20th Century, and by 1919 America had a number of all blue rabbits: American Blues, Blue Beveren, Giant Blue Beveren, Barbancon Blue, Blue Imperial, Blue Vienna and Blue Flemish. It should be noted that Beveren was spelled "Beverin" in the standards of the National Breeders and Fanciers Association of America.

The first White Beveren did not appear until 1916 as sports from a litter of Blues, which occurred in Derbyshire, England. These Blues were from a strain of Beverens which were produced from the Barbancon Blue, which had also been considered Blue Beverens, but of a smaller type.

While the Americans settled on three varieties of Beverens, even today England boosted at one time; Blue, Blue-Eyed White, Ruby-Eyed White, Opal-Eyed White, Black-Eyed White and Black. Today the Beveren in England comes in Blue-Eyed White, Black, Blue, Brown and Lilac. There is also the Pointed Beveren, but the British have classified them as their own breed.

Beverens have never been very popular in any of the countries which they are known to be raised, but again, the breed has a small dedicated band of followers that continue to maintain this old Flemish native. Beverens weigh 8 to 11 pounds (3.6 to 4.89 kg).

BLANC DE HOTOT

erived from Hotot-en-Auge, geographically nestled in a lush green valley of Normandy near the port of LeHavre in Northern France, an area known for its apple cider and superior dairy products, comes the name and the rabbits we call Blanc de Hotot (White of Hotot).

Madame Eugenie Bernhard, chatelaine du Calvados, who owned a large rabbitry of Geant de Flanders (Flemish Giants) and Geant Papillion Francais (Checkered Giants), has been given total credit in originating the Blanc de Hotot. It should be noted that Bernhard was one of the very few women of the time who created a new breed of rabbit, as it was pretty much a man's thing. Eugenie Bernhard's goal was actually to produce a large white rabbit with black eyes of multi-purpose qualities for meat, fur and show. The actual year which she began her breeding program to produce the Hotot rabbit is rather clouded. However, published dates lead us to believe it was in 1902. She first undertook crossing the Papillions with various white rabbits of the time, including the White Vienna and White Flemish Giants. These crosses did not give her any great results. Bernhard consulted Jeanne J. Lemarie, who was the creator of the Large Russian (Large Himalayan), and she explained that she created this new breed strictly through many years of selection using only the Himalayan. Bernhard then resolved herself to work only with the Giant Papillion Francais. Through process of elimination, Bernhard saved only the animals which were lightly marked. A mental picture can easily be drawn of the tremendous goal that the baroness had set for herself and the numerous (500-plus) matings, that would produce the Hotot rabbit we now have today.

The first markings to disappear were the flank spots. The ears and spine markings proved to be extremely difficult, in spite of the various splits in these markings. The last

Dedicated to the late Margaret Henderson of New Mexico, who received the second shipment of Blanc de Hotots to America. Margaret loved her Hotots and maintained them until her health failed and she was forced to give up her rabbits.

of the markings to fade were the eye circles (bands), being almost impossible to eradicate.

Several years would pass, and Eugenie Bernhard would refuse to sell any of her stock, as litters were still throwing the marked rabbits. Mr. Frederick Joppich, a great German judge and breeder of the Hotot for over 30 years, confirmed this, stating, "The marked rabbit throw-backs were nearly impossible to eliminate, as in the English Spots and Checkered Giants." The Hotot rabbit we now have had the desired characteristics since 1912.

Madame Eugenie Bernhard, with what was called the Giant Blanc de Hotot. Photo taken October 14, 1914.

Until World War I, the Blanc de Hotot was not known under an actual name. In his journal, Eugene Meslay talked of a white giant with black eyes of Madame Bernhard. It was not until 1920 that Mrs. Bernhard showed the breed for the first time at the Exposition Internationale d'Aviculture in Paris, calling the breed Geant (Giant) Blanc de Hotot.

The standard established by Bernhard was officially recognized and accepted by the Commission des Standards de Francaise on October 13, 1922. In the original French text, there is no mention of the black bands around the eyes, but of black eyelashes and lower eyelids, more or less colored gray. Entries at the Paris exhibition from 1923 to 1930 comprised about ten animals, with the most being shown in 1927 with a total of fifteen Hotots. During World War II, the breed nearly vanished in France. Switzerland imported the Blanc de Hotot in 1927, and it was here that the breed found the greatest recognition of all. Berne, Switzerland and the surrounding area became known as the "stronghold of the Hotot rabbit," as reported in *Revue Avicole*.

Frederick Joppich, was probably the greatest supporter of the Blanc de Hotot, having begun raising them in 1930 and maintained a large rabbitry of them, appreciating their fertility and fine meat-producing qualities. It was unfortunate that Joppich would become trapped into eastern sector of

German when the country was divided, and would die just mere days before the "Wall" came tumbling down in November of 1989. Although the breed was pretty much locked up in East Germany, credit must be given to Doctor Kissner, who started in 1960 to spread the breed

Earliest known illustration of the Blanc de Hotot, France, 1920.

throughout the Federal German Republic. At the big Stuttgart show in 1970, there would be 62 Blanc de Hotots entered. In Holland, a well-known rabbit fancier, in the person of L. Hamaker de Haarlem, recreated the Hotot by crossing the Lorrains and Charlie English Spots. His work was published in the Dutch review *"The Rabbit Stockbreeder"* on May 31, 1955, which confirmed the same process that Mrs. Bernhard used at the turn of the century.

The early French Standard makes no mention of the glasses or eye band, as Bernhard actually worked very hard to eliminate them completely and was successful in some cases. When the Swiss took up the breed, they seemed to appreciate the unique markings of glasses, and bred for the qualities, which give us the Hotot of today.

While living in Saudi Arabia, this author went to Paris with a friend to bring back a Burman cat, but while there I visited the French Federation of Cuniculiculture and secured addresses of Hotot breeders. Upon returning to Arabia, I contacted these breeders and arranged two shipments to be sent to the states. The first shipment of two pair, with the does mated up, arrived in Houston, Texas at 2:45 p.m. on June 25, 1978. This shipment came from Mr. Fernande Eberti of Saint Louis, France. The second shipment I had sent to my dear late friend, Mrs. Margaret Henderson, of Albuquerque, New Mexico. The three does and one buck arrived on July 2, 1978, and came from Mrs. Silvea Amen of Castres, France.

The first litter of Hotots kindled in the U.S. came on July 24, 1978, and consisted of eight: six Hotots, one Boxer (a Charlie with just one eye band) and one Silver Piebald (similar to a mismarked Dutch, yet the black sections would silver out as in our Silver Fox). These mismarked animals were never used in the breeding program.

American's first public viewing of the Blanc de Hotot was at the New Mexico State Fair when Henderson and I exhibited two 6/8 does. These rabbits were judged per the translated French standard on September 17, 1978, by Judge Jack Munhenk.

Three of the original Blanc de Hotots brought to America, June 25, 1978.

Eleven Hotots were presented at the 55th ARBA Convention at Saginaw, Michigan where the ARBA Standards Committee recommended the acceptance of the Blanc de Hotot to the Book of Standards. On March 5, 1979, the ARBA approved the breed into the organization when the standard was published in Domestic Rabbits magazine May-June issue, Vol. 7, No. 3.

Fourteen interested fanciers joined together and founded the Hotot Rabbit Breeders International, with the ARBA approving and accepting application for charter on May 21, 1979.

Tucson, Arizona would be their first official showing at a National Convention in 1979. Oren Reynolds did the honors of judging the breed, with an outstanding entry of 41 animals. By the close of the convention the Club boasted a membership of 64 and steadily growing.

Those early Blanc de Hotots, although good in size, were certainly a rough lot, when dealing with the hindquarters, but the fur was beautiful, uniquely long and the most wonderful frosted white sheen. In order to improve bodies, breeders mated in first White Beverens, so not to lose that fur. Other breeders chose to cross with White New Zealands and White Satins, and though the bodies have

A not-so-gray author in 1978 after the Blanc de Hotot was approved by the ARBA Standards Committee in Saginaw, Michigan.

110

been greatly improved, that frosted white fur seems to have been lost.

The Blanc de Hotot today, though rare, has a very dedicated following of breeders determined to keep the breed alive in America. Demand for stock is always high, and attempts are currently underway to introduce new blood for the gene pool from Europe.

Now you may be wondering why it is just called Hotot today and not Blanc de Hotot. Well, that is a good question. The breed was accepted as Blanc de Hotot, in the 1981 through 1985 Standard it is listed as Blanc de Hotot. When the ARBA issued their official Guide Book in 1984, the name appeared as just Hotot, with the 1986 through 1990 Standard listing also as just plain Hotot. No one seems to know just how or why the name was changed.

America's first Grand Champion Blanc de Hotot, bred and owned by Walt and Bernadine Hawkins of Salinas, California.

BLANC DE POPIELNO

Poland is the home of the Blanc de Popielno rabbit, and is locally known as the Bialy Popielnianski. It was developed by the Institute of Popielno and recognized as a breed in 1986, with the stud book being maintained by the Central Animal Breeding Office. Blanc de Popielno is a rather unique cross using Polish rabbits (the breed) with Giant Whites, which are probably the Giant Blanc de Bouscat of France. This midget to giant breeding has produced an ideal meat rabbit for Poland in the medium-size class. Rabbits are well developed, with shoulders and rump at the same depth, with no dewlap allowed in either sex. This all-white rabbit with pink eyes weighs in at 4 to 5 kgs. Litter size is typically eight kits.

BLANC DE VENDEE

rance is the home of the Blanc de Vendee, and was created by Mrs. Douillard in 1911. The type of the rabbit is said to be a "reversed mandoline," and is an all-white rabbit with pink eyes. In a special rabbit issue of *The Life in Champagne,* on June 15,

1920, it said, "The White Rabbit of the Vendee, created by Mrs. Douillard, is presented in the form of a race of value and a future because of its qualities; it is rustic, prolific, and its fur is remarkable." For many years Douillard wanted to create a breed

Blanc de Vendee.

of rabbit with a closely cropped coat of white fur, but with a skin large enough in size for the furriers, that would resemble the coat of the Pole (Polish). Specialists of the time thought that simple selection of the white rabbit races of the west of France would produce Douillard's goal. Mrs. Douillard flatly claims that the Blanc de Vendee was the product of a pair of purebred Blue Beverens, and from that appeared a pair of white rabbits in the litter with a closely cropped fur that she was looking for. She continued to mate these for five or six generations, with not a single blue rabbit appearing.

In J.J. Dybowski's book, *Rabbits With Furs,* 1927, Dybowski quotes Poey d'Avant, the nephew of Mrs. Douillard, who had taken over the breeding of the Blanc de Vendee upon her death, shared notes that she had left behind, confirming a very similar story as she had said in the beginning. The breed was officially recognized in France on November 9, 1924.

Mr. Jacques Arnold wrote on February 1, 1983, that he doubted Douillard's story, as albinos are an extremely rare phenomenon of nature, and that in all likelihood the breed was developed through the crossing of Blue Beverens and Angoras. This 3.5 kg. breed is not very widely kept in France today.

BLUE OF HAM

elgium is the native home of the Ham Blue or Blue of Ham. The breed was created in 1900 by Mr. Ulysse Horemans, who was from the village of Ham-sur-Heure, in 1900. The breed was immediately recognized for its beautiful deep blue coat, thick and soft fur, excellent fertility, and fine meat-producing qualities. Ulysse

Horemans used White Vienna and Flemish Giants to create the Blue of Ham. The breed was picked up by other countries; being shown in St. Petersburg, Russia in 1912, Florence, Italy in 1914, and later to Madrid, Spain. World War I nearly wiped out the breed in Europe, but

Blue of Ham.
Photo courtesy Johan Van Hyfte, Belgium.

their creator maintained a number of the Blue of Hams in his rabbitry. This early breed had massive weights at up to 8 kg (nearly 18 pounds), which caused considerable confusion with the Blue Flemish Giants of the country, so a strict weight limit was placed on the Blue of Ham at 6 kg max (13.5 lbs).

Ham Blues appeared to have become extinct and were dropped from the Belgium standards during the 1960s. In 1968, a Mr. L. Herens, from the region of Vise, was raising a similar Blue of Ham, and in 1972 efforts were made to have the breed recognized again, but because breeders were few and far between, it was rejected by the national organization. Efforts were again in place to have the Blue of Ham recognized; two men, Willy Engels and Francis Coppee from Philippeville, had been breeding the rabbit for years. Both men put up large amounts of money and demanded that the Blue of Ham be incorporated into the 1975 standard, but that they should be accepted without the inspection and presentation process. This demand was not well received, and things became rather violent. Animals would be eventually presented to the examining board at a show in 1976, and on September 4, 1976 a new standard was in place and the breed recognized to be able to be shown beginning in 1977.

The Blue of Ham, although rather rare in Belgium, has a distinction that no other breed has, as it was "Money" that saw the breed's recognition.

BOURBONNAIS GREY

France is the home of the Bourbonnais Grey or Gray of Bourbonnais. For a long time in central France, especially in the region of Allier and Saoneet-Loire, existed a gray rabbit which was probably the result of crossing of the Gray Flemish Giant and common farm rabbit of the country, which was very highly desired in the local markets. Mr. Mazet, who was the founder and president of the Avicolous Union Bourbonnaise, requested that a Mr.

Bourbonnais Grey.

Chaponnaud further develop this breed as a superior meat rabbit and of a uniform color. Mr. Chaponnaud was a breeder of the Normand breed, which he introduced the genes of the Normand into the Bourbonnais breed.

There is a second theory of how the breed was created, but the first one given is usually the accepted history. It is said that Mr. Chaponnaud crossed Flemish Giants with wild rabbits; these offspring were further crossed with the Blue Vienna, which gave the breed its muscular features. The Bourbonnais Grey was shown for the first time in Vichy in 1921 and then again in 1922 at the famous Paris exhibition. The breed is not widespread throughout France, but still to this day is centered around the region where it was created. It is a fine meat rabbit, which weighs 3.5 kg to 5 kg.

BRAZILIAN

ust as the name would imply, the Brazilian rabbit or Rustico, as called by the native people, are from Brazil. This is a rather amazing animal, to say the least. From just where they came and what breeds have been involved in their evolution will never be

Dedicated to Dr. Kathleen Blair, who discovered the breed in 1978 in the Santa Dumar Mountain range of Brazil, and has maintained them now for nearly 25 years.

Brazilian Buck.
Photos courtesy of Kathleen Blair, Arizona.

known. It is strongly believed that when the Portuguese sailed from their native home to settle the country, it was at this time that rabbits were introduced to Brazil.

Brazilians are unique in that they are genetically fixed for dilution; that is, they come in a self blue and opal being the most common colors. Other colors to be found in the breed include blue pointed whites, silver-gray or blue chinchilla, lilac with a white lacing, barred feet and white belly, blue tortoiseshell, and the rarest color, a white with very faint silvery blue ticking to the tips of the guard hairs.

Brazilian doe.

All of them have blue-gray eyes, regardless of their body color. They may also come in a broken pattern. However, they will not have a butterfly marking, which is not at all typical of the patterned breeds.

Rusticos, which translates to rustic, are a naturally docile breed. Does and bucks may be kept together with no fighting. Bucks are known to assist the does in raising the young, will guard the hutch before the doe kindles. The race is extremely hardy to a great variance of cold and heat. Brazilians thrive on mere scraps of food in their native homeland. It was in the jungle and villages of Santa Dumar Mountain range where this breed was first found, running amongst the pigs, chickens, dogs and cats, where some of the poorest people live.

The body type is not that of the American commercial type, but rather of European meat type. They have a semi-arched back, almost mandolin, with broad shoulders and back. Rather heavy in bone with large hind feet, ears are somewhat thick and are typically carried cocked forward in an open "V" position. Fur is rather dense, with long guard hairs that are somewhat coarse. They are not at all bothered by flying insects; it is as if they have formed an invisible shield. Does are much larger than the bucks and have a lengthy face and body type, whereas bucks are quick blocky. Bucks typically weigh about 7 pounds (3.175 kg), with does being much larger at 10 to 11 pounds (4.53 to 5 kg). Does have large litters and are known for their excellent maternal instincts, making great foster mothers. Young are born large and grow quickly at first, then slowly but steadily until they are over a year old. Since they mature later than most breeds, they should not be bred until about eight months old.

Kathleen Blair, now of Arizona, went to Brazil as a Peace Corps volunteer in early 1978, after finishing graduate school in Oklahoma. As a wildlife biologist, she was chosen for the mission of doing a ecological inventory of the Caparao National Park, near the Tropic of Capricorn. It was here that she found the Brazilians in the open air markets and villages. During her three years in the country, returning to the States in late November of 1980, Dr. Blair began a rabbit breeding program to put a high protein meat on the tables of the poorest of the poor, and her chosen breed was these rustic native rabbits which she named Brazilians. With the rabbit breeding project, she got the children involved. With her mission complete and time well served, Kathleen Blair distributed all of her rabbits, except for a pair she had named Pipoca and Poppy.

I had the pleasure of meeting Kathleen Blair in 2003 at the ARBA Convention and Show in Wichita, Kansas, where she told me about these amazing rabbits, and in April 2004 I acquired my first trio of Brazilians, a blue doe, an opal doe and a frosted white buck, which have been line bred by Kathleen, with pedigrees kept since 1978. To me, the Brazilian rabbit may be destined to become an ideal commercial rabbit for the extremely hot and cold environments of the world in the future. We shall just have to wait and see.

BRITANNIA PETITE

 n elegant name for an elegant little rabbit that hails from Britain, but the breed is nothing more than the Polish breed of England (see Polish). The first importation of the British Polish took place in 1973, when Flo and Ted Gordon of Oregon, along with Wendy and Warren Pocha of Canada, joined by Charles Chinn of Washington state, imported six animals from Tony Cannell's stud located in Market Drayton, England. Additional imports were made by Dr. and Mrs. Paine of New Mexico from the famous strain of Bert Clipsham, while they were visiting the Bradford Championship Show in 1974. All of these imports were the Ruby-Eyed White Polish.

During the 1973 ARBA Convention, Flo Adams announced that a new name would have to be chosen for the breed if they hoped to get the breed accepted in America, because the ARBA already had a Polish. William "Bill" Sharland suggested the name Britannia, and Flo said, "How about Britannia Petites?" So the new breed to America had a new name, and I might add a very fitting one.

During one of the presentations at the 1975 ARBA Convention in Milwaukee, Wisconsin, the late Richard "Dick" Bernhardt has been invited by Standards Committee Chairman Al Meir to sit in on the presentation of the Petites. Bernhardt was greatly concerned that the Britannia Petites would be crossed with the American Polish and Netherland Dwarfs which, of course, had been happening with the Dwarfs and Polish for some time. Dick Bernhardt would later write in 1978, "I was assured by the chairman of the Standards Committee that it was strictly understood that the Standard on Petites was to be granted for WHITE ONLY, and that it was understood no effort would be made later to produce Petites in all of the numerous colors of Dwarf." Well, we know that statement did not take place. The Britannia Petites were given breed status in 1978.

BRITISH GIANT

he British Giant, of course, comes from Britain and was the creation of a Mr. Richard "Dick" Kirk, with the help of a Mr. J.H.L. Bridge. For many years Kirk's father and grandfather worked with various strains of giant rabbits. Those early strains were mostly from the Continental Flemish Giants. When Dick Kirk became involved with the rabbits, he imported additional blood from Europe, which was brought over by seamen to the docks of Grimsby and Boston during the early 1940s. After World War II, J.H.L. Bridge went to America and purchased Flemish Giants in a number of colors to mix with their Giants. These two men were not happy that the British Flemish Giant was only recognized in one color in England, which they felt hampered the

Mrs. Clark of England, with an early British Giant, circa 1960. Photo courtesy Fur & Feather, England.

breed from becoming popular. British Giants are a mix of Flemish Giant and other giant breeds.

There was a standard in place for Giant rabbits prior and during the last world war, yet the British Giant was not actually named until the early 1960s when they were first exhibited at the Alexandra Palace Show in London. A British Giant Club was formed and a standard was submitted and recognized by the British Rabbit Council.

Richard Kirk lived on his 24-acre farm called Wood Lane. The Giants were maintained in abounded outside pigsties, and during the summer months does and their young were turned out into the pig yards, since these were all separate units. He always would say that he would like to breed his rabbits to the size of pigs, which he never lived to see, yet he produced British Giants topping the scales at over 20 lbs. A White British Giant is the world's record holder at 32 lbs.

British Giants are said to be the largest of all the British breeds, with weights no less than 12-1/2 lbs., but must be over 15 lbs. to gain an additional 10 points under the judge. The breed has a very dense coat of fur, and the breed, although large and roomy, is flat over the back. It is bred in Black, Dark Steel Grey, Blue, Brown Grey, Opal and both Ruby and Blue-Eyed White. The British Giant is not a very common sight in the show-rooms of the United Kingdom.

BROWN CHESTNUT OF LORRAINE

France is the original home of the Brown Chestnut of Lorraine, having been developed by Charles Kaufmann during the years 1921 to 1925 while

Brown Chestnut of Lorraine.
Photo courtesy of Jean-Claude Periquet, France.

he resided at Vitry-on-Flowering Ash of the Moselle, which is a small village overshadowed by Lorraine iron and steel basin. Kaufmann took the common wild rabbit, which in France is known as Garenne, and mated it with various Black and Tans. Charles Kaufmann showed his new creation for the first time at an International Exhibition in Metz, France, in 1925, where the breed was appraised by a commission of judges belonging to the Union of Judges d' Aviculture of the Low-Rhine, Haut-Rhin and of the Moselle, which gave the rabbits very favorable comments. Since the overall color of the rabbit was the brown of the sweet chestnut, Kaufmann decided to give them the chestnut name "Brown of Lorraine."

The breed is rather small, weighing in at just 2 kilos, but it is said that the meat is excellent, fur is dense and a beautiful deep coloration. Does are excellent mothers and produce large amounts of milk for their offspring. The before-mentioned commission, with a few changes in the standard with Kaufmanns' approval, was recognized at a meeting on April 19, 1931. World War II arrived, which devastated most of Europe, and by June 28, 1948, the Brown Chestnut of Lorraine was no longer in the French standard, believing the breed did not survive. Much to the surprise of everyone, a Mr. Muller Oscar of Metz managed to have a large rabbitry filled with the breed. It was once again placed into the French standards in 1958.

CALDES

Spain is the home of the Caldes rabbit, which was developed on an experimental farm in Caldes de Montbui (Barcelona, Spain), which began in 1983. Six different lines of 14 does and 2 bucks were selectively crossed to produce an ideal meat-producing rabbit. The breed is not in the general public's hand, but instead are maintained on governmental and commercial breeding farms. It is a large white rabbit with pink eyes, which adapts well to the Mediterranean climates.

CALIFORNIAN

 alifornians are truly an American breed, and named for the state in which it was developed by George S. West. The sole purpose of creating this breed was purely commercial, as George West wanted a better rabbit for meat and fur, with showing being a secondary consideration. West had been a fur buyer for a number of years and was well aware of what the fur manufacturers most wanted in rabbit fur qualities. During those early years, breeders had introduced Angora into the New Zealand Whites to improve on the quality of the fur. While the fur quality did greatly improve, breeders would be plagued for many years with woollies, continuously cropping up in the litters. The Woollies became so bad that some breeders were reporting half of their litters were carrying this type of rabbit. Having taken some genetics when he took a pre-veterinary course, West decided in 1923 that he would try and produce the idea commercial fur and meat breed.

George West was a native of Salina, Kansas, but would move to 3131 Burton Avenue, Lynwood, California. West had an acre of land, on which he built a 300-hole rabbitry filled with New Zealand Whites. His herd was considered one of the best in the country and were genetically pure with no Angora genes in his stock. West was a prominent fur buyer, shipping bales

of fur by the tons to the Stetson Fur Houses of New York. During this time, approximately 80% of the American rabbit fur was being used in the felt industry for making hats, but when the soft fur of the woollies would not blow or separate properly for the making of first-class felt, the entire bottom of the Californian fur market fell out.

Dedicated to the late George West of California who developed the universally produced Californian rabbit for meat, fur and show.

120

Wesley Dixon.

West began to make experimental crosses using Standard Chinchilla and Himalayans. Chinchilla was chosen for the denseness of coat, but the breed's fur of the time was rather soft, Himalayan was used because their fur was a bit coarser. After many trials, errors and re-tries during a period of seven years, he finally obtained a Chinchilla colored half-breed buck, which weighed six pounds and had the superior fur George West was looking for.

The mixed Chinchilla buck was then line bred to New Zealand White does, and by 1928 George West had developed an 8.5 pound rabbit with the markings of the Himalayan, but with a very dense fur of excellent texture and length. The Californian breed had arrived, yet not of that name; the early name for the breed was Cochinelles. While many people who had seen the Californians wanted them, West refused to sell them, except to two men he held in high respect: Wesley Dixon of Glendale and Roy Fisher of Pomona, California. Both of these men received a trio each of the new breed. Dixon and Fisher were both top breeders of the day and were extremely honest in their dealings. George West would give credit to both Dixon and Fisher for perfecting the Californian breed.

The breed was shown for the first time in South Gate, California in 1928, but did not make a show appearance in the east until 1932, at the ARBA National Convention in Pittsburgh, Pennsylvania, and were shown by A.P. Nutsch from California. It was a long wait before the Californian breed was given a working standard by the ARBA, which came in 1939. The Californian Specialty Club was found in 1946 by Arthur O. Kelley, Jr. from University City, Missouri, who

Roy M. Fisher.

121

Californian. Photo courtesy ARBA.

would serve as the first secretary-treasurer of the new organization, and Roy Fisher, the first president.

It should be noted that George West invented the wire stretcher for furs. Prior to this time, wooden board stretchers were being employed. West was the first person to use the all-wire hutch system, and brought in the first pelleted rabbit feed from Crown Mills of San Francisco, California in 1933.

Just like the New Zealand breed, Californians have spread to every country of the world where rabbits are shown, plus have greatly improved the lives of people living in developing countries, where rabbit breeding programs have been established for the people. It is to the Americans that credit must be given for perfecting this breed as an excellent show animal. Weights are 3.6 to 4.7 kg or 8 to 10.5 lbs. A four-pound fryer can be expected to dress out at 60% of its live weight. While only one color is recognized in the U.S., the breed is recognized in Black, Blue, Chocolate and Lilac by the British Rabbit Council.

Californians showing outstanding dark points.

CARMAGNOLA GREY

Italy is the native home of the Carmagnola Grey rabbit, which was developed from local populations on the farms around the city of Carmagnola, in the Piemonte area of northwest Italy during the 1950s. The breed almost completely disappeared at the beginning of 1980 as a pure breed. The available animals then came from crosses which had been made with other breeds: Blue Vienna, Burgundy Fawn and New Zealand Whites. In 1982, a stock of these rabbits were taken into the Breeding Unit of the Department

Carmagnola Grey.

of Animal Science at the University of Turin in Italy, in a last ditch attempt to recover the breed from extinction. The breed is strictly in governmental hands, with a breeding population of about 500 animals, which would classify the Carmagnola Grey rabbit as critically endangered. This chinchilla coated rabbit is a rather large breed at 5.5 kg. and is docile.

CHAUDRY

The Chaudry rabbit comes from France and is strictly a commercial breed, which was developed by Mr. Alex Wiltzer, one-time president of the national rabbit governing body of France. Mr. Wiltzer crossed all the white breeds of France to create the Chaudry rabbit, without the infusion of Blanc de Hotot or White Vienna blood, since these two breeds are not considered pure for albino. The minimum weight for the Chaudry is 4 kg, or 8-3/4 lbs. And the breed is quite prolific with a minimum of seven young to a litter.

CHECKERED GIANT

arge spotted rabbits have been noted in France and Germany since well into the middle of the 19th century. In the later part of the 1800s in the German region of Lothringen, Flemish Giants, French Lops and spotted rabbits were bred together which produced the Land Kaninchen, which weighed in at 10 to 12 pounds. These rabbits did not have the butterfly marking on the nose. The Land Kaninchen were not bred to be an attractive show animal, but rather a better rabbit for the meat market. Spotted rabbits soon spread throughout Germany, where they were further crossed with Flemish Giants, and a breed was produced and named the Lorraine rabbit, also called Deutsche Riesenschecke (Great German Spotted). These early rabbits again did not have the distinct but-

Dedicated to the true patron of the American Checkered Giant, the late Frank Eichert of New Jersey, circa 1920.

terfly smut markings to the nose, but did resemble a large English Spot, with a wide range of colors, but typically of the wild agouti coloration. It should be noted that the Deutsche Riesenschecke of today in Germany does have the butterfly.

Mr. Otto Reinhardt, of Reinfalz, Germany, is given credit in producing what we know as the Checkered Giant. In 1904, Mr. Reinhardt bred Deutsche Riesenchecke to a Black Flemish Giant. However, some authorities say it was a Gray Flemish. He was shortly after joined in his work by Mr. Phillip Keller of Leipzig and Mr. William Lemke of Kaiserlanden, Germany. The new breed quickly spread throughout Europe and would arrive in America for the first time in 1910. Between the years 1910 and 1912 a total of four shipments had been received by the New Jersey and

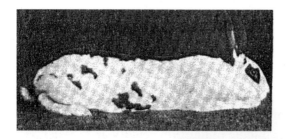

Land Kanchinchen, the beginning of the Checkered Giant. Notice there is no butterfly marking, circa 1900.

Italian illustration of the Land Kanchinchen, circa 1897.

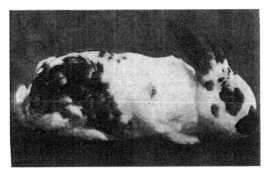

New York Rabbit Clubs. The Checker Giants were starting to take off in America, in the infancy of the rabbit fancy. The first Standard for the breed was quickly written up. In these early days Checkered Giants were known and ad-

vertised under a number of different names: German Spotted, Spotted Giants, American Spotted Giants, Checkers and American Checkered Giants. We simply call them today, Checkered Giants, "The Rabbit Beautiful," which is the adopted slogan of the National Specialty Club.

In the year 1918, Mr. Frank Eichert, of Jersey City, New Jersey, secured a permit from the United States government to import additional shipments of Checker Giants from Germany. By 1920, he had received a total of 12 shipments with no more than eight animals in each consignment, at a cost of between $25 and $40 for each rabbit, which included all shipping costs. Offspring of these imports were sold to Walter B. Garland, of North Canton, Ohio; Tom Nimohay, Dr. C.E. Exline, and Charles Weirick, all of Canton, Ohio; and to a Mr. W.D. Woolson of Springfield, Vermont. Frank Eichert is considered to be "The true patron of the American Checkered Giant" and dedicated the

tenth edition of the American Checkered Giant Rabbit Club, Inc. Guide Book in 1975 to this 90-year-old member, having been with Checkers for no less than 57 years. All of the above-mentioned importations consisted of only marked speci-

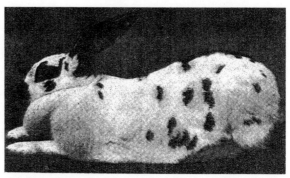

Early German Checkered Giants from 1910, showing quite a difference from what is being bred today.

mens. During the 1930s additional importations were made by William Brinska, of Chicago, Illinois; William J. Schaefer, of Independence, Missouri; Dr. W.D. Peer, of Canal Winchester, Ohio; and a Doc Bender, of Columbus, Ohio. In these importations not only were there marked specimens, but self colored rabbits as well which were beneficial in the breeding programs. The early Checker Giants that were imported were massive animals weighing in at 16 pounds in some cases and had the typical Flemish Giant type. In Europe today, the animals are still rather massive in shape, compared to their American counterparts.

The so-called "Ideal" Checkered Giant of the time was owned by Walter Garland, which he exhibited at the first Challenge Show in 1916 at Philadelphia. The buck was touted to be the "Perfect" example of the breed, and an oil painting was commissioned by Garland.

Walter B. Garland called together local Checkered Giant breeders from the Canton, Ohio area in 1919. They met at Garland's Paint and Glass Store on South Cleveland Ave., Canton, Ohio. Those founding fathers known to be present were: Garland, Tom Nimobhay, Dr. C.E. Exline, Thomas Harmon and Charles Weirick. The American Checkered Giant Club was formed with Walter Garland chosen as president and Charles Weirick as the secretary. The new organization issued their first guide book in 1923, which featured Garland's perfect Checkered Giant on the cover.

Imported Checkered Giant, 1918, scored 95 points at Leipzig, Germany, before arriving at William Schaefer's Rabbitry in Missouri.

In 1920, at the rabbitry of Walter Garland, a litter of Checkered Giants was born. However, there was a strange occurrence in that a pure pink-eyed white sport appeared. Garland kept the rabbit and mated it to a New Zealand Red, and the resulting young born became known as the Tortoise Checkered Giant. In the early days, Checkered Giants were shown in three color classifications, Black, Blue and A.O.C. (Any Other Color)

The "Perfect" Checkered Giant as commissioned by W.B. Garland in 1916.

which included Gray (light, medium and dark), Tortoise, Yellow — well, for that matter, any known color was acceptable in conjunction with white.

The first American Checkered Giant Club Annual Show was held on Saturday, October 8, 1949, when approximately fifty breeders gathered together at the fair grounds in Crown Point, Indiana. There were 186 Check-

Walter B. Garland, in the center, founder of the American Checkered Giant Rabbit Club, circa 1929.

ered Giants entered. James Blyth of Pennsylvania judged the does, and the Reverend Wayne Willmann of Ohio placed the bucks. It is said after considerable deliberation the judges chose a Black Junior Doe as Best of Breed. This rabbit was bred by Lester C. Wells and owned by Frank H. Zimmerman. During the club's business

meeting held at 3:30 that afternoon, without a dissenting vote, it was decided to abolish from the Checkered Giant Standard the A.O.C. class. After April 1, 1950, the Checkered Giants would only be recognized in the Black and Blue varieties.

While there have been a great many wonderful Checkered Giants

Best of Breed at the first All Checkered Giant Show, 1949.

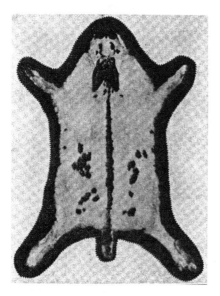

A novel use of the beautiful Checkered pelt, circa 1935.

specimens run up and down the judging tables over the years, and winning their fair share of the prestigious Best Rabbit in Show title, one Checker went a little further in her recognition. A flashy Black Senior Doe named Carr's Dasher, bred and owned by Glen C. Carr of Columbus, Ohio, went Best In Show at the 53rd ARBA National Convention and Show at York, Pennsylvania in 1976, beating out just over 4,400 animals for the coveted title. Now get this, it was the first time that

Glen Carr had ever entered a rabbit at an ARBA Convention. WOW, what an achievement! It appears so acclaimed was this win for the breed, that now, if and when a Checkered Giant does it again, the American Checkered Giant Rabbit Club will award the owner a thousand dollars jackpot bonus.

Glen Carr's Dasher, the only Checkered Giant to win Best in Show at an ARBA convention, circa 1976.

The European Checker (Papillion) of today.

128

Chinchilla, from the Wippell Collection. Reproduced from a Fur & Feather colour plate first issued 6 January 1928.

AMERICAN CHINCHILLA

The American Chinchilla is strictly of American origin (see Standard Chinchilla), having been created by a number of breeders all at the same time. The breed was created using only the normal Chinchilla of the day, that we now call the Standard. American Chinchillas were bred up, by using the heaviest Standard Chinchillas to produce a larger pelt and a finer meat animal. The American Chinchilla was first known as the American Heavyweight Chinchilla.

The Chinchilla breeds of America, circa 1929. Top: Bucks, left to right — Giant, American and Standard. Bottom: Does, left to right — Giant, American and Standard.

129

GIANT CHINCHILLA

 iant Chinchillas were the brain child of Edward H. Stahl of Missouri. When Stahl, purchased the first Chinchilla brought to the United States in 1919, he quickly set out to develop the giant version. The first American Chinchilla Giant, as they were first called, appeared in the basement of Ed Stahl's Kansas City, Missouri home on December 25, 1921. Experiments had been carried out for some time to produce this breed, but it was on this day that the doe, named the Million Dollar Princess, was born, which Stahl felt was as near a perfect animal to the standard he had envisioned. The doe was shown for the first time in a Kansas City Show during the fall of 1922. The Giant Chinchilla has been dubbed the "Million Dollar Rabbit."

The breed was produced by crossing, principally with White Flemish Giants. Stahl started crossing the Standard Chinchilla to a number of the larger breeds: White, Steel, Sandy and Grey Flemish Giants, White New Zealands, Champagne D'Argents and American Blues. The crossing of Light Grey Flemish produced the Chinchilla color most readily, but the ring color was always of a brown or dirt-yellow color. Using the Steel Flemish turned out to be a complete failure as were the crosses using the Champagne D'Argents. In using the White Flemish, although it took longer to get the correct color, it had the advantage over everything else, including a light ring color and the black guard hairs. There would be a noticeable absence of the slate blue under color. During the creation of the new breed, a Chinchilla buck mated to an American Blue doe, youngsters had the correct Chinchilla color. Finally to fix the blue under color, Stahl interbred the offspring of the Chinchilla buck and White Flemish doe, then breeding the progeny of the Chinchilla buck and an American Blue doe. This would fix the genes necessary to produce the Giant Chinchilla we know today.

Stahl's "Million Dollar Princess," the first ideal Giant Chinchilla produced in America, circa 1922.

Dedicated to the late Edward H. Stahl (December 14, 1886-May 22, 1973), a true pioneer of the Domestic Rabbit Industry in America.

STANDARD CHINCHILLA

 he Chinchilla rabbit comes to us from France. A French engineer named Mr. M.J. Dybowski is given credit with producing the breed. Some works state that Dybowski had no definite objective in producing the unique colored rabbit, that it was just a promiscuous mating of a blue doe with an agouti buck. Later the Black and Tan was used to improve the fur structure. Other histories state that a Himalayan doe, a blue doe of unknown origin and a wild buck were used. Dybowski crossed the wild rabbit with the Himalayan, then crossed the wild with the blue. From these two litters the offspring were interbred. Back and Tan blood was also introduced to improve the fur quality. Mr. O. Millsum of England, having spoken with Dybowski, conducted experiments with the first theory in the early 1920s and proved it could be created with such a mating. Mr. Dybowski's Chinchillas were first shown at Saint-Maur, France in April, 1913, and in November at Societe National d' Aviculture, a Paris exhibition. At the Paris exhibition held in November 1914, one of Dybowski's Chinchillas was given the top prize. Some early French breeders, to quote Vie a la Champagne, state that Chinchilla rabbits were being sold on the quays of the Marche auz Oiseaux, Paris, previous to 1913 by an old man called "Le Bonhomme Chinchilla." The new breed named for the South American Chinchilla lanigera, because of its unique colored fur, would become an instant sensation throughout Europe.

The name Chinchilla in the first place is derived from the 15th century Indian tribe known as the Chinchas. The name translates to

The South American Chinchilla lanigera, from which the rabbits get their name. Courtesy United Nations.

131

Chinchilla lanigera.

"little chinta." The fur trading of these little creatures dates as far back as 1500s. When the Spanish conquered the Indian tribe, the Spanish discovered these little fur balls. In Europe in the late 1700s and early part of the 1800s, a Chinchilla fur coat was a must-have for the royals and well-to-do families. A single coat took approximately 100 pelts to make, quickly reducing the wide populations by the end of the 19th century. The Chilean government quickly stepped in, passing laws to outlaw the killing of these animals.

In 1918, a mining engineer named Mathias F. Chapman, who was working for the Anaconda Copper in Chile, saw his first Chinchilla, when a native captured one and tried to sell it at Chapman's camp. Chapman purchased this animal, and his interest began. He sought permission for the Chilean government to capture some for export to the United States. Chapman, along with a party of 23 additional men, spent considerable time trying to capture the now scarce creatures. Of the 11 captured, only 3 were females. The first Chinchillas arrived in the United States in Los Angeles on February 21, 1923. Once Mathias Chapman established his herd, he began to sell these animals for as high as $3,200 a pair. Note the Chinchilla rabbit actually arrived in the United States over three years before their South American namesake.

Chinchilla trophies of England, showing the magnificent $1,000 Sir William Ingram Cup in the center, circa 1919.

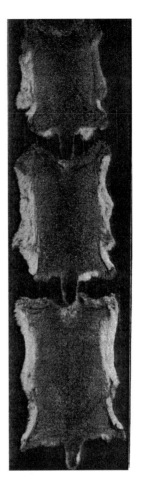

Right: Pelts taken from the Standard, American and Giant Chinchilla.

Mrs. Haidee Lacy-Hulbert, who owned the Mayfield Rabbit Stud in Mitcham Surrey, England, imported the first Chinchillas from France in the summer of 1917 with equal fanfare. Furriers of the day offered breeders up to $4 per pelt. Sir William Ingram was so taken with the new arrivals that he presented a silver cup valued at $1,000 for the Best Adult Chinchilla at the Annual Club show held at the esteemed Crystal Palace.

Chinchillas would arrive on American soil in 1919, when a British fellow sailed the Atlantic with this new breed in tow to exhibit them at the New York State Fair. After the exhibition was over, all of his Chinchillas were offered up for sale, with Edward H. Stahl of Pearl River, NY and Jack Harris of Akron, Ohio grabbing up the lot. Its appearance truly took this country by storm. Marcellus W. Meek was actually the first person to import them a year later in 1920.

The American Chinchilla Rabbit Association was formed in early 1923 with such rabbit greats as Edward H. Stahl, John C. Fehr, Lewis S.J. Griffin, A. Weygandt and Ellis DeLancey, to name but a few at the helm to promote the breed. The first standard was proposed at the Kansas City,

One of the five buildings of Stahl's rabbitry in New York.

A day's shipment leaves for the railroad station at Stahl's Missouri operation.

133

One of many shipments imported from England by Edward H. Stahl, this shipment contained 100 animals, circa 1920.

MO Convention in 1923 and approved the following year at the Lima, Ohio Convention. Leave it up to the Americans, the original Chinchilla wasn't the ideal meat rabbit, because of its small size, so at the Lima Convention a working standard was adopted for the American Chinchilla Giant. That standard would be dropped in 1925 at the Colorado Convention and replaced with the American Heavyweight Chinchilla, our American Chinchilla of today. In November 1928 at the Toledo, Ohio Convention, the American Chinchilla Giant standard was again adopted through the efforts of Ed Stahl, the breed's originator. With the addition of two new breeds of Chinchilla, the original became known as the Standard Chinchilla.

So popular was the Chinchilla breed, that in just nine months in 1928, 9,990 animals were registered with the American Rabbit & Cavy Breeders Association. The record breaker would be from November 1928 to November 1929 when no less that 17,328 Chinchillas would be registered. More 10-cent per rabbit commissions were paid to the club than was taken in that year in memberships. This is a record that has yet to be beaten, to this day. In 1930, the Chinchilla Club had over 1,500 members, and 5,000 Guide Books would be printed in anticipation of the club's growth. It should be noted that Ed Stahl, as he was so fondly known, can probably be considered the "Father of the Domestic Rabbit Industry in

Perfect ring definition of the Chinchilla fur.
Photo courtesy Meg Brown, Scotland.

Right: The first Chinchilla coat ever made in diagonal stripes, worn by Mrs. Fred A. Butikofer of Butikofer Chinchilla Rabbit Farm, circa 1925.

America." He was reputed to own the largest rabbit operation of the time, "Stahl's Outdoor Enterprise Co." in both New York and in Missouri. Stahl oversaw 65 employees and was bringing in a hefty $350,000 per year, all on the sale of breeding stock. He began raising rabbits in 1913 and continued to promote his beloved rabbits and the ARBA, until his death on May 22, 1973.

Whether Mr. Dybowski's creation was by accident or planned, his Chinchilla rabbit would greatly impact the world of rabbits. Sports of the breed have given us our Silver Martens and American Sables in the U.S,. plus Siamese Sable and Sallander breeds abroad. The blood of the Chinchilla runs through the veins of many of our breeds throughout the world, actually more than from any other breed, and is responsible for our breed varieties we called Chinchilla. I think

Two Chinchilla Rabbit Creations actually sold for, left, $550; right, $750, circa 1928. Courtesy Diener Fur Farm, USA.

that is pretty remarkable for one rabbit. Even the sensational boom of the Chinchilla breeds would come to an end, as it did with the Belgian Hares. The fur industry in the United States is pretty much gone these days. Out meat processors now lean toward the more highly developed commercial white rabbits, namely Californians, New Zealand Whites and hybrid animals which have been selectively developed for their rapid gains and meat-producing qualities. All three Chinchilla breeds are kept alive through the efforts of dedicated fanciers and the breed's respective national and state specialty clubs.

CHINCHILLA GIGANTA

hristopher Wren of England began his breeding experiments to produce a giant form of Chinchilla in 1920, using Chinchillas which had been only been brought to England from France in the summer of 1917, and Flemish Giants. Just in case you are wondering why the name Wren sounds so familiar, well, he is a relation to the famous British architect, Sir Christopher Wren. Wren's idea was to produce a large animal for both meat and the ever-growing fur trade, just as Edward H. Stahl in America was envisioning for the Giant Chinchilla in the basement of his Missouri home.

The home and pub where Christopher Wren and his daughter Grace lived, and where the Chinchilla Giganta and British Flemish Giant were developed, circa 1950. Photo courtesy Fur & Feather.

The Chinchilla Giganta was an instant sensation, and the European continent quickly imported animals from Wren's stud. They arrived in Germany by way of the Netherlands, where the breed was further crossed with the giant races and the Angora rabbit. The great German judge and rabbit authority, Frederic Joppich, carried out extensive breeding of this type of Chinchilla, with imported stock from England, by way of Ireland and the normal Chinchilla from France. Through rigorous culling, the Giant Chinchilla of the continent was established, which spread

Chinchilla Giganta, Double Champion Show Girl II, bred by the late Grace Wren, circa 1978. Photo courtesy Meg Brown, Scotland.

over the whole of Europe. The breed was recognized in France on June 28, 1948. It should be noted that Christopher Wren's daughter, Grace Wren, continued in his footsteps, and at the young age of 99 was still keeping her father's Chinchilla Gigantas and Flemish Giants.

CINNAMON

Many of our breeds of rabbits throughout the world have been created by pure accident. Well, the Cinnamon breed is no exception. During the Easter season of 1962, a couple of youngsters by the names of Belle and Fred Houseman of Missoula, Montana were given a young Chinchilla doe by their grandmother. Later on these kids received a New Zealand White buck, and before long crossbred youngsters were in the Houseman household. Their father, Ellis, believed that these crossbred should be used for meat, but young Belle persuaded her dad to let her keep one of the crossbred bucks as a family pet. The children joined the 4-H program and used their crossbred meat rabbits as their project and seemingly did quite well in the marketing category. An unwanted Checkered Giant, crossed Californian doe was presented to the kids, which was mated to Belle's pet buck, and in this litter was a russet-colored rabbit. Again the Checkered cross was mated to the same buck with another rusty-colored rabbit appearing, until one day the doe produced two russet-

Cinnamon

137

colored rabbits, which was a pair. By this time Ellis Houseman told his kids they needed to be keeping purebred rabbits to show, but young ten-year-old Fred, with tears in his eyes, pleaded with his father to let him keep the pair of brownish rabbits., Ellis agreed, as I'm sure most caring fathers would.

The children mated this pair together and 70 percent of the offspring were this russet color, which they called Cinnamon. Now their dad was beginning to take notice of these very different rabbits with the unusual coloration, Ellis also noticed a sheen to the coats of the Cinnamons and the Checkered cross, believing that perhaps there was some Siamese Satin in the gene pool. Ellis Houseman showed these experimental rabbits to Oregon ARBA Judge J. Cyril Lowit, who said he felt they had possibilities, and that for certain there was not another breed like them in the United States. At the encouragement of Lowit, Ellis Houseman would present the Cinnamon breed at the 1969 ARBA Convention in Calgary, Canada, after all the convention was basically in his own back yard. The Cinnamons were approved for their first leg of the journey in becoming a new breed. The year 1970 would prove a bit more difficult; the convention would be in Syracuse, New York, so the rabbits for the presentation would have to travel by air freight, as Houseman could not attend, but to complicate matters more, a virus killed some of the best rabbits. The presentation was made, but did not pass, as the animals were not in the best of form and condition. Just prior to the 1971 Albuquerque, New Mexico convention, a dog broke into the rabbitry, killing three of Houseman's presentation does, but the comments were good and the Cinnamons passed the second hurdle to reaching breed status. While returning from New Mexico, the Housemans hit a severe blizzard, losing a tire off their trailer, which they would abandon, and brought the rabbits home in the trunk of the car.

Ellis Houseman and his family truly believed that the entire project was doomed, but they would realize the fruition of their dreams come to pass when the Cinnamon was recognized and accepted to the ARBA's Book of Standards after the 1972 Convention in Tacoma, Washington. These 8-1/2 to 11-lb. rabbits are only to be found in the U.S., although there is a similar color-shaded breed known as the Thuringer, which is recognized throughout Europe. Cinnamons are by no means a common breed in the showrooms, but they certainly have a dedicated following of fanciers who keep promoting them.

CRIOLLO

Criollo rabbits come from Mexico and other Latin American countries, having been bred there for perhaps centuries by the local people as a food source in the small villages and farms. Through many years, the Criollo rabbit has adapted to the rather hot climates of these countries. The rabbit can be found in many colors and patterns and are by no means a large breed. Criollo rabbits are not highly productive or large in size. In the larger cities, one will find the more commercially developed breeds being used for high meat-producing qualities.

CUBAN BROWN

Cuba is the home of the Cuban Brown rabbit. While researching breeds in developing countries, I spoke with Dr. James I. McNitt at Southern University in Baton Rouge, Louisiana, who told me of this brown rabbit he had seen in Cuba, where it is called by this name. Nothing is known as to the origin of the breed, but it may well be the Havana breed, brought to this island nation many years ago, before the rise of Castro. Dr. McNitt told me that it is a rather small rabbit, totally brown in color. It would make sense that Cuba would want a rabbit which bears the name of their capital city, Havana, although the Havana breed originated in Holland, and was named by a French woman when first shown in Paris.

CZECH ALBIN

Czech Albin are from Czechoslovakia and were created by a Professor Zofka. This all-white meat utility breed is a combination of wild rabbits, blue giants and a mixture of several other breeds that began in 1928 in Kladno-Krocehlavy. Professor Zofka's goal was to greatly improve on the fur qualities, but with the commercial view in mind for a dual purpose animal. One of the main features of the Czech Albins fur is the high gloss to the coat. The breed is not very popular today in Czechoslovakia. Weights are 3.25 kg. to 5 kg.

CZECH SPOT

zechoslovakia is the native home of the Czech Spot. In fact, it is the very first national breed of that country, and was created by Jan Vaclav Kalal, in the area of Tabor. Jan Vaclav Kalal is one of the founding fathers of rabbit breeding in the Czech Republic. The breed is extremely popular in Czechoslovakia, and a club for the breed was created in 1913, which still exists today. The Czech Spot was created with common spotted stable rabbits at the beginning of 1900s. The most popular color is the black, followed by the blue. Agouti marked specimens appeared in 1946 when Kalal crossed the blacks with wild rabbits, but Jan Vaclay Kalal died, so it would be twenty years later that this variety was recreated. Tortoise and Isabella (Beige) marked rabbits were created by Hrdina in 1972. Czech Spots were introduced to the world during the 1936 World's Fair in Leipzig, Germany. Austria imported them in the early 1950s, and a standard was adopted, with the text much like the one used in the breed's native homeland.

Photo courtesy Schweizerischer Rassekaninchenzucht Verband, Switzerland.

In 1910, V. Hruby from Pilsen crossed the Harlequin with various Czech Spots to create a tri-colored variety of the Czech Spot, and this was named the Pilsner Spot and treated as a completely different breed. However, it has since been combined under the breed title of Czech Spot. The breed weighs in at 3 kg to 4 kg.

In 1972 a German fancier by the name Arnold Hirt came up with the idea of creating a small version of the German Checker, not knowing of the Czech Spotted race. Hirt crossed English Spot (Papillon) females which had light chain markings to a Giant Butterfly male. These crosses excited fellow German fanciers who also took up the cause, and followed the same procedure as Arnold Hirt had done. The new German breed was shown for the first time in 1974 by Hirt at Bundes Rabbit Show. Czech Spots were combined with the German breed, which proved to be a spectacular improvement to the German stock. The new breed was recognized in German in 1978 as the Petit Mottled. France recognized the spotted beauties to their standards in 1984 as the Petit Papillon (Butterfly).

DEILENAAR

he Deilenaar rabbit was developed in the fruit-growing region of Betuwe, in the town of Deli, Holland, where the breed gets its name. Mr. G.W.A. Ridderhof developed the breed in the 1930s. However, he did not let it be known what breeds were used in the Deilenaar's makeup. Leading rabbit authorities suggest that Flemish Giant, New Zealand Red, Chinchilla and Tans were used to create the breed we know of today. There is a strong belief that the Belgian Hare may have also been used to produce the rich fiery red agouti color and unique mackereling of black ticking. The Deilenaar was accepted to the Dutch Standard on May 1, 1940, just mere days before the occupation of Holland during World War ll. The breed was slow to reach other European countries because of the war. The United Kingdom recognized the Deilenaar rabbit to the British Rabbit Council's Standards in the late 1980s.

Deilenaars are a friendly, but lively rabbit. They are strong and robust, with a short body that is muscular throughout. The coat is the most eye-catching feature of the breed, be-ing longer than most other breeds. The warm red color is accented by the very heavily spotted black tick-ing referred to as "Mackereling." The coat has a marvelous luster to it, and unique to the breed, the fur is shorter on the head, ears and legs from the rest of the body.

Photo courtesy Meg Brown, Scotland.

DUTCH

ngland gets the credit for the original Dutch rabbit. However, the forebears of the breed came from the Brabant district of Belgium, which is not far from the French border. One can go as far back as 1825, when Belgium and Holland were still united as one country (the Netherlands), when millions of rabbits, known as Brabancons, were being shipped from the Port of Ostend, which is in Bel-

Dedicated to the late James Read of England, no doubt the greatest promoter of the breed. He joined the United Kingdom Dutch Rabbit Club in 1913, was elected president in 1936 and held that position for 40 years, until his death in August 1976.
Photo courtesy Fur & Feather.

gium today, to the markets of London. It should be noted that Belgium became recognized as an independent nation on January 20, 1831. These Brabancons, sometimes referred to as Brabanconne (Son of Brabant), were a rather medium size, that weighed 7 to 9 pounds and cobby in type. The breed was produced in many colors and patterns. They were known to be prolific, and the mothering instinct was outstanding. Those early Brabancons lent their genes to the creation of a number of breeds: Beverens, Brabancon Blues, St. Nicholas Blue, Vienna and the Dutch.

Rabbit fanciers in those early days could go to the market and look over the consignments of rabbits shipped in from Ostend and chose what they believed were fairly well-marked rabbits to establish their own breeding programs. It is reported that the name Dutch had already been given to the breed as early as 1835.

A living ancestor of the Dutch rabbit, the Brabancon of the Ostend meat rabbit of Belgium, circa 1900.

The earliest mention of the Dutch rabbit appears in *Manuals for the Many,* 1865, which states, "This pretty and useful variety is known in France under the name of

Nicard. They are much liked in old Provence on account of their prolific and happy nature and are very largely bred there.

"They are very useful as nurses to bring up the young ones of fancy rab-

The earliest illustration of the Dutch rabbit by name from "Manuals for the Many," 1865.

bits, being such good milkers. It is astonishing to see one of these little creatures bring up five or six young ones in better condition that would be effected by another doe four or five times her size.

"No breeder of fancy rabbits should be without does of this breed. They are of all varieties of colour, both self and parti-colored. Many of them have a white collar round the neck, as shown in the drawing. The chief point of excellence in those little animals is diminutive size, and I have seen some extraordinarily small specimens not weighing more than 1-1/4 lb. This small size is obtained by breeding in-and-in. I cannot see the utility of reducing the size, but such is the freak of fancy."

Colors of the Dutch rabbit in England by the 1880s were listed as: Black-whites, Blue-whites, Tortoiseshell-whites, Grey-whites, Yellow-whites, and Blue-fawn-whites. It was also during this time in history that a battle raged in Britain over the style markings to be bred for: the Old Style or the New Style. The Old Style is the Dutch that we recognize today world-wide, and the New Style was a Dutch with a narrow collar of white, the typical blaze marking and four white feet. The so-called New Style was very rarely ever seen, or even

Mr. Gilbert's Dutch Rabbit, showing the "Old Style Marking," circa 1889.

produced for that matter.

The first Dutch to be exported out of England to Europe would be to Germany in 1882 and, of course, it would spread rapidly to other countries.

Mr. H. G. Gilbert seems to have presented the first standard for the breed during the 1880s, and illustrated the standard also. "I append a scale of points for the Dutch, taking in rotation those most difficult to obtain."

Mr. Rayson's Dutch Rabbit, showing the "New Style Markings," circa 1889.

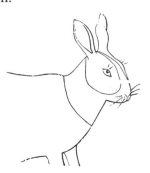

New Style markings.

Old Style markings.

Points of the Exhibition Dutch Rabbit
(Old style markings)

1. Blaze		25
2. Collar		20
3. Hind feet		15
4. Size (diminutive)		10
5. Colour		10
6. Condition		5
7. Head		5
8. Ears		5
9. Eyes		5
Total		100

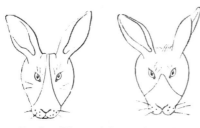

Perfect Blaze / Imperfect Blaze.   *Hind Feet Markings.*

The United Kingdom Dutch Rabbit Club was said to have been founded in 1879. However, no records can be found to substantiate this claim. In a letter to the *Stock Keeper* on May 4, 1883, a Mr. W.C. York called for the establishment of a Dutch Club. Then in 1884, Mr. R.O. Edwards placed adverts in various magazines and papers: *Poultry, The Field,* and *The Bazaar,* requesting all interested parties in forming a National Dutch Club to forward their names and that if enough names were received he would call a meeting. Edwards did receive quite a few responses, and a meeting was scheduled to be held in Kettering on Tuesday, December 30, 1884. In the *Kettering Observer,* on January 2, 1885, appeared this report.

"On Tuesday, December 30, 1884, the first day of the Ornithological Show, a meeting was convened at the Temperance Hall with the object of forming a National Dutch Rabbit Club. There was a fair number of fanciers present, Mr. W. Radford of Burton-on-Trent being unanimously voted to the chair.

"The chairman thought they were much indebted to Mr. Edwards, who had officiated as hon. Sec. Pro. Tem. Their object was to form a club and get more classes for Dutch at the principal shows. Personally he did not care for any variety except Dutch, and believed one thing would have to go against was 'trimming' and 'faking' among Dutch fanciers (Hear, hear).

"Mr. R.O. Edwards, editor of the rabbit department of *Poultry* magazine, said they ought to get the best part of twelve classes at a rabbit show if they formed a club, offered specials, or if possible a challenge cup. They might set to work at once and form a committee.

"Mr. G. Johnson, as one of the oldest Dutch fanciers in the room, said he fully endorsed what had been said as to the formation of a club, and he thought it would be a good thing to have a show once a year in different parts of the country. He said the judgment of the present day was dissatisfactory, and advised having as extensive committee.

"Some discussion ensued as to the amount of the annual subscription, and the matter was left for the committee to decide.

"Mr. Edwards took the names of those who expressed a willingness to

A winning Grey Dutch of 1890.

join, and the members enrolled, then proceeded to elect officers.

"Mr. Andrews (London) was elected president and Messrs. Atkins (Coventry) and Radford (Burton-on-Trent) vice-presidents, with Mr. R. Edwards, secretary and treasurer.

"Over twenty names were submitted as eligible to serve on the committee. Fifteen were elected, the voting taking place by ballot. The result was as follows: Messrs. Phelps (London), Enfield (Gravesend), Gillet (Banbury), Johnson (Kettering), Machin (Sutton-in-Ashfield), Gabb (Birmingham), Ellis (Bath), Allison (Sheffield), Roberts (Leeds), Foster (Kettering), Tottle (Bristol), Gilbert (Rugby), Lund (York), Street (Tunbridge Wells) and Shewell (Derby). The committee was thought by all to be a fairly reprehensive one."

This would appear to have been the very earliest record of a Dutch Club being formed, but matters are further complicated with the following writings. In *The Dutch Rabbit,* written by Mr. G.A. Moss, in 1902, he writes, "It was in 1887 that I first became attached to the Dutch Club; and I believe it was in this year that Messrs. Graham, Outhwaite, Gilpin and others started the club with Mr. Outhwaite as secretary."

A notice which appeared in the *Rabbit Keeper,* from July 5, 1888, "The foundation of the club to commence from July 2, 1888," was quoted by the Dutch Club.

It would appear that there must have been a split between the members of the first club which was founded on December 30, 1884.

Dutch rabbits were brought to the United States from England, during the Belgian Hare boom days at the beginning of the 20th century, and were among the first breeds recognized by the National Pet

G.A. Moss wrote the first book of The Dutch Rabbit, circa 1890.

Stock Association when founded in 1910. There would be three variety classifications: Black, Blue and Any Other Color, which allowed for all the rabbit colors known.

The beautiful little Harlequin or Tri-colored Dutch first

Tortoiseshell Dutch as illustrated by Wippell, circa 1912.

appeared in the Netherlands and was shown for the first time in 1922. The variety was created by Mr. Vijlbrief. Two other breeders also developed the variety: Mr. Versteeg and Mr. W. Wasink, who showed their results at the Rotterdam Show in 1925. It should be noted that W. Wasink wrote a nice little book on the breed, called *De Hollander,* and gives a large portion to the Tri-colored variety. Oddly enough, the Tri-colored Dutch in the United Kingdom is actually treated as a separate breed. This particular variety is no doubt the most difficult one to even attempt to produce the perfect specimen, probably of the marked breeds of rabbits throughout the world.

Black and Blue Dutch, from the Wippell Collection. Reproduced from a Fur & Feather colour plate first issued 23 January 1931.

147

In the land of windmills and tulips, the Dutch rabbit is accepted in all the known recognized rabbit colors: red agouti, chestnut agouti, light steel, cinnamon, opal, lynx, brown steel, blue steel, black, brown, blue, yellow (white belly), orange, tortoiseshell, blue tortoiseshell, lilac tortoiseshell, lilac, chinchilla and tri-color (black, blue and brown in conjunction with yellow).

DWARF HOTOT

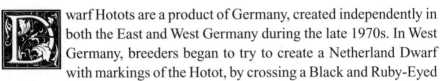 warf Hotots are a product of Germany, created independently in both the East and West Germany during the late 1970s. In West Germany, breeders began to try to create a Netherland Dwarf with markings of the Hotot, by crossing a Black and Ruby-Eyed White Netherland Dwarf. It is reported that one of these matings produced a Dutch marked Dwarf, but when bred back to the Black Netherland Dwarf produced somewhat of a Dwarf Hotot, although the rabbits had colored ears and spots on the back, but with the eye bands of the Hotot. Through further crossing of these rabbits, Dwarf Hotots were produced and of a true dwarf size. These Dwarf Hotots, being so small, were hampered in their reproduction capabilities and lacked vigor.

An enterprising East German breeder took a totally different approach in his breeding program by crossing a standard Hotot buck (Blanc de Hotot) with a Ruby-Eyed White Netherland Dwarf doe. The resulting litter was six, a buck with Hotot markings, two Dutch marked, and three Ruby-Eyed Whites. At five months, the Hotot buck weighed 1.6 kg (3.55 pounds) and had an ear length of 2-3/4 inches. This buck was mated back to his mother, and with the introduction of additional Dwarf blood, he had achieved a larger Hotot than the ones to be found in the West. These Dwarf Hotots had the vigor and produced much larger litters than those in the West.

Now we must remember that Germany was a divided country at this time, as with the East and West being closed off from one another

Dedicated to Marylouise Cowan of Maine, long-time secretary of the American Dwarf Hotot Rabbit Club and 25-year chair of the ARBA's Research and Development Committee, who helped raise over $150,000 for research.

during the early morning hours on Sunday, August 13th, 1961, and did not open back up until 7 p.m. in the evening on November 9th, 1989. Somehow these dedicated fanciers managed to exchange stock across the border with one another in 1979, which was probably a major feat of accomplishment for the fanciers and the Dwarf Hotot breed. The mar-

Photo courtesy America Rabbit Breeders Association.

riage of the two Dwarf Hotot breeds greatly improved the size and stamina of the Dwarf Hotot we know today.

Elizabeth Forstinger of California imported the first Dwarf Hotots to the United States. Forstinger went to attend the huge German Bundesschau, held at Stuttgartner Messe Gelaende in Stuttgart, West Germany in February of 1980. There she saw for the first time the "Eyes of the Fancy," with fourteen Dwarf Hotots on exhibition. Elizabeth Forstinger would write later that she felt very fortunate to have been able to purchase seven animals to bring back to America at this show, but was able to purchase additional stock from two other breeders, one in the West and the originator of them in the East, which would give her a broad gene pool to work with. She culled hard in the early development of the breed in the States, mismarks were culled at birth, and again when their eyes were open, destroying those with blue or marbled eyes.

The road to acceptance in America began in the fall of 1981, when Elizabeth Forstinger showed fifteen Dwarf Hotots at the ARBA Convention in Syracuse, New York, when the breed was accepted for their first showing. They were accepted again at the Seattle, Washington Convention in 1982, and approved for their third and final showing at the Colorado Springs, Colorado 1983 Convention. The Dwarf Hotot was officially recognized to the ARBA Book of Standards in early 1984 as its own breed, and not a variety of the Netherland Dwarf.

DWARF PAPILLON

Germany is the native home of the wonderful Dwarf Papillons or Zwergschecken, as they are known in that country. The breed was created by Paul Fischer and his grandson, Falko Freund, beginning in 1977. To create the breed, these gentlemen used the Dwarfs and small Papillon breed known as Czech Spot/Kleinschecken (Little Checker). The breed was officially accepted to the book of standards for Germany in 2002, with the following varieties recognized: Black, Blue, Brown and the Black/Orange tricolor pattern. This new breed is for sure going to become very popular, weighing in at 1.20 to 1.80 kg or 2.75 to 4 lb.

DWARF SWISS FOX

The little Dwarf Swiss Fox are a fairly recent creation in both Holland and Germany, where breeders have mated the standard Swiss Fox breed with Netherland Dwarfs/Polish of their countries. The breed is beginning to spread to other countries after they were recognized to the Book of Standards in the Netherlands in 1994. Typically these little beauties are found in the Ruby-Eyed and Blue-Eyed Whites only.

ENDERBY ISLAND

 hile researching early modes of rabbit keeping on February 2, 2003, I came across a tidbit of information that caught my fancy. The more I researched, the more fascinated I became, as this remarkable story unfolded before my eyes. Be prepared to take a remarkable journey of hope, survival, fortitude, lifesaving, rescue, destruction and preservation. This story is like no other in the world of domestic rabbits.

Dedicated to Sitereh Schouten, New Zealand, who since the mid-1900s has promoted the Enderby Island rabbits and is determined to keep them from falling into the category of "Extinction." Sitereh and I have become partners in completing the entire history of this amazing breed of rabbit.

On August 18, 1806, Captain Abraham Bristow of the 401-ton whaler OCEAN discovered the Auckland Islands some 390 miles south of New Zealand and called one of the islands Enderby. Whales were plentiful in the waters that surrounded the Aucklands, and the shores would prove to be rich with sea lions. Sealing activity would reach a peak in 1822, and by 1830 the seals were almost extinct.

Rabbits were first introduced to Enderby Island, the northernmost island of the Auckland Island chain by Captain James Ross of the HMS EREBUS and HMS TERROR expedition in November 1840. In October 1842, the ship HANNAH brought Maori natives, plus flax from the Chatham Islands. The party of 30 Maori under Chief Matiro,

The Samuel Enderby, hand-colored engraving by W.J. Huggins, 1835.

along with 30 Moriori slaves, would settle on Enderby Island. Sir Charles Ross, a noted Antarctic explorer, suggested to Charles Enderby of London, that a whaling station be established on the island. In December 1849, 150 British settlers would arrive at Port Ross, brought by the ships SAMUEL ENDERBY, the BRISK and the FANCY. The South Seas Whale Fishery Company was given a royal charter, with funding by the British Government to ship whale oil back to light the streets of London. The settlement would become a total flop and was disbanded in August 1852, just two years, nine months old. It would go down in the history books as the shortest lived British colony. The Maori and Moriori natives would leave the island over a several month period in 1854, having eaten all the man-introduced animals.

Shipwrecks were abundant in the rough and dangerous waters surrounding these six volcanic islands called Auckland. Castaways would attempt to survive for weeks and months, in hopes of a rescue ship finding them. Back in Australia, the Acclimatization Society of Victoria was formed in 1861 by a Mr. Edward Wilson, who had emigrated to Australia from London in 1842. Edward Wilson would become the Society's first president.

The goals of the Acclimatization Society was in the introduction of exotic plants and animals to suitable parts of the colony and to procure animals from Great Britain and other countries.

From the minutes of the 12th meeting of the Acclimatization Society of Victoria, held on May 13th, 1861, "Mr. Wilson laid on the table a sample of a prepared skin of a Chinchilla-rabbit and remarked that this kind of rab-

Edward Wilson, 1813-1878.

bit had been placed on an Island in the coast of Tasmania by Lady Franklin, and after the peculiarities and qualities of this description were pointed out (all of the next part of the minutes are crossed out, most likely due to the fact that a decision was made that they were not relevant to the minutes). Mr. (T.J.) Sumner and Mr. Wilson agreed to import from hence a Shipment of these rabbits to the amount of Twenty Pounds or Twenty Four Pounds on their joint and personal account, and observed that on the arrival of the shipment the Committee should have the option of purchasing."

Lady Jane Franklin, 1791-1875.

No doubt the term Chinchilla, for the Silver-greys, was taken from the writings of Charles Darwin (see Silver history), who was quite active at this time in history. Darwin called the captive bred Silver-greys, Chinchilla, and the wild ones of the warrens were considered Silver-greys.

At meeting 44 of the Society, on January 28th, 1862, there is mention of Wilson's trip to Tasmania, "The president announced that during his stay in Tasmania he had succeeded in establishing an Acclimatization Society at Hobart Town under the most favorable chances of success and that he had presented the six native bears sent by the vice president." I would assume that the rabbits would have been brought back at this time which Lady Jane Franklin had released.

Edward Wilson, in early 1862, presented the Acclimatization Society of Victoria with four Silver-grey rabbits. The society met weekly and at the 210th meeting held April 25th 1865, "The Park report was read requesting instructions on how to deal with the silver-grey rabbits as they had now so largely increased in numbers. The secretary explained that these were originally presented to the Society by Mr. Ed Wilson with the understanding that they should not be parted with. In consequence of this, it was decided to return a portion of these animals to Mr. Wilson's warren at Arundel." I am unable to determine whether they actually sent rabbits back to Wilson's Arundel warren, but it is known that this wealthy newspaper man moved back to England in 1864, settling at Hayes near Bromley in Kent, where he continued with his love of animals by establishing a menagerie which included kangaroos. It appears that the gift of the Silver-greys was more or less a farewell gift than anything else.

From page 656 of the 232nd meeting held on October 3rd, 1865 at the Society's offices. "Present were Dr. Black, vice president, Dr. Mueller, vice president, Professor McCoy, J. Stevenson Esq. The minutes of the last meeting were read and confirmed. A letter was read from the Commissioner of Trade and Customs stating that the steamer "Pharos" would be ready to embark the hog deer from Cape Liptrap on the 9th inst. And the secretary requested and received permission to send down at the same time for liberation some game guinea — a few fowls."

"A second letter was read from the Commissioner suggesting that the Council should place on board the 'Victoria' for liberation at Auckland Islands various animals in order that they might be of use to any persons who might be shipwrecked there. The secretary reported that these had been sent on board that day: 12 goats (2 rams, 10 ewes), 12 silver grey rabbits (2 bucks & 10 does), 8 game fowls (2 cocks & 6 hens) & 2 guinea fowls with all necessary forage for the voyage. After some conversation it was decided to send in addition 3 pigs (1 boar & 2 sows) and 3 geese (1 gander and 2 geese), and the secretary was directed to write and thank the Commissioner for his kindness in giving the Council this opportunity and to intimate that they would be prepared at any time to do the same kind of thing."

In a letter dated 3 October, 1865, Jas. G. Francis, Commissioner of Trade and Customs, advised Commander William Henry Norman of the H.M.C.S. VICTORIA I to search the Auckland Islands for possible persons in distress and "With the view of making provisions, to a certain ex-

HMCS Victoria I, the ship that took the rabbits to Enderby Island in 1865. A wooden steam sloop of 580 tons, mounted with seven 32-pound shot cannons, it was proclaimed the "First Vessel of War, built to the order of a British colony." Launched June 30, 1855, from the River Thames in England. The Victoria was taken apart at Williamstown in 1895. Painting owned by Com. Norman's great-granddaughter, Mrs. Elizabeth Marsden, Australia.

tent, for any persons who may hereafter be wrecked or in distress upon these islands, the Acclimatization Society have put on board a number of animals, which will be good enough to let loose on the island." There would be 12 rabbits on board ship that set sail Wednesday, October 4, 1865. It is here that I must mention, through a complete chance of luck I was able to locate Mrs. Margaret Levin, of Queensland, Australia, who is the great-great-granddaughter of Com. Norman. She became fascinated with my research project and has provided pictures of the ship, the commander, her crew and, best of all, copies of the journal and log books of this historic voyage. It should be noted that Margaret was also a rabbit breeder while living in Victoria.

From Com. Norman's Journals. "Saturday, 14th.

Commander William Henry Norman (March 3, 1812-December 12, 1869). He was Commander of the HMCS Victoria I from 1855-1869.

— No traces of pigs or other animals being observed near here; landed four goats, sent by the Acclimatization Society. Some small patches of English grass growing about the old settlement. Later in the day, one of the men reported having seen a dog. This deterred me from landing some rabbits and fowls as I had intended." There is

HMCS Victoria I looking aft, Commander Norman with telescope, circa 1865. Courtesy Mrs. Margaret Levin, Australia.

an error in his journal as he writes Monday, 18th, and this would actually be Wednesday, 18th "At 4:30 a.m. started for Enderby Island, and anchored in the sandy bay referred to yesterday, at 5 a.m. Sent on shore ten goats and twelve rabbits; these at once took to the English grass, on which I have no doubt they will thrive well. Weighed

Crew of the HMCS Victoria I, circa 1865. Note what appears to be a crate at the bottom right (12 silver-grey rabbits?). Courtesy Mrs. Margaret Levin, Australia.

The Mega Shrubs of Enderby Island. Photo by Wayne Costello, New Zealand.

155

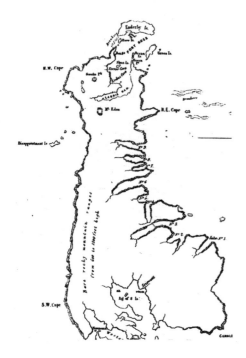

Map sketched by Thomas Musgrave of the Auckland Island chain. Enderby Island is at the very top.

again at 7:30 a.m., and steamed slowly round the island." The H.M.S.C. VICTORIA I returned to its home port, Hobson's Bay, at 1:30 p.m. Monday, November 27, 1865, having found no castaways.

Enderby Island is 1,700 acres in size, cold, windy, rather wet and with high humidity, just a really harsh environment. However, it is considered by many to be the most beautiful of the seven-island chain.

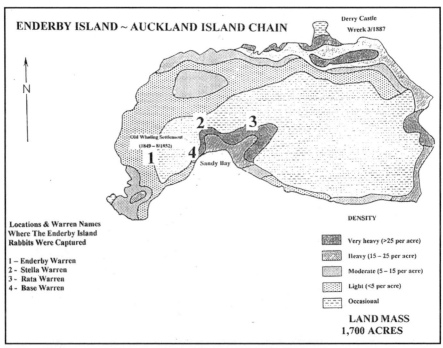

Distribution of rabbits on Enderby Island in 1966, also showing the four capture sites in September 1992. Note: Sandy Bay where the rabbits were rleased in October 1865, showing the greatest density of rabbits.

Except for the coastal cliffs and rocks, along with a few acres of sand hills, short and twisted rata forest, the island is pretty much covered with a dense blanket of peat. The 12 rabbits would thrive and multiply, burrowing into the sandy hillsides and dry peat. In 1867, the survivors of the GENERAL GRANT caught many rabbits, as did the survivors of the DERRY CASTLE in March of 1887.

During the next 100 years, the rabbits of Enderby would be up and down in population. In 1874, H.M.S. BLANCHE found the island "over-run with black rabbits." 1886 in a report to the Royal Society of Victoria it was reported that the rabbits were fast dying out or rather starved out, having eaten most all the grass and reverting to thickly set mossy plants. By 1894 the HINEMOA reported, "Rabbits swarm, and greatly reduce the value of the pasturage ... one of the party shot over twenty in the course of short excursion. 25 head of cattle and many rabbits were reported by Oliver in 1927. In 1932 the pastoral lease of the island ended and in 1934 the New Zealand government made the island a reserve for the preservation of all native flora and fauna.

The NZ National Parks and Reserves Authority approved the Auckland Island Management Plan on January 12, 1987, to eliminate all man-introduced animals from the islands. A study by B.W. Glentworth in 1991 showed a rabbit population of between 5,000 to 6,000 rabbits. Rabbits were destroying the native vegetation at an alarming rate and playing havoc with the threatened Hooker sea lion's pup population. The numerous rabbit burrows along Sandy Bay is an important breeding ground for this sea lion species, and the pups would become trapped in the burrows and die. Of

Feral rabbits on Enderby Island, 1995. Photo by Wayne Costello, New Zealand.

special interest was a film produced of the wildlife of Enderby Island in 1982 by Natural History New Zealand, which is part of the Fox Television Studios Company. This film is wonderful production, showing the rabbits running about the island along with the cattle and other wildlife.

The Canterbury Chapter of the Rare Breeds Conservation Society of NZ (RBCSNZ), having heard of the rabbit's eradication plan, began setting up a project to rescue a breeding population of the Enderby Island Rabbit.

Rabbits being rescued from Enderby Island in round cages, September 20, 1992. Photo by Wayne Costello, New Zealand.

Michael Willis and Dr. Dave Matheson, D.V.M. of the Rare Breeds Society, along with Wayne Costello (expedition leader) and Trevor Tidy from the NZ Department of Conservation (DOC). The members of the DOC team's objective was to determine the suitability of various baits and to determine the acceptance rate of one particular bait type. All would travel on board the NZ naval diving tender ship, HMV MANAWANUI, arriving on Enderby on Tuesday 15, September, 1992 at 11:30 p.m.. A permit was secured to trap 50 rabbits in just a very few days. Various modes of trapping were used, baffle traps and funnel nets at the warren entrances, soft-jaw leg hold traps, proved to be of little use, but 200 meters of wing netting would be the most successful. All of the Enderby Island cattle had been shot and semen collected from the bulls. I do not know their logic by destroying an entire breed of cattle, only known to exist on this small island! It should also be noted that the 50 rabbits which were liberated from Enderby Island left from Sandy Bay, which is the same location from which the original 12 rabbits arrived. The 49 rabbits (one died of a back injury) would arrive at Somes Island in Wellington Harbor on September 25th at 6 p.m. to begin a one-month quarantine period which ended on October 28, 1992. There would be three kits (young) born during this period. Each rabbit was carefully inspected, handled, identified with an ear tag and given a permanent tattoo. Rabbits were split into three different destination groups, one for Wairarapa, another for New Plymouth and the rest going to Christchurch. All rabbits born were carefully recorded in the stud book by Mrs. Catreona Kelly. The rabbits were the property of the DOC. However, ten dedicated caregivers would be

The capture of Lady the cow in 1993. Sandy Bay in the background, with Hooker sea lions on the beach, where the rabbits were released in 1865 and liberated in 1992. Photo by Wayne Costello, New Zealand.

entrusted with the rabbits, under contract, with the RBCSNZ.

It was during this capture that an amazing discovery was made; fresh hoof prints were discovered of a cow and calf. The Enderby Island cattle were not extinct after all. The cow named Lady and her calf, which soon died after capture, would make world history, as Lady became the largest mammal ever cloned, first cow cloned, the first clones to calve, and the first attempt at cloning to save a rare breed. On July 31st, 1998, the first clone named Elsie (LC for Lady clone) was born — well, this is another book in its own self.

In a new contract dated October 19, 1994, the DOC vested the ownership of the rabbits to the RBC. The eradication program took place from February 9 thru May 8, 1993 with a team of four people and a specially trained rabbit tracking dog named Boss. February 14th (Valentine's Day), Lady and her calf were caught within 15 minutes using a helicopter and a net gun, fired from the chopper. The cow and calf, along with the Rare Breeds team, would leave the island

Lady, the sole survivor of the breed from Enderby Island.

159

All cattle photos by Dr. Karen Nicoll, New Zealand.

Left:
Lady's three clones.

Right: Clone with calf.

Darby, the bull born to Lady using artificial insemination.

on the 15th of February on the Marine COUNTESS. The rabbits would be killed with a green dyed cereal pellet containing Brodifacoum, which was sowed using a helicopter under the capable hands of pilot Allan Bond. February 15th the chopper would drop no less than five tons of bait in just five hours. On the 19th the first dead rabbits were found; by the 21st dead rabbits were seen everywhere on the island. The last Enderby Island rabbit would be shot and killed on April 12, 1993, thus ending a 127-year period of natural selection.

Through the determined and dedicated efforts to keep the breed alive, Sitereh and Chris Schouten of Nature's Pace near Christchurch, the Enderby Island rabbit was given breed status by the Rabbit Council of New Zealand in April, 2002, when it was accepted into their book of Standards.

Enderby Island rabbits are the world's rarest breed of rabbit, with less than 100 animals in existence. Most are black, there are but five known cream-colored ones and even fewer blues. The breed evolved from the English Silver Greys, and not the Champagne de Argente as previously reported in various papers and scientific journals. This author has been a collector of old rabbit books for 30 years. In my research some of the earliest works state that the Silver came from Siam and was brought to England

Stella Hut was built for castaways, which is the capture site for the sole Cream Enderby Island rabbit. Photo by Te Papa's History curator, Michael Fitzgerald, New Zealand, 1987.

by traders. Other works say that Silver Greys existed thousands of years ago in India and were brought to Europe by Portuguese sailors early in the 17th century. Gervase Markham in 1631 wrote that rabbits with silver tips to their hairs were being kept in the warrens of England. It is well documented that Silver appeared in the warrens of Lincolnshire, England amongst wild rabbits, and were known as Sprigs, Millers, Lincolnshire Silver Greys, Chinchilla Silver Grey, Riche and more simply put, Silver Greys. English breeders have perfected the silver breed to have an even silvering over the entire body, including the head, ears, feet and tail. The fur is sleek, with a fly back coat. In one of my early books, *Manuals for the Many, The Rabbit Book,* 1865, there is a wood engraving that screams Enderby Island Rabbit. I quote, "The head and ears are nearly all black with a few white hairs. These white hairs are more numerous on the neck, shoulders and back; but on all the lower parts, such as the chest or belly, the number of white hairs is greater than those of a blue or black colour."

Today's Enderby Island rabbits are small at 3 to 3.5 lbs., fine in bone, narrow in body, eyes very bold, head is a perfect "V" laid

Silver Grey from "Manuals for the Many," 1865.

Clare Kiminmonth of Katz n K9z of Christchurch, NZ was the shipping agent for the Enderby Island rabbits to come to America. She is at the vet's office getting the Health Certificates. Photo by Sitereh Schouten, New Zealand.

on its side, and the head appears quite small for the body. Ears are fine and carried in a "V." The body is rather heavily silvered in most animals, with about 80% silvering. The extremities, i.e., the head, ears, feet and tail, are much darker and only lightly silvered, with a pronounced butterfly marking on the nose. The coat is unlike the Silver breed, being more open, longer and soft in texture. The youngsters can be rather slow to silver in some cases, and may require six to eight months to complete the cycle. Adults become more silvered over the years. Litters are rather small with two, three and four kits, with a record being eight. Genetically, it is the PUREST breed of domestic rabbit in the world and the ONLY breed that has evolved without the touch of man. It was simply created by nature. So there you have a VERY condensed version of a remarkable story, some 250-plus generations, of natural selection during a course of 127 years of near total isolation on a Subantarctic island called Enderby, where a nucleus of 12 rabbits would evolve to become their own breed called Enderby Island. There is much Thanks to be given to the Rare Breeds Conservation Society of New Zealand for having saved this primitive breed.

This author, while doing the early research of the Enderby Island rabbit, quickly began putting into motion the task of importing some of these rabbits to America, which actually turned out to be no easy task. It turned out that this was the first time ever that rabbits were being exported from New Zealand to anywhere in the world. Government protocol had to be established between the two nations. It was through the efforts of Dr. Roger Perkins, United States Department of Agriculture, clearance was given for the rabbits to be shipped to America. After a 30-plus hour journey, changing five different planes, ten rabbits (three bucks and seven does) arrived in Houston, Texas on March 11th, 2003.

Blue English, from the Wippell Collection. Reproduced from a Fur & Feather colour plate first issued 29 April 1927.

ENGLISH SPOT

Spotted or parti-colored rabbits have been in existence in England for well over 200 years. Yet little attention was being paid to them until the beginning of the 1800s, when the term "Smut" was first mentioned in Bonnington Moubray's work, *A Practial Treasties on Breeding, Rearing and Fattening, All Kinds of Domestic Poultry, Pheasants, Pigeons and Rabbits,* in 1816. Moubray wrote; "Of late years, in London, the term smut has been applied

Dedicated to the late James L. Blyth (1895-1991), founder and first president of the American English Rabbit Club. James Blyth was one of the rabbit greats, started in English Spots in 1916 and raised them for more than 70 years. He served as Secretary of the American Rabbit Breeders Association for 27 years. Photo courtesy ARBA's Domestic Rabbits.

The earliest patterned rabbit, forerunner of the English, circa 1850.

as a mark of distinction in the rabbit. Thus there are single and double smuts. The smut consists of a black spot on the side of the rabbit's nose; when there are two black spots, one on each side of the nose, it constitutes a double smut. Generally, the rabbits are prized for the number of these black spots upon the head and body, and for the fineness and length and size of the ears, which occasions their falling about the head, in a manner different from the common rabbit. Black and tortoiseshell are the favourite colours." Now it is here that there is little doubt in my mind that the lop-eared rabbit is beginning to make its appearance in the United Kingdom. These so-called smuts were further mated to the smaller tame rabbits of the time.

E. Sebastion Delamer, also known as Reverend E.S. Dixon, wrote his book in 1859, *Pigeons and Rabbits,* highlighted a chapter with "MARK-INGS: THE SMUT AND THE CHAIN — CARRIAGE" writes: "Other points in fancy rabbits are more conventional and variable and depend more upon individual taste. Peculiarities which are the rage today may be only coldly looked upon tomorrow. Amongst these are those varieties of the animal which are discriminated by the combination of colours respectively belonging to them. We quote a paragraph from Mr. Rogers: Note, Rogers, wrote of the rabbit in the 1820s, and has been quoted quite a bit by our earliest authors on rabbits. Rogers writes; "The fur of fancy rabbit may be blue, or rather lead colour and white; or black and white; tawny and white, that is tortoiseshell-colored. But it is not of so much importance what colours the coat of the rabbit displays, as it is that those colours should be arranged in a particular manner, forming imaginary figures, or fancied resemblances of certain objects. Hence the peculiarities of their markings have been denoted by distinctive designations. What is termed the 'Blue Butterfly Smut' was for some time considered the most valuable of fancy rabbits; it is thus named on account of having bluish or lead-coloured spots on either side of the nose, considered as having some resemblance to the spread wings of a butterfly, what may be termed the ground-work of the rabbit's face being white. A black and white rabbit may also have the face marked in a similar manner, constituting a 'Black Butterfly Smut.' But a good fancy rabbit must likewise have other marks, without which it cannot be considered as perfect model of its kind. There should be a black or blue patch of fur on its back, called the saddle; the tail must be of the same colour with the back and snout; while the legs should be all white; and there ought to be dark stripes on both sides of the body in front, passing backwards to meet the saddle, and uniting on the top of the shoulders, as the part called the withers in a horse. These stripes form what is termed the 'chain,' having somewhat the appearance of a chain or collar hanging round the neck. Among thorough-bred fancy rabbits, perhaps not one in a hundred will have all these markings clearly and exactly displayed on its coat; but the more nearly the figures on the fur of a rabbit approach to the pattern described, the greater will be its value, so far at least as relates to colour. The beauty and consequent worth of a fancy rabbit, however, depends a good deal on its shape, or what styled its 'carriage.' A rabbit is said to have a good carriage when its back is finely arched, rising full two inches above the top of its head, which must be held so low as for the muzzle and the points of the ears to reach almost close to the ground."

Now I will say here that it is in all likelihood, although I do not have total proof, but it was Mr. Rogers who coined the terms, "Butterfly and Chain markings," that we still recognize today throughout the world. Rogers was certainly correct in saying the numbers one could expect to have with the correct pattern.

There is very little written of the early history of the English Spot, other than the previous mentioned works, except for the writings of James Salter on the breed, published in *Fur & Feather* in 1891. James Salter was a highly respected man of the time, being a member of the Royal College of Physicians, Fellow of the Royal Society, Fellow of the Linnaean Society, Fellow of the Zoological Society, plus a number of other learned bodies. He would be the first president of the English Rabbit Club. James Salter wrote; "It is a law in the

James Salter would give us the earliest history of what would become known as the English in Britain and English Spot in America. He was the first President of the National English Rabbit Club. Circa 1890.

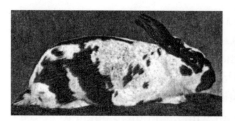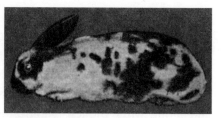

Early English Spots of the later 1800s.

colouration of these rabbits, and indeed with all those that are broken colored, that the white starts from beneath and the colour from the back, and where they meet they are broken up, prevailing variously. In the small English rabbits, the distribution of colour in the broken-colored specimens had not been bred for, and no beauty in that direction had been attained. Which prevailed to a great extent. There was the characteristic colored stripe down the flank, the points of the ears coloured, and often a certain amount of irregular colouring round the eyes. But the smut character about the nose and the chains of spots on the body, especially on the shoulder region, which distinguished the high bred forms of the variety, were wanting."

Salter then writes of his earliest association with the spotted beauties of the time; "I am writing in the past tense for the double reason; first, because the days of my boy rabbits are indeed past, and secondly, because it was at that time that the English fanciers bred them at their best. I must allude to one circumstance of a personal nature. I had the good fortune to possess, as an uncle, a distinguished naturalist, the later Professor Bell, professor of zoology and natural history in King's College, London. He was greatly interested, in its scientific aspect, in the breeding and variations of domestic animals, and, among others, he kept double smut rabbits as they were then bred in the highest perfection, the boys' English rabbit glorified. These rabbits were shown at the Zoological Gardens, Regent's Park, about the year 1836, and it was from that stock that Professor Bell obtained his, and it was from him that I first received a pair of these beautiful creatures. To me they were indeed a surprise and a revelation. I had no idea until then that such rabbits existed. I will now proceed to describe the large English rabbits as they were about 1838, when I first made their acquaintance. But I must ask my readers who may keep this variety to remember that I am not writing in a controversial sense in any way, nor with a desire to enforce a particular standard to be now adopted. My description may be considered historical, and as recording what the standard was at the time to which I refer."

"The smut rabbit, double or butterfly, was large, reaching seven to ten pounds in weight. Its general form was that of the lop-eared rabbits as they existed at the time when the English were at their zenith — rather small in front, with large, somewhat high, rounded hindquarters — a shape about intermediate between the Belgian and the Lop of the present day. The heads were small and refined looking, the ears were rather large, about five inches in length, remarkably thin and delicate in structure. When young, they were carried somewhat loosely, but in good specimens they became sufficiently stiff in adult to be held much as those of Belgians. Those specimens that were thought to be sufficiently good to show at the meetings of the rabbit clubs always had erect ears, but half lops were not unknown and were always discarded as failing in one essential point. The most marked characteristic, however, was the pattern of the colouring, which in perfect specimens was striking and beautiful. The largest area of the fur was white associated with either of the ordinary rabbit colours, but black and blue were the favorites. My own preference was for the fawn and white. Perhaps the most striking were the tortoiseshell, where the head markings were nearly black, while those on the body were fawn, the large area of white between the two obliterating the merging of the one colour into the other. I do not recollect ever to have seen one of these rabbits self-colored."

James Salter now would write concerning the markings of the early English: "Taking a black and white specimen, the following would be a description of the 'double smut': extending from the shoulders backwards over the spine was a black stripe beginning and ending with a point and gradually widening across the end of the back and loins. On either side from the widest part numerous more or less circular spots, stretching downwards and spreading over the flank, and in their course becoming smaller and more separate. Similar but smaller spots were spread over the shoulder. The markings of the head were, however, the most remarkable and important; and, indeed, it was upon them that the fancier's efforts and selection in the breeding mainly turned; if the head were well marked, the body would not be far wanting. The head was white for the most part; around each eye was a circular black ring, free from any projection or spur, either upwards toward the ear or the nose, in which directions in mismarked specimens there was a tendency to excess of colour. On each side of the nose, close to the nostril, was a perfectly round and sharply defined black spot, from the size of a four penny piece to that of a shilling. Those two nose spots, one on either side, constituted the "double smut" point, and were essential. They were more constantly true than the eye circle, which was prone to break and spread to the ear, especially if the latter was heavily colored to the root. Where there is much colour and the patches are near, there is always a tendency for them to run together, or at all events to approach. The ears, in good specimens, were white at the roots and black above. The distinctness and roundness of the spots, with symmetry of the two sides, both body and head, were the gauge merit, and it was marvelous to see how wonderfully perfect some of the specimens were; and, in the multitude of their sound spots, remind one of the Dalmatian coach dogs that formerly ran by the chariots of the wealthy and fashionable. If the rabbits had been artificially coloured, with the aid of a measure and compasses, many of them could have not been surpassed."

James Salter closes his piece by saying; "I now come upon rather delicate ground, but I must be historically true. The breeders of these lovely large English rabbits, at the time I am writing of, more than fifty years ago, did not look with favour upon what are now called 'butterfly smuts'; they considered them mismarked and tabooed them accordingly. This was the opinion at the rabbit clubs, though I believe it was not reduced to writing in any hard and fast standard of perfection. There were no shows then, nor professional judges, merely an occasional gathering of fanciers, and this was the conclusion arrived at by a general consensus of opinion. The "butterfly smut" refers to the marking of the nose, in which the double smuts spots have become so enlarged as to meet over the front of the nose, and there to coalesce, often sending up a spur of colour in the middle line, which represents the body of the butterfly, while the patches of colour on either side typify the wings. It was found that this confluence of the nose spots was nearly always associated with a degeneration of the clear, defined spot character of the markings generally, the eye circle would break out and extend to the ear, and the body spots would become confused and angular. This was the experience then, and opinions of what was right were regulated accordingly. I express no opinion myself; I simply record. Other ideas may prevail now, and clouds of colour may be preferred to spots. This rests with the fanciers of the variety, and how they desire to select and breed. Either may be adopted or both."

Prior to the 1880s, the "Double Smuts," "the 'Butterfly Smuts," or "English," as they would finally become known, were always shown in the Any Other Variety classes, where they usually always won. By the later part of that decade, show committees saw the growing number of English

Early winning English from the United Kingdom, circa 1905.

Spot fanciers, and began to provide the breed with its own showroom classes, which would further promote the breed throughout England.

Fur & Feather would publish a suggestion by Mr. W. Fisher of Southport, England on December 18, 1890 that a national breed club be formed for the English. In the following next issue of *Fur & Feather,* a Mr. E. Salisbury of Blackburn supported the idea and asked for the assistance of Mr. E. Biggs, Mr. J.W. Harrison and Mr. G. Allsop. With Biggs from Southport spearheading the project, a meeting was held in Liverpool on January 28, 1891, but only three gentleman attended the meeting, Biggs, Harrison and a Mr. J.W. Morris. However, letters of support were sent in by the following men; Allsop, Cross, Hagger, Hunt and Slater. At the small meeting it was resolved that the English Rabbit Club be formed and that the previously mentioned men be considered members, along with a Mr. J.B. Fothergill, become members. Biggs would be appointed secretary pro tem, until an election could be held.

The club's first election results were announced in *Fur & Feather,* on March 12, 1891, with James Salter, as President, J.W. Harrison as vice-president, Committee members in the persons of G. Allsop, T.S. Dawson, W. Fisher, J.W. Morris and E. Salisbury, Secretary E. Biggs, Judges; T.B. Mason, E. Biggs, J.H. Roberts, O. Moses, J.E. Aldred and W. Lumb. It was at this time a standard of points were adopted for the breed, although this caused quite a bit of controversy among the fanciers of the day.

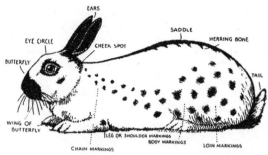

A major turning point for the breed came on July 30, 1892, during the Mytholmroyd Show. There was the largest gathering of English breeders yet when a meeting was called to order. During this meeting, sketches were submitted by the members of what they believed constituted the proper standard for the breed. There would be, of course, considerable discussions on the subject,

The ideal English appeared in America's first rabbit standard in 1917.

A Dutch illustration of the ideal English, circa 1900.

so a committee was formed of the following men; Biggs, Mason, Roberts, Winn and Womersley. On January 12, 1893, would appear in the pages of *Fur & Feather,* the ideal English Spot rabbit, that the entire rabbit world uses today. The young 23-year-old artist would be none other than Ernest George Wippell, (6-19-1869 to 6-12-1961). There is little doubt in my mind that James Slater, the club's first president, secured Wippell through his connections with the Zoological Gardens, to illustrate the ideal English Spot. Ernest Wippell would become very famous for his painting and drawings of all sorts of animals, especially in his renditions of the "Ideal" in all sorts of show poultry, pigeons and rabbits, to name but a few. During the early days of the American Rabbit Breeders Association, Wippell was contacted to illustrate in color all our known breeds of rabbits and cavies of the time. However, Wippell never followed through, due to his advancing age. If one is lucky enough to find an original Wippell and can afford to purchase it, do so, as his talented work is priceless.

Germany imported the breed in 1889 and it was well received, although breeders were not allowed to show them, since the shows of the time only catered to the more commercial meat and fur type breeds. The English breed

soon spread to neighboring
countries, thanks to the efforts
of the Germans, being called by
various names English, English
Spot, English Butterfly and
Papillon, which is French for
Butterfly.

English Spots began arriving in America from England
in the beginning of the 1900s,
as the Belgian Hare boom was
waning. Colors in those early
days were only recognized in
the Black, Blue, Gray and Tor-

*Left to right: Mr. W. Harris, purchaser; Mr. W.
Watmouth, editor and founder of Fur &
Feather; and C.B. Thompson, breeder of the
English, which sold for $1,000 in 1938.*

toise. Europe quickly set out developing many other varieties, and today
there is even the beautiful Tri-colored English Spot, which is particularly
appreciate by the Swiss and Germans. The Chocolate English Spots were
the creation of Mr. Henry Noble, of Honley, England, who began in 1913
using Havanas to Black English. Henry Noble spent a full 24 years developing this variety before it was accepted by the national club in 1937. It should
be noted that Noble also developed the Chocolate Dutch. A national specialty club for the breed was formed in the United States in 1924.

One of the most noted importers of the early English Spots to America
was none other than the born-into-wealth Margaret "Peggy" Guggenheim,
of Babylon, Long Island, New York. Guggenheim was born August 26,
1898. Her father, Benjamin, would go down on the ill-fated Titanic in 1912,
just before Margaret's fourteenth birthday, a father whom she adored, and
it was said that she never overcame the loss. Benjamin Guggenheim died
gallantly, for he ran to his cabin, dressing in his
finest evening attire, then assisted the women and
children into the life boats, before going down with
the ship. What Margaret wanted, Margaret got. She
not only imported English Spots, but Belgian Hares,

*William J. Seyfrield was the first Secretary of the Ameri-
can English Rabbit Club and served for many years.
When he passed away in 1980, he had bred English Spots
for 66 years. Photo courtesy ARBA's Domestic Rabbits.*

Dutch and English Lops. All animals from the finest specimens in the showrooms of the England and continent. She was an important exhibitor at Madison Square Gardens, Boston Poultry Show and other east coast exhibitions. She showed at

Grey English buck, illustrated by Wippell in 1911.

the 1919 National Convention in Cleveland, Ohio, after having just inherited $450,000 from her father's estate. Near the close of the convention, the officials refused to allow her to remove her rabbit from the showroom. She then picked the Dutch rabbit up, placed it on her person and defied any of them to stop her. The late James Blyth wrote to her for a price of a pair of English Spots, and she wrote back they would be $50 each, so Blyth turned her down. She ended up moving to Paris, France, and began an extensive collection of modern art, buying works from the great artists of the time for mere cents on the dollar, before the Nazi occupation. She said she did not like the United States for the way they treated the Jewish people, and would

The ideal English Spot, as illustrated by Ernest George Wippell in January 1893.

eventually settle in Venice, Italy after the war. When she died on December 23, 1979, she had amassed one of the world's largest collections of modern art, some 266 pieces, valued at more than $35 million. Now that was an interesting rabbit lady!

FAUVE DE BOURGOGNE

 rance is the native home of this very old breed of rabbit known as the Deer of Burgundy. Fawn-colored rabbits have been known on the farms in the Burgundy region for many years, and those old specimens were usually marked with some white on the head, neck and legs, but this didn't deter the old farmer, as he knew his fawn-colored rabbits processed fine meat-producing qualities for his family. Stock breeders then decided to fix the traits, most notably of them a Mr. A. Renard, who has been given credit in founding the breed.

Mr. Renard wrote in an issue of *The Acclimatization,* in 1919, on the history of the Deer of Burgundy, "Its geographical surface is rather frequently in Burgundy, starting from Dijon, in the Gold Coast, it is seen in Nieve only until Clamecy, for then entering Yonne where it is met more commonly than everywhere else, but hardly exceeds the line of the departments of Yonne and the Paddle, as a good neighbor, it leaves this part of Champagne to his "Argente brother." Here he is speaking of the Argente breed, known as Champagne. Mr. Renard collected a number of worthy specimens from it seems various areas, and began to make the breed a fine show animal, but without losing its outstanding commercial properties. His work began at the beginning of the 1900s, just when Americans on the west coast were creating the New Zealand Red. The Fauve de Bourgogne has spread throughout Europe and into England. However, they have not reached the United States. It is often used in breeding programs in the developing countries of the world where rabbit breeding projects have been estab-

Fauve de Bourgogne.
Photo courtesy Jean-Claude Periquet, France.

173

lished. The coat is more of a yellow than red, plus it is a longer coat than normal. The breed is often called the Burgundy Yellow. Their weight is 3.5 kg. to 5 kg. (7 lb. 11 oz. to 11 lb.).

FEE DE MARBOURG

ermany is the original home of the Fee De Marbourg, or Marburger, which was created by Miss Marie Sandemann, beginning in 1912 when she was given a rabbit from the caretaker of the school that her nephew attended, by a Mr. L. Peter. Miss Sandemann also raised Havanas, was delighted with the unusual color of this rabbit, which was a doe, and had been bred from Mr. Peters Havanas. She mated the doe with a Silver colored male, and all of the offspring were Black. The doe died when the litter was ten weeks old, so she selected a Black doe and bred it back to a Havana. In this litter were mostly Blacks and Havanas, but one animal, a male, was the beautiful gray coloration of the original doe. Marie Sandemann quickly set out to fix the color, and showed the breed first as "Feh" in 1915. There was tremendous excitement from fellow fanciers when they saw the lilac gray rabbits which carried a light reddish cast to the fur, which is like our Lilacs today. A rabbit judge by the name of Kemp became excited about the breed and dedicated himself to having them recognized. The breed was given a standard and approved by the Reichsverband Deutscher Kaninchenzuchter in 1924 under the name of Feh de Marbourg. The term "Feh" has been chosen by German furriers to indicate the color, which greatly resembled the Siberian Squirrel. Although the breed is actually a Lilac, the Germans have bred for a deeper color, which sets this breed apart. The breed is recognized in a number of European countries and weigh in at 2 to 3.5 kg or 4 lb. 6 oz. to 7 lb. 11 oz.

Fee de Marbourg. Photo courtesy Meg Brown, Scotland

Flemish Giant, from the Wippell Collection. Reproduced from a Fur & Feather colour plate first issued 26 May 1922.

FLEMISH GIANT

here is little doubt that Belgium is the native home of the mastodons of the rabbit world we call Flemish Giants. Giant rabbits have been recorded as far back as the 16th century. In *De Quadrupedibus digitalis,* 1637, U. Aldrovandi, describes on the authority of a number of early writers such as Scaliger, in 1557, that rabbits of various colors, some like a hare. He further states that P. Valerianus, who died a very old man in 1558, saw in Verona rabbits four times bigger than normal.

Just exactly when the genes for "Giants"

Dedicated to the late Vern Ashton (1892-1980). Vern started raising Flemish Giants in 1914 and continued until his health failed in 1978, a full 64 years. He was President of the National Federation of Flemish Giant Rabbit Breeders for 34 years, plus an ARBA director for 30 consecutive years.

appeared no one will ever know for certain. The oldest breed from the old Flemish country is the Steenkonijn or Stone Rabbit, which has been bred for centuries in Belgium for meat. These rabbits typically weighed the old world measure of a "Stone," 3.5 kilos or 7 lb. 11 oz. This author believes that the

Flemish Giant doe that won the Crystal Palace Show, London, 1887.

Steenkonijn, was the foundation blood of the early Flemish Giants, with additional blood added over the years.

There is also the Patagonian breed, a massive rabbit of the day which would have contributed its genes to the Flemish Giant, before it became extinct at the end of the 19th century, as the early Flemish were the same color as the Steenkonijn and Patagonian.

To a more recent time of a hundred and fifty years ago, we know for certain that six clubs existed for the giant breed, in the suburbs around Ghent, Belgium, where the height of breeding activity took place. The societies had rather unusual names to say the least; "Them Without Fear," "Virgin of Ghent," the "Young Tradesman," "Country of Promise," the "Court" and "Brothers of Sunday." The organizations had fixed meeting days where all the members had to gather, otherwise be fined. They would organize weight contests, both as individuals and by groups or teams. These gatherings of the 1860s would eventually become what we know as rabbit shows. At one competition in 1867, held by the Country of Promise group, a doe was the winner, with an unbelievable weight of 8.5 kilos or nearly 19 pounds. It is reported that several of the early Flemish Giants approached these weights. A baker from the Kortedagsteeg in Ghent sold a giant at this weight for 45 BEF, which would be the wages for 2 to 2-1/2 months of labor in the day. The first standard was written for the breed in 1893 by Albert Van Heuverzwijn, a stanch supporter of the breed. Some people did not agree on the standard, and soon there were different directions being followed. The breed suffered in quality and weight. At this time there were but two colors recognized, the Gray Agouti which had a white belly and the Iron Gray with a dark belly — the latter color being the preferred color by most fanciers. It was at this time that new colors were being developed, mostly through the efforts of the members of the Court. The giant rabbits of Flanders began to move into other countries.

In Germany a Giant Club was founded in Leipzig in 1897. The breed was known as the Flemish Giant until 1937, when the breed became known as the German Giants.

Christopher Wren and A.J. Watts of England were the very earliest supporters for the breed in the United Kingdom. Their choice was the Iron Gray variety (Dark Steel Gray). This is today the only recognized color accepted by the British Rabbit Council. The Flemish Giant of the British Isles is so far removed now from the Flemish Giants of the rest of the world that they have become easily their own recognized breed (see Flemish Giant, British).

The first Flemish Giants to reach America came from both Belgium and England during the 1890s during the height of the Belgian Hare boom days. A Fred Dewey of Maryland went to Belgium and brought back giant rabbits in July 1900 (see Belgian Giant and Belgian Hare). By the late 1890s the American Flemish Giant Club was formed with Mr. A.M. Bush serving as secretary of the club. I'm not quite sure of what these odds are, but today the secretary of the National Federation of Flemish Giant Rabbit Breeders is a Mr. A. Bush, too.

Edwin E. Vrooman wrote for *The Belgian Hare Guide,* 1900, which was a book published by Inland Poultry Journal Co. of Indianapolis, Indiana, "As to pedigreed Flemish Giants, the beginner will be disappointed if he expects to get a pedigree of several generation, for we have not been able to get any from Belgium, and other breeders tell us of the same experience; and from England we have gotten only pedigrees going back two generations. One can buy stock direct from England, out of a prize winner or a prize winner itself; but that is about all the pedigree he can get.

"Judging from the demand and inquiries relating to this class of hares (Flemish Giants), we are convinced that he is fast being recognized by and for his good qualities, and we pre-

An American bred Flemish Giant doe from 1899.

dict that ere long he will be quite popular, as he certainly deserves to be."

The Standard adopted by the American Flemish Giant Club is as follows:

MATURITY — Twelve months, weight to be not less than 12 pounds; size to be as large as possible.

OFFICIAL WEIGHT — For immature specimens, 3 months old, 6 pounds; 4 months old, 7 pounds; 5 months old, 8 pounds; 6 months old, 9 pounds; 7 months old, 9-1/2 pounds; 8 months old, 10 pounds; 9 months old, 10-1/2 pounds, 10 months old, 11 pounds, 11 months old, 11-1/2 pounds. Official Cut. — For under size, one-half point to the ounce of shortage.

SIZE — Large and imposing 30

COLOR — To be dark gray, with no inclination to sandiness, and as free from white under belly as possible, except under tail, even ticking 20

HEAD — Large, shapely and firmly set on 5

EARS — Erect, moderately tick, six inches long 6

EYES — Dark brown, bright, large and expressive 6

BREAST — Broad and massive 6

FORELEGS — Straight and heavy boned 4

HINDLEGS — Shapely and heavy boned 4

BACK — Long and broad 4

HAUNCHES — Wide and massive 5

DEWLAP — Does to have good size and evenly carried 5

CONDITION — Firm in flesh and close coated 5

Total 100

It is not known when the American Flemish Giant Club disbanded, but no doubt it was during the time of the bust of the ever popular Belgian Hare. Then in 1915, a Captain Gay W. Akin, with his wife, Mrs. E.M. Akin, of Denver, Colorado, conceived the idea of uniting the Flemish Giant breeders throughout the nation into a club. They invited a E. Taylor of Golden, and Lewis S.J. Griffin of Colorado Springs

Lewis S.J. Griffin of Colorado was the first President of the Flemish Federation.

A Flemish Giant from its native homeland. Photo courtesy Het Belgisch Raskonijn VZW, Belgium.

to their home on Sunday, November 15, 1915, and thus was born the idea of the National Federation of Flemish Giant Breeders. Letters were sent to several noted breeders of the day. In 1916 the club was founded, with Lewis S.J. Griffin serving as the first president and Bill Taylor, the first secretary. These two gentleman also wrote standards for the Light Gray, Black and Steel Flemish. In 1919 the Blue and White Flemish Giant would be recognized. Sandy Gray Flemish were recognized in 1924, but the name is now known as just the Sandy. For a short period, the Silver-Tipped Flemish Giant was recognized, and in 1929 appeared a working standard for the Flemish Giant Rex. The seventh and final variety, the Fawn Flemish, was recognized in 1938.

The only Flemish Giant to ever win Best in Show at an ARBA National Convention. Photo courtesy ARBA's Domestic Rabbits.

One famous Flemish Giant was a Sandy Junior doe, bred and owned by Joey Shults of California which won Best in Show at the 1987 American Rabbit Breeders Association Convention and Show in Portland, Oregon, beating out 4,921 rabbits for the coveted title.

FLEMISH GIANT (BRITISH)

The English Flemish Giant was developed in England, by the late Christopher Wren, during the early 1920s. It is certain that Flemish Giant blood runs through the rabbit's veins, but I'm sure some other breeds as well can be found in its genetic makeup. At the time, Chris Wren had imported

Dedicated to the late Grace Wren, who continued to breed her father's Flemish Giants and Chinchilla Gigantas into her 99th year. Photo courtesy Fur & Feather, England.

Flemish Giants from Europe and England and had already recognized a "Giant" rabbit. Wren set out to create his own giant rabbit, which met with come dissension of the Giant fanciers. Wren's Flemish is truly a genetically unique rabbit as it is a false steel, very dark in color, yet it has a white belly. It is certainly the smallest of the Flemish Giants; bucks should not weigh less than 11 pounds (4.97 kg) and does not less than 12 pounds (5.44 kg). English Flemish Giants are only recognized in the dark steel gray color. Oddly enough, the stan-

British Flemish Giant Dark Steel bred by Christopher Wren. Photo courtesy Meg Brown, Scotland.

dard for the breed calls for the type to be large, roomy and flat, shoulders and hindquarters are to be broad. This type of Flemish is totally restricted to the United Kingdom, as other countries of the world prefer the true

The late John Sandford on the left, a famous author of rabbit books, and his mentor, Christopher Wren, who developed the British Flemish Giant. Sandford spent his afternoons after school and weekends cleaning hutches for Wren to learn all he could about rabbits. Photo courtesy Fur & Feather, England.

Flemish Giants of massive size. This fairly old breed could well become extinct in the not so distant future, as less and less are being shown today in England.

FLORIDA WHITE

lorida Whites were originally developed in the state of Florida, by a rabbit judge by the name of Orville Miliken, during 1960. It was during the 1962 Tampa, Florida ARBA Convention and Show that many breeders were fortunate enough to be able to visit the Mililiken Rabbitry and were able to see several stages of the development of the new breed, although there were very few all-white rabbits, due to the introduction of the Dutch genes. Through careful selection and line breeding, Orville Miliken developed a compact strain of all-white rabbits. The Florida White was recognized as a breed by the American Rabbit Breeders Association in 1967, at the Syracuse, New York Convention and Show. Miliken's goal was to produce a smaller albino laboratory animal and a small meat rabbit. The initial breeds used in the development of the breed were said to be an albino Dutch, Ruby-Eyed White Polish and a small, yet typie White New Zealand. Miliken's original purpose did not quite materialize, as scientists are rather hesitant to change from one laboratory breed for another, especially when little biological information is available on the genetic makeup of this new breed. Also, it could easily be understood why the breed never made the meat industry cut, for it made no sense to have a small fryer, when it was just as easy to dress a larger rabbit as it would be for a smaller one. Today's Florida Whites are known for their fine bone and have been ranked in the top five rabbit breeds for weight dress-out percentage. The early Florida Whites were far different than one finds today, especially in heaviness of bone and type.

A major turning point for the breed came when the meat type master of rabbit breeding, Fibber McGehee of Oklahoma, began to breed Florida Whites, beginning in 1970. Fibber thought just mating quality Polish to New Zealand Whites would reduce the size enough to work with, but it did not prove that easy. According to Fibber, the New Zealand was used in the breeding program just once. Through selective breeding, Fibber fixed the type of the breed. Dale Allison, also of Oklahoma, while visiting Fibber McGehee's rabbitry, decided he really liked the little white rabbits and wanted to work with them solely, so Fibber gave Dale the lot. Dale Addison

Dedicated to Eabert "Fibber" McGehee of Oklahoma, a master breeder of Florida Whites, who has done much to perfect the breed. Shown here with his 1999 Best in Show winner from the ARBA National Convention in Louisville, Kentucky. Photo courtesy Heinold Feeds.

would do quite well with the fairly new little breed, with his biggest win being Best Rabbit in Show at the 1977 ARBA Convention and Show held in Houston, Texas. Other early contributors to the development of the breed included: Oren Reynolds, Billy Dodge, Kat Stearns, Larry Petty and Dr. T.E. Reed.

In 1978, Fibber once again decided to keep the breed, and went back to the same previous drawing board. This time while visiting Dennis Holcomb's home in Deepville, Pennsylvania, he noticed in a rabbitry they were visiting one day, owned by a person known as Gillham, who was well known for his Rex rabbits, a small white buck, of unknown origin. Fibber said, "You might think I'm crazy, but I'd rather have that little white rabbit than any of them!" Dennis asked what in the world for, and McGehee replied that he felt it would be just right for his Florida White breeding program. Well, Fibber did eventually get that buck, and the Florida White breed has continued to move forward ever since.

The Florida White Rabbit Breeders Association was granted a charter by the ARBA in 1972, with Dale Allison serving as the club's first president. A National Florida White Specialty Show was started in 1975. The Florida White would again make history when Fibber McGehee won Best Rabbit in Show at the 1999 ARBA Convention and Show in Louisville, Kentucky.

Florida White. Photo courtesy American Rabbit Breeders Association.

FURLESS

 urless rabbits were first discovered by the famous English genetist, W.E. Castle, in 1933. The Furless is a recessive ff gene and only the double recessive ff will have no fur. Well, actually the Furless rabbit will have a few hairs, as seen in the photos. These types of rabbits are extremely rare throughout the world, as breeders culled extensively to remove them from their herds whenever they should

Dr. Steven Lukefahr of Texas with a Furless rabbit and a White Mini Lop. Photo courtesy Dr. Steven Lukefahr.

appear on the rare occasion. Because the Furless rabbit carries a lethal gene, there is little doubt that this breed of rabbit will never be recognized by any national rabbit governing body of the world, which caters to show animals. Work has been put into motion in Texas for the last three years to breed these most ugly creatures that only a mother could love.

Dr. Steven Lukefahr, professor at A&M University-Kingsville, heard of a rare furless Mini-Lop being born in El Campo, Texas called Fuzz. Fuzz was believed to be the first of his kind born in the United State. However, a litter of Polish born in the 1950s had three furless kits. Dr. Lukefahr borrowed Fuzz and mated him to does at the university, from which all of

Furless rabbit. Photo courtesy American Rabbit Breeders Association.

the progeny were furred. Upon breeding brother and sisters, appeared Furless rabbits in the litters.

Dr. Lukefahr reports that the naked rabbits were about a half-pound heavier, and that the body temperature one degree lower than furred rabbits. Also, for the south Texas climate, the Furless were far more active.

Andrea Rogers, a graduate student working with Lukefahr, and a visiting professor from Poland, Dr. Marian Brozozowski, with Dr. Lukefahr, came up with names for the various degrees of Furless. Those with the most fur missing were called Baldies, those which had a bit more fur were termed Fuzzies, and rabbits with still more fur were called Woolies.

Dr. Lukefahr's goals were to produce the Furless rabbit as a meat animal for developing countries where there is extreme heat. While this could prove beneficial, I just wonder about problems with sunburn, hutch burn, sore feet, and especially biting insects.

GABALI

Sinai and the Western Desert in Egypt is the native home of the Gabali rabbit, which was stabilized by the Desert Research Institute in Maryout, which is on the northwestern coast of Egypt. Gabali rabbits are a uniform wild gray color and average

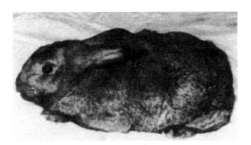

Gabali rabbit.

weight is 3.3 kg. Gabalies are known for their large litters of up to 12 young, and are very well adapted to the harsh desert conditions. The population of the Gabali rabbit is considered endangered with 1,200 to 5,000 rabbits.

GEANT HONGROIS

Hungary is the native home of this giant breed of rabbit, also called Magyar Orias by the local people. The creator is not known, but the Geant Hongrois first appeared in 1920, and was a crossing of the rustic wild rabbit of Hungary, along with French Lops and Flemish Giants, and recognition was given to this declining breed by the National Institute for Agricultural Quality Control in 1993. It is a solidly built rabbit, with no noticeable rise from the shoulders to the hips, with both males and females reaching 5.50 kg. to 7.0 kg. Does are known for their very large litters of up to 16 kits, which are mainly bred for meat.

GIANT BLANC DU BOUSCAT

 ne of the few giant breeds of rabbits was developed by Mr. and Mrs. Dulon in 1906. The Dulons lived in southern France, but more precisely in Bouscat in the Bordelaise suburbs. Mr. and Mrs. Dulon originally called their new breed "Hermine," but soon changed the name to what we know today as the Giant White of Bouscat. Champagne d'Argents, Flemish Giants and An-

goras are the breeds which flow through this breed's veins. Their goal was to produce a closely cropped hair on a white rabbit, but with the silky texture of the Angora. The first crossings were between the Champagne and the Angora; this produced rather attractive small white rabbits, which were then coupled with a

Giant Blanc du Bouscat.

Gray Flemish Giant. These matings initially produced colored rabbits, but through selection, the Giant Blanc du Bouscat was produced.

The new breed was shown for the first time in Paris in 1910, then later in Province on June 20, 1924, when it was adopted into the French Book of Standards. The coat is rather long and with a pronounced frosty sheen, and the males weigh in at 5 kg and the does a hefty 6 kg. It is still a rather popular breed today through its native France.

GIANT PAPILLON

Giant Butterfly rabbits are of the same origin as the Checkered Giant of America, which originated in Germany (see Checkered Giant). France began calling the breed Giant French Butterfly or Geant Papillon Francais since 1954. In their native home of Germany, they are known as Deutsche

Dedicated to Reinhard Danninger of Austsria, for no other reason but for raising this outstandingly magnificent picture-perfect Giant Papillon buck in 2001.

Risenchecken, and in Holland, Groot Lotharinger. The best of this breed of spotted rabbit are found today in Germany. The main difference in the Giant Papillon and the Checkered Giants is the hip spots. Americans pretty much settle for elongated spots of two to three, while the

Giant Papillon, circa 1910.

Papillons of Europe want smaller spots of at least three, with the ideal being six to eight. Weights should be 5 to over 6 kg or 11 to over 13.4 lbs.

GIZA WHITE

From the land of the pyramids comes the Giza White rabbit of Egypt, which is used for meat, but more oddly, for milk as well. The Giza White has been an established breed since 1932, when native domestic rabbits of Egypt of various colors and sizes were bred by the Animal Breeding Department of Cairo University at Giza. The University was attempting to create a breed with uniform charac-

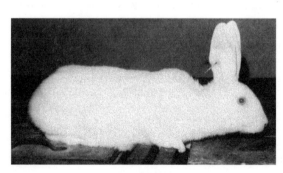

Giza White.

teristic. Both black and white varieties were genetically segregated, with each selection being carefully documented. About 1937, a systematic breeding operation took place with the main objective of fixing the albino types, for large litter size (7 kits), and a high growth rate for the hot climate of their country. The Giza White today is a white rabbit with a soft silky fur, with an average weight of 2.75 kg. Populations are said to be endangered with 1,500 to 10,000 animals.

GOAT

 oat rabbits originate from France, and yes, you read it correctly, the Goat rabbit breed, is so named because of the color and markings of a rare breed of goat known as the Poitevine. The Goat rabbit is an old breed kept on the farms, most commonly found in the areas of Charentes, Gironde and the Dordogne. Jean Coutard wrote of the origin of the Goat rabbit, "In the years 1990, whereas member of Conservation Association of the Races of Aquitaine we traversed the area, especially Pyrenees, with the research of the animals belonging to races threatened to supplement or create inventories we were far from doubting to us that pleasant surprise awaiting us one kilometer and half from our premises, of all the new Conservatory Farm of Leyssart. At the time of our visit in a neighbor, we discovered in his rabbit burrow a rabbit whose color intrigued us much because I remembered very well the dress of these rabbits that my family raised in the sixties under the name of rabbit-goat, I had never re-examined some since. It should be said that the rabbit burrow of the farms always are not very well exposed, often relegated under hangars. The questioned farmer say to me that it had had of it formerly and that it had just found some recently. As for the name, with his accent, he says to me 'ole a rabbit goat.' I was a little interdict by also finding close to on our premises a variety of rabbit which I loved much when I was a child because the color was remarkable."

Some of these rabbits were purchased, raised

Dedicated to Mr. Pascal Desautard of France who attempts to have the Goat rabbit recognized as a breed in France.

187

Goat rabbit photos. Courtesy Federation Francaise de Cuniculiculture, France.

and presented at various shows. It was reported that a small number of visitors recognized them from years gone by as the Goat rabbit, so the name was certainly fixed.

In January of 2000, a Mr. Pascal Desautard, who lives close to Riom, contacted the National Commission of the Standards in France to recognize the breed. Mr. Desautard was asked to present some animals on June 11, 2000, at a one-day technical training session for judges to be held at Lezoux in Puy-de-Dome. Mr. Desautard, along with a Pierre Edmond Desse, brought four animals: an adult buck weighing 3.5 kg, and two adult does, with one doe's youngster of one month of age.

The gentlemen, joined by several other breeders of the Goat rabbit, would have to fix the type and coloration of the breed, and eight animals, consisting of four bucks and four does of various ages, would have to be presented during three consecutive years before the National Commission of the Standards. The first presentation was made on December 16, 2000, at St. Flour. As of this writing the Goat rabbit has not been officially recognized, but the breed is an Otter pattern, and the colors are Black, Blue and Brown for the moment.

GOLDEN GLAVCOT

olden Glavcots are a British breed which had been extinct for many years, until it was recreated by Mr. J. Irons in the late 1960s. To create the breed, Irons used three brown breeds: Brown Beveren, Havana and the modern-day Siberian. They were exhibited at the famous Bradford Championship Show at Doncaster, England

Dedicated to Meg Brown of Scotland, who worked for many years perfecting her beloved Golden Glavcots, until her doctor ordered her to give up her rabbits. Meg is shown here with the breed. Photo courtesy Judy Le Marchant, England.

in January of 1976. The Golden Glavcot was not liked by most fanciers, but one special lady in particular did, and that would be the famous rabbit lady from Scotland, Miss Meg Brown. Irons told Meg Brown how to carry on with the breed, which she did until 2002, when forced to give up her rabbits due to health reasons by order of her doctors. Dear Meg told me that she crossed in wild rabbits to improve the color of the Golden Glavcot. No one seems to know just why the name Glavcot was ever chosen for the breed. There was a Silver Glavcot during the first quarter of the 1900s, which appears from a print that I have to have been a Lilac form of the breed, but this color is long ago extinct. The breed is only recognized in the United Kingdom, and being kept alive by a small band of fanciers. A rather small breed, which weighs in at 2.26 to 2.72 kilos, or 5 to 6 pounds.

GOTLAND

Sweden is the native home of this ancient breed which has been around since
the 1500s. This is not a show animal.
However, there is a Gotland Rabbit Club
which sponsors this breed, and a Stud
Book is maintained. The Gotland rabbit, which comes in a vast array of colors and patterns, is especially appreciated for their hardiness, lean and delicious meat. The Gotland rabbit in the
olden days could be found running
freely in the byre amongst the cattle, and
they were usually cared for by the children of the farms. Gotlands weigh in at
3 to 4 kilos, or 6.5 to 9 lbs.

*Dedicated to Mirjam Gille of Sweden, who continues to raise this very old breed of
rabbit. Mirjam is holding a Gotland rabbit. Photo courtesy Bjorn Lidman, Sweden.*

GREY PEARL OF HALLE

Belgium is the home of the of the Grey Pearl of Halle (Gris Perle
de Hal) and was created by Monsieur Vervoort, from Halle, near
Brussels in the year 1912. According to Vervoort, he obtained a
Havana from the region of Binche, and mated him to five Ha-
vana does, all sisters, and in all five litters appeared all of a silver color. He
showed the new breed
in Brussels during the
World War I. He fur-
ther crossed the breed
with Blue Beverens at
the suggestion of Pro-
fessor Frateur. There
is another story as to

Grey Pearl of Halle.

the creation of this breed, that Havanas were crossed with the Argente Bleu, which gave rise to the white ticking over the entire body of a very soft, near Lilac gray color. The Grey Pearl of Halle is a rather small rabbit, weighing in at 2 to 2.5 kg or 4 lb 6 oz to 5 lb 8 oz. It was imported into England in the early 1920s by Lady Layland-Barratt, of Torquay, directly from the shed of Monsieur Vervoort. Lady Layland-Barratt wrote in *Fur Producing Rabbits,* 1929, "Monsieur Vervoort has maintained his policy of silence. This silence may be due to the fancied security of definite knowledge or to an uncertainly occasioned by the perception of various possibilities sensed but not defined." The breed became extinct in England, but was reintroduced at the turn of this century.

HARLEQUIN

 arlequins are said to be natives of France, or could they be actually from Japan as the original name implies? Mr. N. Naudin wrote in the French publication, *Avicolous Review,* in October of 1894, "We saw appearing, at the time of the open competition of 1887, in the class of common rabbits, a variety which had excited curiosity highly. They were tricolour and bore the Japanese name." It is believed that the first Japanese appeared in the suburbs of Paris in either Belleville or Montmarte from the old world Brabancon breed, which is the forerunner of the Dutch and common tame rabbits. In France's *Hunting and Fishing,* 1894/1895, a writer wrote of the Japanese, " Let us not manage we from there to discover the very recent origin of this rabbit very common, but multi-colored the made-to-order of the tricolour cat or scale of tortoise, in English tortoiseshell. We know that this color is obtained by the crossing of black rabbit with the russet red one.

Dedicated to the late Carroll Terhune of Kentucky, fondly known as "Mr. Harlequin," who worked over 25 years to promote the breed and see it distributed throughout the United States.

Tri-Colored rabbit, circa 1894.

Wouldn't the joker who it first launched as Japanese like to be rather pleasant to make known himself? The amateurs could then address their congratulations to him."

Proof is shown that parti-colored and tri-colored rabbits were being bred and exhibited in Japan during the years 1872 to 1874. The keeping of these rabbits was particularly popular in the cities of Osaka and Tokyo. This was the ending of the Edo period and the beginning of the Meiji period in Japan's history. Many rabbit shows were being held for the parti-colored and calico rabbits. The calico rabbits were highly esteemed for their colors and patterns, just as the beautiful fish, the ornamental carp, known as "Koi," are today. The calicos would fetch extremely high prices for a fine marked specimen, and would sell for as much as a house. As the rabbit trade increased, serious problems arose, with so much crime taking place because of these unique rabbits that the Tokyo government had to establish laws which required rabbit keepers to notify the authorities of their dealings and to once a month pay a one-yen tax per rabbit. These new harsh regulations would cause the demise of the fancy rabbit in Japan.

There exists a three-piece multi-colored wood block print from 1873, created by Utagawa Yoshitsuya II and titled *Ryuko usagi shukkai zue,* which translates Rabbit show

An Italian illustration from 1897.

exhibition list, that shows a great many rabbits, both parti-colored and tri-colored, which would prove the existence of these rabbits during this time period in Japan. Perhaps there is indeed some true meaning to the original name of the rabbit, once called Japanese by the British and Americans. It was during the Edo and Meiji eras that Japan resumed trade and diplomatic relations with the western countries. Could these rabbits have been brought into France and released on the estates for the amusement and pleasure of the land owners?

In 1895, Charles Rayson, a most noted rabbit authority of the time, went to Paris to secure a pair of these rabbits from the Jardin d' Acclimatation, which were sent to Jersey in the Channel Islands. Rayson wrote in his book, *Rabbits for Prizes and Profit,* 1897, on the Japanese, "It is now some years since this interesting rabbit was first introduced to the notice of English fanciers, and it still remains almost as unknown as in the year '93, when a short notice was published in a fancy paper. Like most other new varieties introduced from abroad, it is susceptible of very great improvement, which, like the Dutch and the Himalayan, it will doubtless experience once its merits have been recognized.

"The Japanese rabbit is a large and stoutly built animal, shaped like the Dutch rabbit, but probably twice as heavy and half as large again. Its head is massive, and the ears — at present its worst points — are large, and in old specimens especially, somewhat apt to fall over at the tips like those of the Patagonian.

"The coat is beautifully fine and soft and somewhat open texture, and the markings, which as yet are sometimes inconstant, are curiously and attractively arranged in stripes, running around the body like two belts. Some specimens, very well marked, were exhibited at a show in Paris several years ago; but it has been found impossible to trace their subsequent career, and as French fanciers do not take the same interest as their English brethren in

A German illustration from 1910.

A magnificent Harlequin. It is amazing what one can do with an airbrush. Photo courtesy Meg Brown, Scotland.

keeping their stock pure, they seemed to have crossed the Japanese in an irritating and foolish way, whereby they have gone far to spoil an original and lovely variety. In the summer of 1895 the writer paid a special visit to the Jardin d'Acclimatation in Paris, with the object of acquiring the best possible specimens of the breed, the French Zoo being the only place where they could be obtained, and the rabbits purchased on this occasion were afterward sent to Jersey, where they have been successfully bred from.

"The Japanese rabbit has many advantages to recommend it beyond its undoubtedly quaint and handsome appearance and its size and weight, which would make it valuable from an economic point of view. It is docile and gentle, and must be hardy, or it would not have survived the apprenticeship it had served in the Jardin, where the rabbit-houses, although elegant in appearance, are most unsuitable sanitarily, being built of terra-cotta and stone. It is prolific, and the does are good mothers, while for the size of the animal is not a large eater.

One of the original Japanese imported to America in 1917.

"There is, moreover, an opening of much interest to the true fancier in the opportunity of offers of improving and fixing the characteristic markings. Some of the Japanese in the Jardin d'Acclimatation had evidently been crossed with the Dutch, an absurd pro-

The ideal marking of the Japanese appeared in the first American Standard in 1917.

cedure which introduced white into their colouring, hitherto composed entirely of fawn, orange, and black, except the small white mark on the nose. The proper colours for a Japanese rabbit are the three former only, and any other white on the head or face shows the Dutch cross, which should be bred out as quickly as possible. The body is, or should be, entirely fawn-colored underneath; the head and ears are fawn, the latter laced with black; the back is orange, with regular stripes of black going across it and down the sides, as shown in the accompanying illustration of a real Jap. The rabbit illustrated in not idealized, and it will be observed that the hinder stripe is much narrower than it should be in parts. The markings of the nose — the smut and white patch — are very characteristic."

Now I hope that all Harlequin fanciers took note of Charles Rayson's writings, that the early animals were not the checkerboard pattern that is strived for today, but instead had a banded body only.

France ruled in 1899 that the Japanese could no longer carry white in the coat. Japanese were first imported to America by Meek Court and Company of Chicago, Illinois, in 1917, and rabbits were advertised by Mr. Marcellus W. Meek for $40 adults and $30 for youngsters. The breed was recognized that same year by the National Breeders and Fanciers Association.

The first standard for the Japanese in the United States reads:

Early American Japanese, circa 1924.

IRREGULAR MARKINGS
Of an unequal distribution of the color bands .... 30 Points
UNDER COLOR
Distinct and shiny, from cream and egg gold to a brick red ...... 20 Points
SHAPE
Rather short and thick set with strong limbs, weight about 8 pounds
.... 20 Points
EARS AND HEAD
Undercolor to match body and spotted over with black patches
.... 10 Points
FUR
To be thick and even .... 10 Points
CONDITION
.... 10 Points

Total = 100

Above: The Japanese rabbit, circa the 1880s.

The Japanese Rabbit's color is intended to represent the rising sun and has circles running around the body at irregular intervals; the bands forming the circles are not regular in size or width; the circles

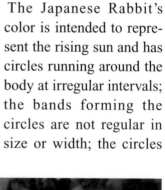

represent the sun's rays and the under color the sun. Defects are unclear color of bands showing a mottled appearance. Undercolor fading out till it shows pure white spots.

Once again, we see no mention of alternating ear markings, divided face, or al-

Right: Harlequin showing excellent head markings. Photo courtesy American Rabbit Breeders Association.

ternating pattern to the front and hind feet and legs.

The downfall of the Japanese breed name in America would begin on December 7, 1941, when the Japanese chose to bomb Pearl Harbor, bringing the U.S. to war with Japan. The name Japanese was dropped and changed to Harlequin both in America and England in the mid-1940s; yet in all other countries the name remains Japanese today.

The Harlequin made world headlines during the 1980s when it went Best in Show at the huge Europa Show, having scored 98 points. Rabbit owned by W.J. Tummers.

It was also in the mid-1940s that Blue, Chocolate and Lilac Harlequins appeared, and it would be the British who developed the Magpie version by introducing the Chinchilla to the Harlequins' genetic makeup. The name Japanese and Magpie in the U.S. and UK would be used to refer to the color groups in the Harlequin breed.

HAVANA

he Havana originated in the Netherlands in the year 1898 in a small village called Ingen, near Utrecht, Holland. They were produced through a chance mating, as a black and white marked common farm rabbit, a doe, was turned out in a stable with a number of other common rabbits that were meant for export for table use on the farm of Mr. Honders. This doe produced the first Havanas. However, it is unknown which rabbit sired the litter. These new brown and white rabbits were given the name of Ingensche Vuuroog or translated "Fire-eye from Ingen," because of the unusual ruby glow to the eyes when viewed in good light. Noted breeders, Mr. Van der Horst, Mr. Jacobs and Mr. Muysert, greatly stabilized the color. The new breed was introduced to the public for the first time at the Ornithophilia Show at Utrecht, in 1899. It should be said, they were also called Castor and Beavers (Castor meaning Beaver in French). The Beaver name was considered by many of the leading rabbit authorities of the time as being too much like Beveren, and would likely cause confusion. France imported them at the turn of the 20th century.

Havana, from the Wippell Collection. Reproduced from a Fur & Feather colour plate first issued 1st July, 1927.

Mrs. Jeanne J. Lamaire showed the brown rabbits under the name of Havana at a Paris show in 1903. Mrs. Lamaire believed the color to be more like the color of the famous Havana cigar. However, Lamaire claimed that the ones she showed were not of Dutch origin, but had been bred by her using French breeds. Mr. M. Meslay, a well-known French breeder, believed that she had obtained them by using a blue rabbit. The first Havanas were said to be a very strong dark red/brown color, more like the color of a dark squirrel and weighed in at a hefty 7-1/2 pounds, yet the type

was widely different in the various European shows. From France, animals were exported to Switzerland, and from Switzerland the breed went into Germany, where they were exhibited for the first time in 1907 at the Drachenfels Show in Leipzig. Miss Mabel

Dedicated to the late Lee Owen Stamm of Illinois, who raised Havanas for some 31 years and developed the Blue and Black varieties. Stamm even went so far as to develop a White Havana. Only in America would someone take a color breed and make it into more colors.

198

Illingworth imported the first Havanas to England from France in 1908, with later imports coming from Holland. Illingworth entered one animal at the

Two Havana does imported by Mabel Illingworth, circa 1908.

Cambridge Show in 1909, taking a fourth place in the Any Other Variety Class. The first class for Havanas was sponsored by Miss Illingworth at London's famous Crystal Palace Show of 1910. The National Havana Club in England was founded in October 1920.

The early Havanas, though large, had problems with milky-white spots about the coat and white feet. There was much crossing with the other breeds being carried out in Europe. Crosses with Black and Tan was given credit with eliminating the white feet, and crosses with Himalayans greatly modified the size, shape and fur qualities.

Havanas were imported to the United States in 1916 by William A. Lyons, of Waukegan, Illinois, first from Miss Illingworth, when the Blue Imperial (now extinct) were also introduced to this country. After 1918, a great many importations were brought over to America. Mr. Lyons did a great deal to promote the breed. In 1919 it was reported that the breed was becoming quite popular in the U.S., but rather difficult to breed, and the size was 7 pounds and over. Havanas were introduced to the west coast by Marcellus W. Meek in 1921. Ten Havana breeders met in Akron, Ohio, in September 1925 and organized the Havana Rabbit Club, which changed to American Federation of Havana Breeders and finally to the present Havana Rabbit Breeders Association. It should be noted that there was actually a Havana Club first founded in 1920, according to Marcellus Meek, in his *The Standard of Perfection for American Domestic Rabbits,* 1928. In the 1930 Book of

An imported Havana from France, circa 1918.   Standards, we find there were

two types of Havanas being recognized, the Standard Havana with a weight of 4-1/2 to 7 pounds and the Heavyweight Havanas at 7 pounds and up, with the ideal being 9 pounds. The standard was pretty much the same for both breeds with the exception of weight and length of ear. These Heavy-weight Havanas, though especially developed for the meat market and fur trade, were never very popular and were removed from the standards in the mid-1950s. There is still a large version of the Havana being raised in Sweden, known as the Stora Havana, although it is grave danger of becoming extinct.

Mr. Walter Huey, of Pendleton, Indiana, while inbreeding his Standard Havanas to improve the near mink chocolate color, discovered by chance in 1934 Havanas with an intensified sparkle to the coat. A new rabbit mutation had occurred that would soon spread world-wide into every rabbit-producing nation. These shiny rabbits were first shown with the normal Havanas, but quickly a storm of protest went up, and the new coat mutation was given the name called Satin. Satin Havanas were recognized for a number of years under the umbrella of the Havana Club until the mid-1940s when the American Satin Rabbit Breeders Association formed in 1946 and the name was changed to Chocolate Satin.

The late Lee Owen Stamm, of Dakota, Illinois, who was secretary of the Havana Club for many years, developed two additional varieties of Havana. In 1959, a Chocolate Havana doe produced two blue sports in a litter, which were both males. Stamm did the same mating; this time the doe produced another two blue sports and both were does. He bred these Blues together and produced six all Blue youngsters. Through line breeding — father to daughter, mother to son, he had fixed the new variety. The Blue variety was ac-

Katie and Brad Boyce, with their Best in Show Black Havana. Photo courtesy Heinhold Freeds.

cepted in 1965, after working on the color for six years, and 15 years later in 1980, Stamm's Black Havanas were recognized. The latter two varieties are not recognized in any other country. Lee Owen Stamm died on January 23, 1981, shortly after the Blacks were accepted.

One might ask the question if there is a famous Havana. Well, I believe the answer would be yes. On October 8, 2002, a little Black Havana junior doe, bred and owned by Katie and Brad Boyce, took Best In Show at the 79th ARBA National Convention and Show, held in Peoria, Illinois, out of an entry of over 12,000 animals. Lee Owen Stamm would have been very proud of his worthy creation.

There are a number of breeds that have been created with the genes from the Havana, such as Alaska, Lilac, Marburger, Perlfee, Thrianta, with the most famous breed of all being the Satin rabbit.

HERMELIN

ermany imported the first Polish to their country from England in 1884, with further imports taking place into the early 1900s. The maximum weight was set at 1.5 kg., heads were to be short, strong and well-rounded, with eyes large and prominent. Ears to be short, rather broad at the base and pointed at the tips. Bodies are as small as possible, short coupled and very broad. Finally, the fur was to be short, fine, tightly set and shining white. At that time in history, Hermelins were known as Poles. The breed made little progress in Germany because of the First World War, as the economic situation was not exactly favorable for small rabbits, as the larger breed skins were in high demand over the smaller pelts, and a larger carcass was far more appropriate to satisfy the requirements of the family's consumption. Luckily for the Polish breed, there were the dedicated stock keepers that preserved the original breed through selection for size and type. Some enterprising fanciers began to sell the small pelts of the Poles as an imitation of the true Ermine fur, which was extremely expensive, but high in demand. This would then become the death of the Pole name and the beginning of a breed known today as the Hermelin (Ermine in German is Hermine).

An early Hermelin in Germany, circa 1910.

In 1918 appeared the Blue-Eyed Whites, bred by a Mr. Kluge of Hohndorf and a Mr. Lohse of Dippolswalde, Germany, by crossing the Ruby-Eyed Whites with Dutch and White Viennas. They were shown for the first time in Leipzig in 1919 as Hermelin of Saxony. By the 1920s there were drastic morphological changes taking place in the breed, and a true dwarf rabbit was being created.

HIMALAYAN

imalayans have perhaps been christened with more names than any other breed of rabbit: Antwerp, Chinese, African, Egyptian, Egyptian Smut, Polish, Black Nosed Rabbit, Lapin d'Anver, Russian, Mock Ermine, Warren Rabbit and the Windsor Rabbit. During the 150-plus years of its being, huge debates have been waged over the animal's original homeland. Kempster W. Knight, in his monumental work, *The Book of the Rabbit,* Second Edition, March 1889, has this to say, "Although this neat animal is said to be found in great numbers on the chain of mountains from which it takes its name (the meaning of which is 'the adobe of Snow'), which extends 1800 miles from Brahmapoorta, in Assam, to the western extremity of the Hindoo-Koosh, in Cabul, the popular idea has no foundation in fact. It is asserted to be a sacrificial rabbit with the Chinese, who are said to annually offer up 30,000 upon 1600 altars, with prayers that the crops and fruits generally may be as prolific as rabbits. Be this as it may, the rabbit is frequently spoken of as 'Chinese,' also 'Black-nosed Rabbit from China,' and was so labelled, we believe, in the Zoological Gardens, when first introduced into this country."

A modern writer says: "The name Himalayan has been objected to on the ground that the animal is not to be found on the hills bearing that name. Perhaps not, but my own impression is

Dedicated to the late Francis P. Riffle of Ohio, who raised Himalayans some 37 years, and served as secretary of the American Himalayan Rabbit Association for over 20 years.

202

that they are natives of northern India and China, and perhaps some of the contiguous states. My information on the subject was gathered from the remarks of a traveller who had traveled in that quarter, and who told me that they existed in great force on

From "Manuals for the Many," 1865, appears this illustration titled CHINESE.

both sides of the hills, but he would not vouch for their existence on the summit." Owing to the value of the skin as an article of commerce, the breed has been imported into and cultivated in a great many countries, including Russia, Poland, Egypt, Germany, France, the Netherlands and our own land. A natural result is that the breed boasts of many names, such as Egyptian Smut, Polish rabbit. They have been entered at exhibitions as Antwerp rabbits; we need hardly say that the Himalayan is quite distinct from the Polish rabbit."

"The Himalayan as a fancy rabbit appears to have been a very recent acquisition, for until 1862 we do not find it mentioned in any of the handbooks devoted to rabbits; but in *Rabbits* (which, by the way, is very largely indebted to 'Bonington Moubray, Esq.,' although it does not acknowledge it), published in that year, there appears a small illustration of it, but without letterpress description."

From the *Cottage Gardner and Country Gentleman,* a show was reported held at Nottingham, England, in January 1858, where four classes for rabbits were provided. In the fourth class, "Any other breed," the winner of first prize was W.H. Ralph's Chinese, and the second prize went to T.

Himalayan Rabbit, circa 1880s.

Gilbert's Russian rabbit. There is little question that both of these rabbits were no doubt the early Himalayans.

Although a picture may not have appeared before 1862, text concerning the rabbit certainly pre-dates this time. From the *Cottage Gardener*, June 2, 1857, "WHITE RABBITS WITH BLACK POINTS — Having observed in your journal of the 12th of March an inquiry as to the origin of the white rabbits with black noses, ears, feet and tail, and with pink eyes, a pair of which were exhibited at the Crystal Palace Show, and which according to your correspondent, amongst other names, have been styles 'Africans,' I believe I can give some information on the subject, as I am most certain that the stock now sold in London and the vicinity at such high prices was bred from rabbits of my own of nearly an opposite colour. About nine years back I commenced breeding Silver-Grey tame rabbits from a stock of a few Silver-Greys and blacks, which I procured from a dealer in Leadenhall Market; and for four years after, though I bred some hundreds, no other colours were ever thrown than silvers, blacks, or sprints — i.e., only partly covered with the silver points. About that time I introduced a buck which had been bred by crossing the produce of a wild Silver-Grey buck and tame doe twice with other tame Silvers, consequently having one-eighth of wild blood in him. Amongst the first litter bred from him and a Silver-Grey doe appeared a white rabbit similar to the Crystal Palace pair; and during that season my does occasionally bred by him these white Africans, and also a sandy one. The following season, to change the blood and improve the quality of the fur, I introduced some half-wild Silver-Grey bucks, bred from a Lincolnshire warren buck and tame doe. When the two wild strains united, the Africans became more numerous (about one-third in number to two-thirds of Silvers). On two occa-

A beautiful illustration from 1874.

An early British winner of many medals and cups, circa 1900.

sions, five and four years ago, I sent some Silver-Grey does, and also a number of Africans, to a dealer in Leadenhall Market, and from him I have no doubt those in London and the vicinity were bred. My reason for this opinion is that, except the dealer above mentioned and those who have purchased from him, no other person but myself, and about seven others to whom I have sold them within the last year, is in possession of a pure Silver-Grey tame breed crossed with a wild. I sold the greater part of my stock to a gentleman last year, retaining only a few Silvers, which I selected as not breeding Africans; and out of about 60 rabbits bred last season, there were only three, and those sandy, one of which I now have. I understand that on the Norfolk Silver-Grey warren, where the rabbits have been much intermixed with the common grey, numerous sandy and white Africans appear; but I never heard of any on the pure Silver-Grey or common grey warrens. It would seem, therefore, that these extraordinary colours appear only when the wild Silver-Grey is mixed with a different variety. Why it is so must be left to the physiologist to determine. It strikes me that, at some distant period, the wild Silver-Grey breed may have been produced by a cross from the white and sandy Africans (obtained from some other country) and the wild black rabbits."

There are quite a few early breeders of the Silvers which allude to the same facts as presented above, in that Himalayans were appearing in their Silver nest boxes. However, at no time have any of them reported obtaining Silvers from the pairing of two Himalayans. Charles Darwin, in his *The Variation of Animals and Plants under Domestication,* 1868, also mentions these findings of the Himalayan rabbit. Darwin writes, "We come now to the Himalayan breed, which is sometimes called Chinese, Polish or Russian. These pretty rabbits are white, or occasionally yellow, excepting their ears, nose, feet and upper side of the tail, which are all brownish-black; but as they have red eyes, they may be considered as albinoes. I have received several accounts of their breeding true. From their symmetrical marks, they were at first ranked as specifically distinct, and were provisionally named *L. nigripes.*" Now it should be noted here that the "L" would stand for the Latin word *Lepus,* for hare, and a yellow Himalayan, so many years ago.

A Mr. Bartlett, reporting in the *Proceedings of the Zoological Society,* 1861, London, "was led to make a careful trial in the Zoological Gardens, and he found that by simply crossing Silver-Greys with chinchillas he could always produce some Himalayans." Now when chinchilla is mentioned here, it is not the Chinchilla breed, but actually a name that Darwin used to refer to the tame Silver-Greys, and when Darwin writes of Silver-Greys proper, he is speaking of the wild type found in the warrens of England.

Cuniculus writes of the Himalayan in his book, *The Practical Rabbit Keeper,* 1880, "REFERENCE to our plate will show the extreme beauty of the rabbit to the description of which this chapter is devoted. There is much difference of opinion as to the prettiest rabbit extant, but we certainly uphold the Himalayan as being unexcelled, even if equaled.

"The animal comes from China, and hence is sometimes very properly called the Chinese rabbit. Its locale is not confined to the Celestial Empire, and the Himalayan is frequently found at both sides of the mountain from which it takes its name. We have had in our rabbitry newly imported specimens of the variety, and have, without exception, found them superior to the average English caste, and to have been invaluable for breeding purposes.

"The Himalayan is not a large rabbit. At one time the whim was to keep it down, but this, happily, is a thing of the past now; and size, although by no means a sine qua non, is considered of some importance. Six and seven pounds very lately were the average weights of our show specimens; now we think they would run at least a pound heavier, and we unhesitatingly say that the movement is in the right direction. Imported rabbits are often as heavy as 8-1/2 pounds, when not too severely pulled down by the voyage.

"The animal is well-built, sometimes a little lanky, but more frequently inclined to be stumpy, and there is a firm feeling about the flesh that is indicative of great constitutional strength. In disposition the Himalayan is timid, but can be tamed by gentle means, and when it acquires confidence in its keeper soon becomes very affectionate and tractable."

I only wished that Cuniculus had written where he had imported his Himalayans from, but according to his writing, they were indeed a large rabbit, compared to the breed today. Several standards for the breed were floating around during the 1880s.

The earliest standard, for which there are two, comes from Cuniculus' book, which has been previously quoted.

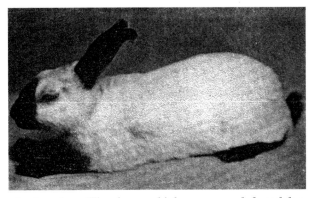

An American Himalayan which was never defeated during the years 1917 through 1920.

Nose points 20
Ear points 20
Feet points 20
General uniformity 25
Condition and eye 15
Total = 100

Another standard was offered by a friend of Cuniculus and presented as follows:

Nose points 15
Ear points 15
Fore-feet points 15
Hind-feet points 15
Uniformity 20
Condition 5
Quality of fur 5
Eye 5
Carriage 5
Total = 100

The National Himalayan Rabbit Club of England was founded in 1888 and continues today. This organization recognizes four varieties; Black, Blue, Chocolate and Lilac. Himalayans arrived in America at the turn of the 20th century, and were recognized as a breed by the National Pet Stock Association founded on January 10, 1910, yet only in the Black variety. The first standard given for the breed in the United States is as follows:

```
Size and weight (4 pounds)............................................................... 11
Color: Head (white with black smut on nose,
    egg-shaped up between eyes......................................................... 14
Color: Ears (black with clean cut white between. No white hairs)....... 15
Jaw: (Lower jaw black)
Eyes: Pink
Color: Check, back, belly, flanks, white.
Color: Fore legs (black to top of legs and clean cut) ........................ 15
Color: Hind legs (feet black) ............................................................ 25
Color: Tail (black) ............................................................................ . 6
Dewlap (none)
Condition: Flesh, solid and firm; fur fine, short, close, silky,
    Free from hutch stains ................................................................ 14
                                                        Total  =  100
```

The first Himalayans to arrive in America were imported from England in 1912, and were to become very popular both on the East and Pacific Coast as a fine fur animal and, of course, as an attractive exhibition animal. Marcellus W. Meek imported additional animals in 1919, which included a famous champion buck known as Grand Duke York.

England was the first to develop the Himalayan in other colors. It was during the 1930s that self Blue English Spots were crossed with the original Himalayans. During the late 1940s, Chocolate Himalayans were produced, again using the self Chocolate English. It was just a matter of time, by crossing the Blues and Chocolates, that the Lilac Himalayans were produced.

In America, Blue Himalayans were imported from the United Kingdom and recognized by the American Rabbit Breeders Association on October 30, 1962. The late Don Lovejoy of California imported a trio of the Blues in 1963. Though quite rare in America, the Blues were pretty much localized to the west coast. Credit is given to Ron Smelt of California for developing the Chocolates, by using the same methods as did the British, and his Lilac Himalayans came about by crossing in Lilac Mini Rex.

HULSTLANDER

n 1977, Mr. J. de Graaf of the Netherlands began to cross-breed Blue Eyes White Netherland Dwarfs (they are known as Pools in Holland) with a small White Vienna. Mr. de Graaf did this as he wanted to investigate the inheritance of certain characteristics of the Vienna color (Blue Eyed) rabbits. His first attempt was unsuccessful, as he failed to breed any young rabbits using the small Blue Eyed White Netherland Dwarfs. Mr. de Graaf then tried another route to reach his goal. He obtained a large German Ruby Eyed White Netherland Dwarf (they are known as Hermelin in Germany) which he could mate to a small White Vienna. He used the German Ruby Eyed Netherland Dwarf, because they are generally bigger than the Blue Eyed White Dwarfs, and also because the German Dwarfs are bigger than those found in the Netherlands. This time Mr. de Graaf was successful in producing some youngsters in a variety of colors. To obtain the blue-eyed rabbits he was looking for, he next mated the youngsters to each other and to the Blue Eyed White Dwarfs from the Netherlands. This gave him two strains to work with, one with blue eyes and the other with red eyes. Mr. de Graaf noted that the Blue Eyed strain had some very desirable fea-

tures unlike any other breed of rabbit and began working intensively to set these characteristics on his new breed. In 1984, Mr. J. de Graaf's Hulstlander was accepted to the standards of the Nederlandse Konijnenfokkers Bond (Dutch National Rabbit Organization). The Hulstlander gets its name from the district in the Province of Overijssel where Mr. de Graaf lived and developed the new breed.

Jac DeGraaf of Holland, who developed the Hulstlander.

IBICENCO

Spain is the home of the Ibicenco rabbit, with the main population to be found on the Island of Ibiza. Locally the Ibicenco rabbit is called Conill Pages or Conill Eivissen.

The breed is a multi-colored mottled rabbit of 2.2 kg. and are considered a rustic breed, which is used for meat. Data collected in 1996 showed a rather low population of 1,000 animals and are considered endangered.

ISABELLA

The Isabella is from Sweden and recognized in all the Scandinavian countries. It is basically the same rabbit as the Beige of Europe, with the exception of color. Isabellas are a Blue Tortoiseshell rabbit, whereas the Beige was formally called Isabella when they were first introduced into the United Kingdom in the late 1920s.

JAMORA

 amoras are a rather recent creation from Germany and can be ranked, in my opinion, within the breeds of Angoras. This rather small Harlequin patterned Angora rabbit began in 1983, by Mr. Jhannes Held and Dr. Thimm (PHD) from Blaustein, Germany, and was officially recognized by the National Rabbit Governing body of Germany in 1993. The first matings were with the beautiful German Angoras to the Japanese (Harlequin) which, of course, would give the wool and the Harlequin pattern. To further downsize the breed, Ruby-Eyed White Hermelins (Dwarfs) were used, as the men wanted to get the more rounded face in the breed.

The Jamoras of Germany weigh in at between 2 to 2.5 kilograms (4.5 to 5.5 lbs.), and the wool is to be 5 to 6 cm. (2 to 2.5 inches) in length. Wool is medium fine and of a silky nature, and is not inclined to felt or matt. The wool is not to be present on the head and ears. Because of the introduction of the two white breeds (Angora and Hermelin), white toenails are a problem at this time, plus the standard which the Germans have set is rather tough

Jamora rabbit. Photo courtesy Zentralverband Deutscher Rassekaninchenzuecher.

to achieve, especially with the same pattern called for in the Harlequin breed. The bred is good-natured, curious and lively. Litter size ranges from two to six kits. The Jamoras are becoming quite popular in their native land and have since spread to the Netherlands, Switzerland and Sweden.

JAPANESE LARGE WHITE

 apanese Large White rabbits come from Japan, where they are also called Japanese Jumbo White, Nakayama Jumbo Rabbit, but officially they are known as Japanese Jumbo White Akita Select Breed. As reported by Dr. Steven Lukefahr, there are just two types of rabbits which can be found throughout the developing countries of the world: the improved breeds which have been imported, or the local strains, which have been bred for many years on the farms and in the local villages. The Japanese Large Whites are, of course, a white rabbit, which has pink eyes, and have been said to have been created from Flemish Giants and New Zealand Whites, and are strictly protected by the Japanese Agriculture Association.

Rabbits first came to Japan in the 16th century from Holland. During the Meiji Period and onward, with the increasing difficulties associated with the Russo-Japanese war, rabbit meat and fur became a profitable industry as it was inexpensive to produce. Subsidies were given by the Japanese government for rabbit raising. It was during this time that the Japanese Large White could be found throughout the country, and in 1939 their numbers were estimated to be somewhere near 6.6 million rabbits. Following the end of World War II, the rabbit numbers dropped drastically, as the main purpose of raising them switched to research and for the pet trade.

JERSEY WOOLY

 onnie Seeley, of High Bridge, New Jersey, developed the Jersey Wooly, beginning in the 1970s. Seeley wanted to produce a small wooled breed, with ease of care for the pet trade. Angora and Netherland Dwarfs were the basic breeds involved in the beginning stage. During the selection process, downsizing the animals and the ever-present white toenails plagued the breeding program.

In 1981, Bonnie Seeley, selected three of her early animals to continue downsizing the breed. She chose a 4-pound Chinchilla buck, called Silver which carried the dwarfing gene; a 4-pound Black Silver Marten doe, also with the dwarfing gene named Blackie, and a Blue doe, weighing 4-1/2 pounds, known as Muzzy, which did not carry the dwarfing gene.

Jersey Wooly. Photo courtesy American Rabbit Breeders Association.

By late 1981, she had mated these animal to Netherland Dwarfs, which would produce normal furred animals. Further interbreeding would produce the Jersey Wooly we know today. Bonnie said the early crosses produced about 90% of the progeny with mismatched toenails.

The Jersey Wooly was first presented at the ARBA Convention and Show in 1984 at Orlando, Florida, and accepted, although several of the presentation animals showed mismatched toenails. At the second presentation the following year in Houston, Texas, the Standards Committee rejected the animals for disqualifying toenails. This I find very odd, that they would have been accepted at the first presentation.

Three passing presentations would see the Jersey Wooly recognized as a breed at the Madison, Wisconsin Convention in 1988, and the breed has never looked back. Their fairly easy-care coats have made them one of the most popular of the small breed.

In New Zealand, the Jersey Wooly has been created and is pending acceptance to the standards of the Rabbit Council of New Zealand.

KABYLE

Kabyle rabbits are from Algeria and can be regarded as a breed in danger of extinction, with a total population of less that 500 breeding animals. There is no known study of the Kabyle rabbit prior to 1990 of the native rabbit, but in order to develop the rabbit meat production industry in Algeria, the government imported New Zealand Whites, Californians and Burgundy Fawns in the 1970s, which were crossed with the original Kabyle rabbit. Unfortunately, the old Kabyle population was probably totally lost, because the rabbits of Algeria today are a mixture all four breeds. Kabyles come in a wide range of colors, being bred both on commercial and family farms for their meat. The breed is a small to medium-size rabbit, but good-natured and fairly well adapted to the hot climate of Algeria.

Kabyle Rabbit.

KANEL

Just on the scene has arrived the Kanel rabbit, from Denmark. Kanel translates to Cinnamon. The rabbit was created by the crossing of the Thuringer and Havana breeds. It was presented at the national rabbit show in Denmark in 2003, and is a medium-size breed and is a chocolate tortoiseshell.

Kanel. Photo courtesy Kaninuppfodaren, Sweden.

KLEIN LOTHARINGER

Klein Lotharingers are a smaller Dutch version of the Giant Papillon. The breed was created by a lady named J. M. K. Berman van Schelven, from Emmeloord. The breed was created through crossing Netherland Dwarfs with the Giant Papillons (no easy feat there). Further crossing were made with English Spots which had rather coarse markings. The Netherlands recognized the new breed in 1975 to their standards. Klein Lotharingers became very popular almost overnight in Holland. Germany has their similar breed called the Kleinschecken (Petit Mottled), and there is, of course, the original small checker developed in Czechoslovakia, called the Czech Spot. This Dutch breed is smaller than the other two, weighing in at 3 kg. or 6 lb 10 oz.

LARGE HIMALAYAN

 imalayans of a large size were developed in France, and are known there as the Grand Russe (Russian). The breed was created by Jeanne J. Lemarie, and she began her breeding program in 1908, to produce a larger version of the Himalayan whose

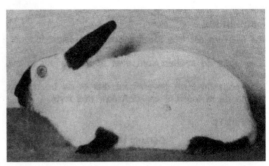

Grand Russe. *Photo courtesy Federation Francaise de Cuniculiculture, France.*

Jeanne J. Lemarie, who developed the breed. *Photo courtesy Pierre Periquet, France.*

fur was so much in demand because of its close resemblance to the true Ermine. Lemarie worked for two years experimenting with breeding the normal Himalayans to each other, selecting only the largest ones to use in her breeding program. She reported that during that time, the results were at best poor, with only 3% of the offspring being desirable. Jeanne Lemarie persevered, however, and by another four years the results were far better with adults now reaching 4 kg., yet some were tipping the scales at 5 kg. Lemarie exhibited a pair at the National exhibition on November 12, 1913, with the buck weighing 4.5 kg. and the doe at 5.5 kg. These two animals were in perfect form and condition, and not at all fattened. She was able to preserve the quality flesh, quality fur and the quick development of the offspring, all by using only Himalayans that weighed just 2 kg. when she started her breeding program.

LARGE SILVER

 here are a number of Large Silver rabbits which have been developed in Europe, by various crosses. In Germany, the rabbits were first developed by the teacher David Gartner, who is credited with the development of the Thuringer breed. Gartner produced a large silvered rabbit during the 1890s by crossing a giant breed called the Lotharinger Risen, of a gray wild color, to a Silver Grey. The rabbits he would eventually breed were exhibited at the Leipzig show in 1900, weighed in at 3.5 to 4.5 kg (7.75 to 10 lb). It appears that the officials did not care for the breed, as the traits were not yet firmly fixed. David Gartner decided to give up on the breed.

A large silvered rabbit was then taken up by a George Stone, of Detmold, who used Silver Greys and it is believed Belgian Giants of an iron-gray color. He would produce a breed which was rather elongated as the Giants (Flemish) and slightly silvered, over a dark base color. A great interest was developed in the breed for the meat and pelt industry, which would last during World War I. George Stone passed away, and the Large Silvers were beginning to lose their following. A Mr. Friedrich Nail, from Neudietendorf, began working on the large silver rabbits. Neil was an acquaintance of David Gartner, and began breeding the Silver Greys to Blue Viennas in 1905, then crossed these with Gartner's Thuringers, and from this union, would produce a Large Silver Blue. These animals weighed a hefty 5 to 6 kg (11.25 to 13.25 lb), a beautiful color and type, which was said to be far superior to Stone's German Silvers. Breeders began to further cross these to the Champagnes, which really messed things up, as there was all sorts of varying degrees of silvering.

In 1926, the national rabbit governing body placed strict standards on the breed, in order to keep the German Large Silver as a

Large Silver. *Photo courtesy Sofie Lundus, Denmark.*

215

separate breed from the Champagne D'Argent. German Large Silvers were highly sought by the restaurant trade during 1939, and for a few years that followed. However, with the outbreak of World War II, the stock was nearly decimated in their native home. A specialty club was founded for the breed on October 8, 1949, with Erich Spreitz serving as chairman. The breed began to gain popularity once again, but due to the untimely death of Spreitz, who surely was the driving force behind the club, the organization soon folded.

Through the years, the breed had its highs and lows, as do most breeds. At the famous Europa Show, held in Stuttgart, Germany, in 1970, there were no less than 195 of the breed shown. A Yellow Large Silver was developed by a Hans Patz, by crossing Silver Fawns, Red New Zealand and the Champagnes D'Argent, and recognized in 1974. Today there are five recognized varieties: Black, Blue, Havana, Brown and Yellow.

LILAC

 ilacs have been produced in a number of locations all about the same time. The first is said to have been Mr. H. Onslow, of Cambridge, England in 1913, who showed them for the first time at the big London show that same year. However, Miss Mabel Illingworth also produced them by using her newly developed breed called the Blue Imperial and Havanas, also in 1913, but she called them Essex Lavenders. Mr. C.H. Spruty, of Gouda, Holland, created the Gouda or Gowenaar in 1917, using Havanas and Blue Beverens, but these were of a greater size. The famous geneticist, Professor R.C. Punnet of Cambridge University, created what he called the Cambridge Blue in 1922, with Blue Beverens and Havanas. All three of the British strains were eventually merged together, and the rabbits of the pinkish dove coloration became known as Lilacs.

Truly there are a number of breeds that

Dedicated to the late Kenneth W. Fehrman of Wisconsin, who was considered "Mr. Lilac." Fehrman faithfully served as Secretary of the National Lilac Rabbit Club for 30 years. Photo courtesy ARBA's Domestic Rabbits.

can simply be called Lilacs, but because of breeder's preference, the colors will vary, as will the size of the animals; therefore, some have been treated as separate breeds.

Lilac.

Lilacs were imported into the United States mostly from England during 1922; however, Americans already recognized the Gouda rabbit. There were a great many more importations which took place between 1924 and 1926. The Gouda shortly thereafter became extinct in America. Lilacs in America have never been one of the most popular breeds, yet they do maintain a dedicated following of those persons who strive for the beautiful coloration of the breed.

LIONHEAD

here has been a lot of speculation on how the Lionhead rabbit began, but it is just that, purely speculation. I'm a history buff when it comes to rabbits and have spent nearly a year trying to piece together just where did our Lionheads come from.

The breed did not first appear in 1996 as previously published, because they first arrived in England in the later part of 1995. It has been said that the Lionhead rabbit was produced by crossing the Swiss Fox and the Netherland Dwarf. That idea was just someone's opinion when questioned as to how they came about. The idea that the Jersey Wooly was also used in the make-up of the breed is totally false. The Jersey Wooly is not recognized in any European country, nor is the breed found in the United Kingdom. One source tells me that while breeders

Dedicated to the late Jo Anne Statler of Minnesota, who would introduce America to the Lionhead rabbit in 2000.

217

The Lionheads of Belgium. Photos courtesy Het
Belgisch Raskonijn vzw, Belgium.

were working on the Angora Dwarf, the Lionhead mutation occurred in a litter of bunnies. That statement there was my beginning lead in piecing the history together. One thing for certain is the Lionhead rabbit is a mutation and the first major mutation in rabbits since 1934 when the Satin rabbit first appeared in a litter of Havanas.

Bearded rabbits can be traced back prior to 1960, when a man by the name of Raoul Verwulgen of Belgium exhibited creatures as the Bearded Rabbit of Ghent for the first time in Het Neerhof in Ghent. This was the one and only time they were exhibited, as Raoul Verwulgen became mad at questions being posed to him. He took his rabbits and left, never to be heard of again.

Raoul Verwulgen tells of the story that he was traveling through France in about 1958, and received two Bearded rabbits as a gift from a man whom he had met accidentally. The man was a hermit, living in the forest, keeping these unique rabbits. He further reports that his does never had more than five young per litter, and by breeding brother to sister, father to daughter, son to mother, he always produced the same bearded characteristics, with no deviation whatsoever.

A Dr. Willem, from the University of Ghent, suggested to Verwulgen that he should exhibit these rabbits and seek out breed status for them. There were doubts in the story as to the breed's origin. When questioned at the exhibition by Mr. Fr. C. Schaedtler, who was a famous Dutch judge and author, Verwulgen became angry.

In *De Ark,* which is a publication dealing with the conservation of rare domestic animals, appeared an article on the Bearded Rabbits, written by Mr. Ronny De Clercq. "Approximately 15 years ago, I discovered at

Zingem, a small village between Ghent and Oudenaarde, a doe of a rabbit breed which still is being known by the inspectors as 'Beardeds of Ghent.' "

Ronny De Clecq continues, "By mating with related animals, I rapidly obtained a race, of which approximately 80% of the offspring did not only have beards, but also belonged to the same type, regarding to color and body type. Around 1985, I obtained a group of rabbits which could be considered as 95% pure bearded. They had a great uniformity regarding color, type and coat. But because of the inbreeding, the vitality of the herd reversed a lot. When initially I had nests of 10 to 12 young ones, which grew up without a great outburst. Later on, I had nests of only 3 to 6 young ones, of which a few of them still died. Furthermore, it became more and more difficult to get the does pregnant. After a few years filled with this kind of difficulties, I decided to bring in fresh blood: I took does, which seemed identical regarding type and color to my bearded rabbits. These does were mated with pure Breaded bucks. From these offspring I selected a few new does, which were again mated with a pure buck. Working like this I obtained a stable breed."

Miss Meg Brown of Scotland is one of the world's leading authorities on the domestic rabbit. She has dedicated her entire life to rabbits and their promotion world-wide, and at the young age of 89 has just finished another book. Meg is a past president of the British Rabbit Council (BRC) and is a Life Vice-President of same. Meg has served on the board of directors for the European Association of Poultry, Pigeons and Rabbit Breeders (EAPPRB) for 26 consecutive years. She has traveled Europe extensively in her research work, visiting shows and rabbit breeders.

Meg Brown recently told me that she first saw the Lionhead rabbit in France in 1966, and they were of a creamy gold color that was being called "Lapin Barbe," which translates to "Rabbit Beard" or "Bearded Rabbit." These rabbits were of medium size and were considered mongrels by the French people. These rabbits with beards also were appearing in mixed litters of bunnies.

The noted Belgium rabbit judge,

The early Lionhead from the 1960s.

Mr. Flor Dickens, wrote me with this information. "The Lionhead rabbit is not accepted in the Belgium Standard today. In the early 1970s, they were shown in Belgium under the name of 'Petegemse Baard' (3-3.5 kilos). However, in the end the breed did not get acceptance. These days, we find the Lionhead dwarfs mainly in pet shops and the animal markets in Belgium. They have lost their popularity nowadays. The Lionhead dwarfs were never shown in Belgium to get accepted." Now to translate, "Petegem" is the name of a little village, actually there are two villages with that name. They are both located in the province of East-Flanders (Oost-Vlaanderen, Flandre occidentale). Capital of that province is Ghent (Gent in Dutch, Gand in French). Belgium is divided into 10 provinces, five Dutch-speaking in the north and five French-speaking in the south of Belgium. Petegem-aan-de-Leie (De Leie is a river) situated near the town of Deinze. Deinze is situated 22 km west of Ghent. The second is Wortegem-Petegem (two villages that have merged and so both names are mentioned) which lays on the Scheldt. This is also a big river (Schelde in Dutch, l'Escaut in French), near the town of Oudenaarde and lays 40 km south of Ghent. The name "Baard" means beard in Dutch; therefore, the rabbit in Belgium is named after the villages for where it first appeared.

Meg Brown's and Flor Dicken's stories certainly have some things in common. The Lionhead's name both contained the word "Beard," both spoke of a medium-size rabbit. This mutation did not make the attention of those who showed rabbits, but were merely used for meat or as pets. To further downsize the "Bearded Rabbit" for the pet shop trade, there is no doubt that the European Pol (Netherland Dwarf) and other small breeds were crossed, giving us the vast array of colors we have today.

In the late 1970s, breeders in France and Belgium set out to create the Dwarf Angora. Meg Brown tells me that breeders were having a difficult time getting the wool covering on the head and ears; therefore, they crossed in the "Bearded Rabbit" which greatly improved this new breed. In looking at photos of the Dwarf Angoras, those heavily furnished and those that are not, you can certainly see our Lionheads, in wool, wool length (minimum 2 inches), ear furnishings, body type, head, stance and weight range (3 lb. 5 oz. to 4 lbs.). Meg has said that she believed the Lapin Barbe of France is now nearly extinct.

Finland began importing the Lionhead rabbit in the mid 1990s from Germany, according to Leea Makela of Finland. Martin Neuberger of California said that he lived in Tokyo, Japan during 1994 to 1996, and saw

Lionhead rabbits in both pet shops and rabbit specialty shops. He says, "Since I desperately was missing my rabbit hobby, I visited the shops often and became friendly with the staff. The Lionheads always came from European imports." It should be noted that these rabbits in Tokyo sold for over $1,000 each. I received communications from a fellow in Singapore and he has purchased Lionheads at a pet shop there for $300, and his rabbits came from a broker in Belgium.

It appears that the Lionhead breed will never be accepted into the European Standard. The European Association of Poultry, Pigeons and Rabbit Breeders was founded on June 18, 1938, and to date they now have over 20 member countries. Through the years they have developed an International Standard of Perfection and in the year 2002 voted not to allow any more breeds of rabbits that are crossed with existing breeds into the organization's standards.

The National Lionhead Rabbit Club was formed in 1996 in England. It was at the Bradford Championship Show in 1997 that a provisional standard was discussed for the Lionhead rabbit. That same year the British Rabbit Council voted that no more long-haired breeds would be permitted into the standards.

Annette Poolock and Clarice Pell of Clarinette Stud write, "Animal welfare associations, the House Rabbit Association and rescue associations all approached the club concerned about the long hair, as many long-haired rabbits ended up in rescue in a terrible state. The club and BRC were also threatened with bad exposure in the national press if we dared to carry on producing these fluffy rabbits. If these rabbits were going to end up in rescue because of their matted coats, then we had to rethink.

"It was agreed that a small rabbit with long silky hair (not woolly) only around the head, not in the skirt area, would be acceptable to all concerned and also would comply with the BRC requirements.

"Next was a discussion with a geneticist to see if it was possible to produce a rabbit with a smooth body and a long silky mane. As the long hair gene and short hair gene had never been produced in the same rabbit before (as required by the new standard), there was doubt whether it could be done. The rest is history, so now Lionhead breeders have proven something to the geneticists and kept the welfare and rescue and hopefully the BRC happy."

Joyce Taylor and Derek Medlock of England attended a show in Bruges, Belgium in 1995, and in one of the many displays there was a large aviary filled with exotic birds and plants and, to their amazement, these cute little

Lionhead rabbits were running about the floor. Arrangements were made to purchase some stock in a month while they were in Holland. Joyce and Derek recently told me that another fellow from England by the name of Allen Fairhall went with them to Holland to get the rabbits. There were 21 Lionheads made available to them from two different breeders; one breeder was from Belgium and the other from the Bel-

Lionhead seen by Taylor & Medlock in 1995.

gium and French border. Allen Fairhall purchased 12 rabbits in various colors, and Joyce and Derek purchased the remaining nine animals all in the Sooty Fawn (Tortoise) color. Allen kept a trio of Seal Points and sold

The Lionheads purchased by Taylor & Medlock in 1995.

the remaining nine animals to other British rabbit fanciers. Fairhall later sold his Lionhead stock and moved to Spain. Joyce and Derek to this day continue to breed their Lionheads and have not crossed them with any other breeds of rabbits. On May 5, 2002, Joyce Taylor took Best of Breed Lionhead at the Southern Championship Show, which was the first specialty show for the National Lionhead Rabbit Club.

The five lionheads that were first brought into northern Minnesota by Jo Anne Statler included a Harlequin (Orange/Black) doe, a Siamese Sable buck (carrier of the Harlequin and Steel), Black sport buck (with a Dutch blaze, a carrier of the Vienna gene), Silver Tipped Steel doe, Broken Chestnut Agouti buck, and a Harlequin

The original five Lionheads imported to America by Jo Anne Statler.

doe. In an attempt to broaden the gene pool, several Minnesota breeders began crossing the Lionheads to various other small breeds, such as Netherland Dwarfs, Britannia Petite, Polish and Florida Whites. Holland Lops have also been used in the Lionhead breeding program, but I still to this day cannot understand why.

LITTLE SILVER

hroughout Europe and the Scandinavian countries you will find the Little Silver rabbit, under various names, such as Klein Silber in Germany, meaning Little Silver. The breed is nothing more than the original Silver of the United Kingdom or the United States. Through a hundred years of selection, the breed has evolved into a much different type, very cobby in shape, broader head, ears and body. The fur, while mostly uniformly silvered throughout, is a night-and-day difference. The coat is more open and doesn't at all carry the tightly fitting and snappy coat that the British and Americans have bred for.

The original Silvers came to the European continent about 1880, of course, from England. The breed reached Germany in 1892; yet oddly enough it appears in the first German standard in 1880. Max Berthold, of Chemnitz, Germany, would write the first true description of the breed in 1900. A Silver Club was founded in Leipzig in 1904, and in 1906 another club was established in Gera. By 1908, there were already five recognized colors. Today, in Germany there are six varieties: Black, Yellow, Blue, Brown, Havana and the Brightly. The Brightly, known as Klein Silber Helle, is the most beautiful creature one can behold, as in all respects it is a miniature version of the

Little Silver of Europe. Photo courtesy Michael Degel, Germany.

Champagne D'Argent.

The Little Silvers are very popular rabbits, especially so in Germany, as can be seen from the numbers shown in 1980 in Hanover, with 1263 animals. Two years later at the huge Stuttgart Show, no less than 2677 Silvers appeared, with no less than 454 being shown by youth fanciers.

Klein Silber Helle. Photo courtesy Franz Josef Wissing, Germany.

LOP BREEDS

AMERICAN FUZZY LOP

Just as the name would imply, the American Fuzzy Lop is an American creation. Holland Lops were, in the beginning, bred in only the solid colors, and fanciers desired to introduce the broken pattern to the breed. Holland Lops were mated to English Spots, which did inject the broken gene; the fur of the Broken Hollands now had a fly back coat instead of the rollback coat called for in the breed's standards. These Broken Hollands were then mated with French Angora to improve the fur, but at the same time introduced the wool gene. Long-coated Holland Lops were occasionally appearing in the Lop litters. The Fuzzy Lops were occurring all over the country, and in-

American Fuzzy Lop. Photo courtesy American Rabbit Breeders Association.

terest in these long-coated little Lops was building.

Patty Greene-Karl decided to fix the traits and develop the American Fuzzy Lop. She worked on the American Fuzzy Lops for four years before presenting them for the first time at the ARBA Convention in Houston, Texas in 1985, in which they were approved for a first showing. The next year at Columbus, Ohio Convention, the breed once again was passed for a second showing. In 1987 at the Portland, Oregon Convention, the breed did not pass, citing a lack of uniformity from one animal to the other. At the request of Patty Greene-Karl, a new standard was written up by Jeff Hardin, which was approved. This standard was basically the same as for the Holland Lop breed, with the exception of having a wooled coat. At the Madison, Wisconsin ARBA Convention in 1988, the American Fuzzy Lop was recognized as a breed to America, which weighed in at 3.5 to 4 lbs.

CASHMERE LOP

 ashmere Lops are a product of the United Kingdom, and their history is pretty much the same as the American Fuzzy Lop. The breed has been created by the long-coated sports for the normal Lops.

At one time a Dereck Ricketts was working on producing the Giant Cashmere Lop for wooly sports from the French Lop, yet little interest was developed in the breed, and it quickly vanished from the scene.

There are two type of Cashmere Lops recognized by the British Rabbit Council: Cashmere and Miniature Cashmere Lop, with the latter pretty much being the same as the American Fuzzy Lop. While the Cashmere Lop should weigh 4 to 5.25 lb. (1.81 to 2.38 kg) and is rec-

Cashmere Lop. Photo courtesy British Rabbit Council.

ognized in many colors and patterns, the Miniature counterpart should not weigh more than 3.50 lb. (1.60 kg) and more limited in the colors: Agouti, Steel, Sooty Fawn, White, Black, Brown, Siamese Smoke, Marten Smoke, Otter in Black, Blue and Chocolate, with any Butterfly pattern of these colors.

DWARF REX LOP

 rance is the original location of the development of the Dwarf Rex Lop, and only very recently has this breed made its appearance to the world of rabbits. The Dwarf Rex Lop is the brainchild of Pierre Periquet, who in 1998 began mating Dwarf Lops with Dwarf Rex. Pierre tells me that the main difficulty was with the length of ear. The animals in the first generation crosses had ears that were too short for the breed. The second generation brought in the Rex coat. With the third generation, the ears were fairly reasonable and the Rexing of the coat stable. While the coat is quite good and ears carried typically like the Holland Lop, or Dwarf Lop of Europe which are known for their ear control, a bit of improvement is needed in the body type and head structure.

Pierre Periquet had a wonderful idea behind creating this new breed; because children are greatly infatuated by the Dwarf Lops and everyone knows that children love to caress their pets, with the Rex fur place on the Dwarf Lops, the need to caress is increased. Therefore, children will tend to take better care of their pets than before. I believe that these cute little rabbits will be spreading throughout Europe in the years to come.

Dedicated to Pierre Periquet of France, who developed the Dwarf Rex Lop which he is holding. From what I have been able to determine, Pierre is the youngest person ever to develop a new breed of rabbit. Photo courtesy Jean-Claude Periquet, France.

Full or Double Lop, circa 1885, from "The Practical Rabbit Keeper."

ENGLISH LOP

nglish Lops are the very oldest of the exhibition breeds, that is, it is the breed which started rabbit shows, especially in the British Isles. The origin of the Lop-eared rabbit, as it was first called, is rather shrouded in history. Some of the early writers say that the rabbits came from Algiers, North Africa, some say from the island of Madagascar; hence the early name for the variety we call tortoiseshell. Another writer places the breed in Patagonia; some say that Lop-eared rabbits were known in the warrens of England, and others clearly state the first Lops came from China, which were then crossed with the larger rabbits of England. Although we will never know for sure the precise origin, this author is more inclined to believe that the rabbits came from China during the mid to later 1700s. I have seen a 16th century Chinese carving of a Lop-eared rabbit. Regardless of their origin, it is the British that took on the challenge to produce the longest eared rabbit.

Dedicated to Miss Meg Brown of Scotland who spent many years promoting the Lops to prevent them from becoming extinct. I would have to say that Meg Brown did more for the Lops, in particular the English and French Lops, than any human, past or present, in the entire world of rabbits. Photo courtesy Fur & Feather, England.

The earliest mention of the Lop-eared rabbit appears in Bonington Moubray's *Practical Treatise,* 1822, in which he writes, "Of late years, in London, the term smut has been applied as a mark of distinction in the rabbit. Thus there are single and double smuts. The smut consists of a black spot on the side of the rabbit's nose: when there are two black spots, one on each size *(I think he meant side)* of the nose, it constitutes a double smut. Generally, the rabbits are prized for the number of these black spots upon the head and body, and for the fineness and length and size of the ears, which occasions their falling about the head, in a manner different from the common rabbit. Black and tortoiseshell are the favourite colours."

Rabbits were first allowed in the agricultural shows of England in the mid 1820s, with the Lops being the only breed. In 1840, the Metropolitan Fancy Rabbit Club was founded in London at Green Gate, City Road. This

Full of Double Lop, circa 1895. From "Rabbits for Exhibition, Pleasure and Market."

228

Mr. C. Garratt's buck, winner of first prize at Crystal Palace, London, 1887.

was the first Lop Club as the word "Fancy" was an early term used to refer to the Lop-eared rabbit, as they were the only fancy breed of the time. The Metropolitan Club was considered the "father of rabbit societies." The first prize for length of ear at their first show was won by a Mr. Lock from London, with a sooty (tortoiseshell) buck with 19-inch ear length. After a few months the club moved to White Horse on Friday Street, where another show was held. Influential members of the club campaigned, and the society finally landed at the British Hotel at Cockspur Street. It was at this location, and its show, where the first Lop appeared measuring 21 inches in ear length. The Yellow and White buck belonged to a Mr. Terry. Local Lop Clubs would soon follow the first organization. These clubs would hold their meetings in various pubs throughout London. Strict rules were put into force regarding not attending meetings, being late, not registering your litters, showing a rabbit over eight months of age. The secretary was required to inspect each member's shed on a monthly basis, nor could a fellow member be refused entry into another member's shed. Lops were not allowed to be shown with

Known as the Double or Full Lop, circa 1865.

less than 17-inch ears. Nine prizes would be awarded at each show: 1 – for the longest ear, 2 – for the next longest ear, 3 – for the next longest ear, 4 – the best Black and White, 5 – the best Yellow and White, 6 – best Tortoiseshell, 7 – best Gray and White, 8 – best Blue and White, and 9 – for heaviest Lop. No member

229

was allowed to take more than one prize at each show. During this time period, the rabbits were not judged for anything but length and width of the ears, except for the one prize of the heaviest rabbit. These rules, of course, pretty much applied to the so-called Double or Full Lop as it was to become later known. Indeed, there were other Lops of sorts; however, these were not considered the true Lop of the day. In *Manuals for the Many — The Rabbit Book*, 1865, I quote and use their engravings for the other type Lops of long ago.

OAR LOP

"The Oar-Lop is so called from the ears in the position resembling the two oars of a boat resting in the rowlocks in the hands of a waterman. This is particularly admired by some fanciers, but is strongly condemned by others. It bears a

Oar Lop, circa 1880.

Oar Lop, circa 1865.

more close resemblance to the perfect Lop than any other variety of this breed. Many rabbits of the best blood will carry their ears in this position, but are unfit for exhibition, unless to compete for weight, in which class the ears are not considered."

HORN LOP

"The Horn-Lop rabbit derives its name from the position on which the ears are carried, drooping forward and a little downwards over the eyes, resembling the horns of a cow. This rabbit, like the Oar-Lop, may be produced by the most highly bred specimens of the Double-Lop variety, and, by judicious mating, may be the parent of first-

Horn Lop, circa 1880.

class stock. It is not the result of a cross with the common rabbit, which in this variety is more often the case, and will show itself through many generations. The Horn-Lop is not often to be met with, but is not to be more valued on that account. It is impossible to

Horn Lop, circa 1865.

make perfect lops of Horn-Lops either by capping or stitching."

HALF LOP

"The Half-Lop variety may be derived into two classes, and, at least, with some benefit to the young fancier; inasmuch as one variety almost invariably bespeaks impurity of blood, while in the other variety we may find numbers of the highest-bred animals descended from the parents of the purest blood and great beauty. It is very difficult to breed a litter of young rabbits from the most perfect specimens without one or two of them being the last-mentioned vari-

Half Lop, circa 1880.

ety of the Half-Lop — at any rate, for some time or until the offending ear be brought to its more proper position by the use of the cap or stitch."

Half Lop, circa 1865.

Kempster W. Knight, in his *The Book of the Rabbit,* 1881, devotes a full 50 pages to the Lop breed, with a very interesting insight of the methods of keeping the breed so long ago, with quotes from the leading Lop fanciers of the day. It is obvious from the previous type Lops that ear control was a problem of the early days. Lead weights, hot wax and stitching of the ears to-gether were once prac-

The Lop ear cap, developed by an American fan-cier, but also widely used in England during the 1880s.

tices used, regardless of how cruel it may have been to the rabbits. An American fancier, writing on the subject of capping, appears in Knight's book, saying: "This should be done at the age of six weeks or two months, in the following manner: Cut from a piece of leather a strip in the shape of the illustration. The places x x are cut so as to act like a flap, and this must be made of such size as will fit the rabbit's head; put the ears through from the under side, and draw the two ends under the throat and tie them. These flaps press the ear down, and after being kept on a week usually a cure. The leather should be the thickness of ordinary boot-leather."

Further torture to the almighty ear was holding the young Lops on the owner's lap in front of the fire, and pulling and stretching the ear, oftentimes with hot oils, or with a coating of wax. Great debates were carried out by the Lop fanciers of yesteryear, concerning the amount of heat that the Lops should be kept in to improve ear growth. Here are some of the fanciers' quotes as to temperatures in their sheds: Mr. Lock of London says: "I never use any artificial heat except a gaslight during the damp weather to produce a more genial heat, and never the high tem-perature of 70 or 80 degrees, which must tend to destroy the constitution

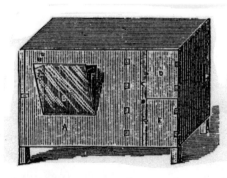

Breeding hutch for Lops, circa 1880. The hutch is covered with tin; there are no ventilation holes; the slant is made of glass to allow light. This hay hopper is backed with a metal grate.

of the rabbit." Mr. A.H. Easton of Hull says: "I at one time kept them in a high temperature of 85 to 90 degrees by means of a stove kept burning all night; but this I found made the air too hot and dry, and there was an escape of sulphur injurious to them. I now rear all my rabbit in smaller hutches, kept dry and warm, and at a tempera-ture of some 60 to 65 degrees, and find it the safest plan to insure strength." One poor gentlemen went as far as 100 degrees on his

Alaska

Altex

American

Angora, Dwarf

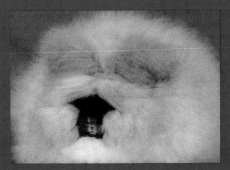

Angora, English

Angora, French

Angora, Giant

Angora, Mini English

Angora, Satin

Argent, Champagne d'

Argent, Creme d'

Argente, Bleu

Argente, Brun

Argente, Noir

Argente, Saint Hubert

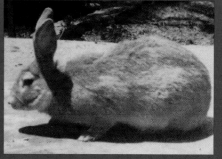
Baladi

Bauscat

Beige

Belgian Hare

Belgian Silver

Beveren

Blanc de Hotot

Blanc de Vendee

Blue of Ham

Bourbonnais Grey

Brazilian

Britannin Petite

British Giant

Brown Chestnut of Lorraine

Californian

Carmagnola Grey

Checkered Giant

Chinchilla, American

Chinchilla, Giant

Chinchilla, Giganta

Chinchilla, Standard

Cinnamon

Czech Spot

Deilenaar

Dutch

Dutch, Harlequin

Dwarf Hotot

Enderby Island

English Spot

Fauve de Bourgogne

Fee de Marbourg

Flemish Giant

Flemish Giant (British)

Florida White

Furless

Gabali

Giant Blanc du Bouscat

Giant Papillon

Giza White

Golden Glavcot

Gotland

Grey Pearl of Halle

Harlequin, Japanese

Harlequin, Magpie

Havana

Hermelin

Himalayan

Hulstlander

Jamora

Jersey Wooly

Kabyle

Large Himalayan

Large Silver

Lilac

Lionhead

Little Silver

Lop, American Fuzzy

Lop, Cashmere

Lop, Dwarf Rex

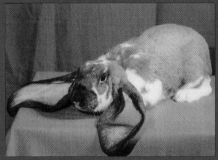

Lop, English

Lop, French

Lop, German

Lop, Holland

Lop, Meissener

Lop, Mini

Lop, Velveteen

Lutino

Lutterbach Ermine

Mecklenburger Scheck

Mini Satin

Moravien Blue

Netherland Dwarf

New Zealand

Normand

Palomino

Pannon White

Perlfee

Petit Papillon Tricolor

Pointed Beveren

Polish

Rex, Astrex

Rex, Dwarf

Rex, Micro

Rex, Mini

Rex, Mini Satin

Rex, Opossum

Rex, Standard

Rhinelander

Rhoen

Sable

Sachengold

Sallander

Satin

Schwarzgrannen

Separator

Siberian

Silver

Silver Fox

Silver Marten

Smoke Pearl

Squirrel

St. Nicholas Blue

Stone

Sussex

Swiss Fox

Tadla

Tan

Thrianta

Thuringer

Vienna

Vienna White

Vit Land

Wheaten

poor rabbits, and also allowed the rabbit's droppings to accumulate so that heat would build in the hutch. Coal, oil and paraffin heaters were commonplace to heat the hutches and sheds. Fanciers, or better yet, Dr. Jeckels and Mr. Hydes of the day, even went so low as to construct all-metal hutches, with little to no ventilation or light for the rabbits.

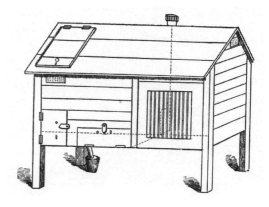

Called the Improved Lop Breeding Hutch from 1880, the above appears a bit more humane than the all-metal hutch of the same era.

Prior to 1875, other breeds of rabbits were almost unknown in London. In the spring of 1875, classes would finally be provided for Dutch, Silver Grey, Himalayans and Any Other Variety, in addition, of course, to the usual Lop classes. In 1879, Angoras were substituted for Any Other Variety, and a class was added for Belgian Hares. So the Lop rabbit was easily proclaimed as "The King of the Fancy." It was by this time that a real standard would come into play for the Lop breed. A Mr. J. Newman of London seems to have displaced the idea that the ears were the only feature to be considered in the Lops. He writes in *Live Stock Journal and Fancier's Gazette,* February 12th 1875, "When I have judged, I have always of late years done so by 'points,' and this is my system: For a rabbit measuring 24 inches long, 6 inches wide, and quite perfect in every way, I would give 100 points, distributed as follows:

Half Lop of 1855, from Bement's book.

Length of ear 25
Width of ear.. 20
Carriage of ear... 5
Colour.. 10
Make and Shape 10
Eye 10
General condition 10
Weight 10

Total = 100 Points

Mr. Newman's point system was one of many that I have found in the early writings of the Lop rabbit. In fact, there are at least six different standards, with points totaling as little as 16 up to 100.

Called the Perfect Lop in 1855, from Bement's book.

From Caleb Nichols Bement's (1791-1868) book, *The Rabbit Fancier,* 1855, which is the oldest known rabbit book written in America, we learn and I quote, "Mr. F. Rotch, of Morris Ostego County, N.Y., imported the first of the large lop-eared rabbits into this country, some 12 or 14 years ago. His beautiful high-bred animals have occasionally been exhibited at the fairs of the State Agricultural Society, for which premiums have been awarded and the highest commendations elicited." So now we have a timeline of between 1841 to 1843 when the first English Lops appeared in America. A flurry of importations would take place during the 1850s. One London fancier was shipping as many as 60 animals a week during the height of the Lops' popularity to the American shores. We can now paint a picture that the Lop-Eared rabbit was the first breed to start a domestic rabbit boom in America.

From *Gleason's Pictorial Drawing-Room Companion,* July 9, 1853, there appears an engraving of a buck and two does, now with young, which had been imported in the spring of 1852, by a George P. Burnham, of

Engraving from "Gleason's Pictorial Drawing-Room Companion," July 9, 1853. This is the earliest engraving that I have been able to locate of a Lop eared rabbit anywhere.

Boston, Massachusetts. "My stock I imported last spring from London, Liverpool and Dublin; and I shall be happy to show those interested, at my residence in Melrose. I am not aware that these pretty animals are now very extensively bred in this country, Mr. Rotch, of Morris, N.Y., and Mr. Rodman, of Dedham, being the only gentlemen that I know who have fine stock; yet I think we shall very soon see more of them, at home and abroad." Mr. Rotch of New York State, a great rabbit fancier, thus writes to the editor of *Country Gentleman,* on the demand for the famous lop-eared fancy rabbits: "I have, with the most persevering pen-and-ink assiduity, replied to the multitude of inquiries and others, which have thronged in upon me the last six months, requesting I would send them rabbits. They have come from almost every State in the Union; distance, it would seem, being as nothing, risk of transportation as a trifle, and price as no obstacle; but it is totally out of my power to meet the demand for these little animals, which thus come upon one from all quarters."

Then appearing in another American publication called *The Northern Farmer,* Vol. 1, No. 2, February 1854, by the editor, "Fancy Lop-Ear Rabbits — The Lop-Ear Rabbit is a superior variety, which originally came from the island of Madagascar, off the coast of Africa, and has been greatly improved in England. They are now much sought for in this country, and several importations were made during the past year, among which, of great size and beauty, is that of Messrs. Bennett & Plaisted, of Great Falls, N.H. The best rabbit in Great Britain, the 'Champion of England,' has recently been added to their stock at a high price, which we learn from those gentlemen, and also from the *Field,* a London paper that notices the sale &c. It appears that the extraordinary value

The Northern Farmer, February 1854.

placed on the 'Champion of England' is for his great size, and enormous length of ears, being 22 inches long. He won the first prize at the exhibition of the Surrey Zoological Gardens, and was purchased by Miss Watts, the celebrated amateur, for Messrs. B. &. P. His color is black and white. We have ordered an engraving of him for our periodical."

The National Lop Club in England finally agreed upon a standard for the breed. Well, actually two standards were issued just before the turn of the century: Limit Classes and Any-Length Classes.

Limit Classes		Any-Length Classes	
Ear Length	15	Ear Length	.25
Ear Width	15	Ear Width	20
Substance and Shape	5	Substance and Shape	5
Shape & Carriage of Rabbit	10	Straight Feet and Tail	10
Colour and Markings	15	Colour and Markings	10
Condition	10	Condition	10
Straight Feet and Tail	10	Shape	5
Eye	10	Eye	10
Size	10	Size	5
	100 Points		100 Points

By the turn of the century, many people felt that the Lops' popularity was falling, but exhibits at the shows would find from 60 up to nearly 100 Lops entered. However, many more breeds were coming to light. One of the greatest supporters of the breed was William Knightbridge, of East London who wrote *The Lop Rabbit, How To Breed, Manage and Exhibit,* 1900, but Knightbridge's life was cut short when he passed away on November 3, 1901, at the age of 40 from Bright's disease. It was during this point in time that 26-inch Lops were fairly commonplace. Then on September 4, 1901, appeared the "Phenomenal Lop." In the editorial which appeared in *Fur & Feather,* September 19, 1901, "Warminster Show, held September 4th, was a success. The weather was good and the entry capital, although we fear the amalgamation of the Lops with the Any Other Variety Class will not please exhibitors generally. The sensation of the show was the young winning Lop, staged by Capt.

William Knightbridge.

Youlton, of Jersey. This exhibit, Mr. Tottle assures us, measured 30-1/8 inches long, by 7-3/8 inches wide — truly phenomenal if correct, but measurements differ so much that we are naturally anxious to await corroboration before accepting these astounding figures. Be this as it may, Mr. Tottle found his 29-inch rule inadequate, and had to secure one a yard long to take the measurement, and this we understand was done before several interested sightseers, the performance naturally causing excitement." Then on September 26, 1901, Mr. W.L. Langley wrote in the same paper, "I can assure you the length given is correct. In fact, I believe it will measure 30-1/2 inches long. However, the Rabbit was a masterpiece, and a credit to Captain Youlton, in producing such a fine specimen." It is a great pity that I have not been able to locate a picture of this specimen.

The downfall of the English Lop would be what had made it so famous, its ears. No breed of rabbit could beat a Lop on the show table, and when one did, near war would break out. Fanciers of other breeds refused to show against the English

A trio of Lops bred by Captain W.B. Youlton of England, circa 1899.

237

Lop, and by 1945 the breed was on the very verge of extinction, both in England and America. With the ears being all the rage, the bodies of the Lop had gone neglected.

Full Lop, circa 1880.

The breed was saved by a dear friend of mine, Miss Meg Brown, of Scotland, as told by her in her book, *Rabbit lopaedia, A Complete Guide to Rabbit Care,* 2000, by Meg Brown and Virginia Richardson, "When I saw my first English Lop, it was a poor thing indeed. It took me three years to buy a pair. Ultimately, I got a three-year-old doe and was offered a sterile buck which turned out to be not so sterile. I had my first litter from that pair. I noted that the body of the Lop had indeed been forgotten, and I was determined to improve it. But how? I read all the rabbit literature available, discovered that the French Lop was a cross from the English Lop and went to France and bought the Paris Show winner for five (pounds)! I took one youngster back and bred it with the English Lop, and 10 years later, when I showed it in Paris, it nearly caused a riot because I had crossed it back to the French Lop. The head judge asked me, 'What have you done to the English Lop? We have never seen such Lop.' I told him that I had looked up the French Lop ancestry and discovered that the English Lop was an ancestor. He laughed and laughed, thinking it was a huge joke, and said 'Now why didn't we think of that?' From there on, the Lop improved and was, from 1960s onwards, a good rabbit behind the ears!"

Meg Brown would send this author two pairs of Lops, English and French, in 1971, and we would again see the Lops taking hold in America. In April 8, 1971, the Lop Rabbit Club of America was issued a charter by the American Rabbit Breeders Association with 32 charter members. In

A world record holder, before they had world records. This Sooty Junior doe measured 29-1/2 x 7-1/2 inches and was Swiss bred. Circa 1940s.

English Lop depicted on a Bulgarian stamp.

1999, at the Louisville, Kentucky ARBA Convention and Show, a total of 370 English Lops were shown in the open show, with 133 in the youth section, making a grand total of 503 English Lops. These are amazing numbers for a breed that came so near to extinction, so I'm confident that the breed is here to stay. It should be noted that the Americans must be given credit for the all-around "BEST" English Lops, as they have improved 100% on the bony bodies of yesteryear.

Lops have appeared on many postage stamps of the world over the years, but the first stamp issue was in 1926. It is a German stamp, and the Black and White Lop that appears is actually a French Lop and not an English Lop as some documents have reported. The rabbit was owned by the great rabbit judge and author, Frederick Joppich.

Due to animal rights people, Germany must ban rabbits with ears over 25.5 inches, and in Holland, 27.5 inches is as long as they

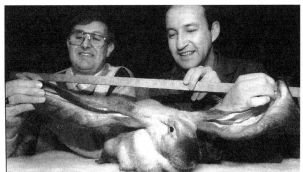

Toby II, a past world record holder, with the owner and breeder, Phil Wheeler, on the left. Photo courtesy Fur & Feather, England.

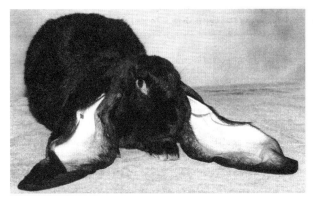

Toby III, a two-time world record holder. Photo courtesy Fur & Feather, England.

Nipper's Geronimo, also known as Guinness, for obvious reasons is the current World Record holder for the longest ears, with a record that will probably stand for many years to come. Photos courtesy Margaret and Waymon Nipper, USA.

CERTIFICATE

The longest rabbit ears measured
79 cm (31.125 in) in a complete span
on 1 November 2003 at the American
Rabbit Breeders Association National
Show in Wichita, Kansas, USA.
The ears belong to an English Lop called
Nipper's Geronimo who is owned by
Waymon and Margaret Nipper of
Bakersfield, California, USA.

Keeper of the Records
GUINNESS WORLD RECORDS LTD

The Guiness World Records Certificate for the longest eared rabbit. Courtesy Margaret and Waymon Nipper, USA.

can be allowed before disqualification.

One of the last three longest eared rabbits which made the *Guinness Book of Records* was a Tortoiseshell buck bred and owned by Phil Wheeler of England. This rabbit was named Toby II, which set the record in 1996 at 29.25 inches and a width of 7 3/8 inches. Then his grandson, Toby III, a Black buck, set the longest eared rabbit record on June 3, 2002 at the Queen's Jubilee Show in England at a record 30.25 inches by an amazing width of 7.75 inches. Toby III was the world record holder before this latest measurement, when first measured on December 3, 2000 at 29.25 inches. The current record holder, and one that surely will stand for a long time, was bred by Margaret and Waymon Nipper of California. Nipper's Geronimo, a Tortoiseshell buck, was measured at the American Rabbit Breeders Association Convention at Wichita, Kansas on November 1, 2003, at a staggering 31.125 inches by 7.25 inches wide, achieving the latest Guinness World Record. Because Nipper's Geronimo was a young rabbit at the time, perhaps he too will be a double record holder.

FRENCH LOP

rance is, of course, the native home of the largest of the Lop tribe we call the French Lop, having been developed during the middle of the 19th century by a bookbinder from Breteuil named Mr. Cordonnier. Mr. Girard, the old acting director of the Botanical Gardens of Lyon, moved to Paris in 1852, and the following year brought English Lops to add to his collection of farm animals. Cordonnier obtained some and mated them to the giant breeds of the time, namely the old breed known as Normand or Picard, as well as the extinct bulldog-headed Rouennais.

Those early French Lops were primarily bred for meat production and not as a show animal. French Lops were soon exported to Germany in 1869, and the breed was to be found in Switzerland in 1899. Oddly enough, in its native home, the French Lop was not recognized and given a standard until March 25, 1922.

It is not known just when the French Lop arrived in America, but surely it must have been in the beginning of the 20th century, as it was among the first breeds recognized when the National Pet Stock Association was founded in early 1910. The standard was the same as the English Lop, but was to have shorter ears.

For many years the French Lop was extremely rare in

Earliest known illustration of a French Lop, Italy, circa 1897.

241

German illustration from 1917.

German illustration from 1917.

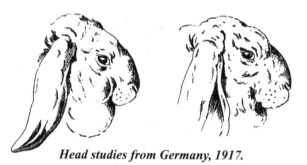

Head studies from Germany, 1917.

North America; in fact, only one known breeder of them was in Canada by the name of Bert Reurs, and he only kept the whites. Some were imported from Switzerland to Texas in 1970 by a Mr. Jordie. This author received a pair of Agouti French Lops from Meg Brown of Scotland in 1971. Further importations took place during the early 1970s from England, Holland and Germany. With the formation of the Lop Rabbit Club of America, both French and English Lops received a renewal of interest and are extremely popular today.

A fine French Lop from France.
Photo courtesy Jean-Claude Periquet, France.

The first stamp to depict a Lop rabbit issued in 1926 and the actual rabbit.

Dutch marked French Lop, developed in Denmark.
Photo courtesy Sofie Lundus, Denmark.

Now for a novelty in the breed, what about the Dutch French Lop? During the early 1990s, Mr. Hans Zoellner, of Sjaelland, Denmark, in the city of Helsinger, mated a French Lop doe to a Dutch buck. The Dutch was only used once in the breeding program. Hans then through selection of the best marked to the best mark created the new variety, which is now being considered for recognition.

Lops have appeared on many postage stamps throughout the world over the years, but the first stamp issued was in 1926. It is a German stamp, and the Broken Black Lop, which is oftentimes confused for an English Lop, is actually a French Lop. This rabbit was bred and owned by the late great rabbit judge and author, Frederick Joppich.

Italian illustration of 1915.

GERMAN LOP

Germany Lops are indeed from Germany, but have been named in Britain. These are nothing more than a larger version of the Deutsche Klein Widder or the Mini Lop of America (see Mini Lop). The British Rabbit Council has accepted a weight range of 2.94 kg. to 3.855 kg. (6.5 to 8.5 lb). The Dwarf Lop of England is more to the size of the Mini Lop of the states.

HOLLAND LOP

 ust as the name suggests, Holland Lops come to use from the Netherlands and can easily be considered the second most popular breed of domestic rabbit world wide, next to the Netherland Dwarf. Mr. Adrian de Cock, of Tilburg, is given total credit in originating the breed, beginning his breeding program during the winter of 1949. The late Adrian de Cock was a renowned breeder of the Tan rabbit; in fact, he wrote a book on the breed called *Het Tankonijn in Woord en Beeld,* in 1946. Mr. de Cock was also an admirer of the French Lop, but felt its main drawback to many fanciers was the massive size, feeding cost involved and large hutches required to keep the breed. Mr. de Cock set a goal for himself to breed a dwarf version of the French Lop. He obtained a French Lop buck and mated it to a White Netherland Dwarf. He felt that the offspring would be smaller than if the cross were reversed. This venture failed, so he did the reverse cross anyway in 1951. After two failed matings, the third time was a charm, as he finally was able to get a litter of six youngsters; yet none of the offspring showed lopped ears.

Adrian de Cock secured a Tortoiseshell English Lop buck and mated it to one of the previous crossbred does in 1952. From this mating, one doe was fully lopped, two had the erect ear carriage, and another was half lopped. The fully

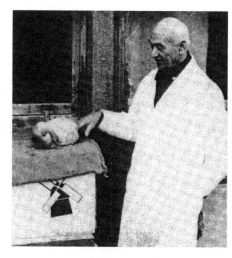

Dedicated to the late Adrian de Cock of Holland who gave the world our littlest Lop.

lopped doe was extremely aggressive and never used in the future breeding program. The half lopped doe was chosen to carry on the experiment, when she was mated to a buck from the first litter of the French Lop x Netherland Dwarf cross, as well as the does from the first cross, bred to bucks from the second litter. Through these crossings a percentage of the offspring had lopped ears,

Holland Lop. *Photo courtesy American Rabbit Breeders Association.*

which were later inter-bred to conform to the French Lop type, as the English Lop blood which was introduced spoiled his vision for the new breed.

After three years of selection, Mr. de Cock had produced animals which weighed in between 5-1/2 to 6-1/2 pounds. He further bred these animals with Netherland Dwarfs to reduce their size, and by January 1, 1964, he had produced his long-awaited goal and presented four animals, all weighing in at less that 4-1/2 pounds to the national governing body in the Netherlands, where the breed was recognized to their book of standards. In 1970, Adrian de Cock called together a dozen of his fellow Netherland Dwarf Lop fanciers and formed the Netherland Dwarf Lop Specialty Club.

The little Lops soon spread throughout Europe, but good stock was hard to come by, and many fast buck merchants tried to get the upper weights raised in the Netherlands, but to no avail. George Scott first brought the little rabbits to England in 1969, via the Netherlands, where they have become known as the Miniature Lop.

Aleck Brooks III, of Ardsley, New York, would be given credit for introducing the breed to the United

Aleck Brooks III of New York introduced the Holland Lop to America.

States. After seeing a picture of the popular little breed in a European magazine in 1973, Aleck, along with his parents, Buddy and Barbara Brooks, went to Holland and befriended Mr. de Cock in 1974, and was able to secure his first trio: a pair of Tortoiseshells and a Sable Point doe. Further imports would follow, as the breed became an instant sensation in America.

The ARBA required the breed to be shown and approved at three conventions, so Aleck and his parents took the challenge, first showing them at Houston, Texas in 1977, and being recognized at the Tucson, Arizona Convention in 1979.

History would be made at the 57th ARBA Convention in Milwaukee, Wisconsin in 1980, when the Holland Lops, as they became known on U.S. soil, were shown at convention as an official breed for their first time. Aleck Brook III won Best In Show in the Four Class breeds with a Tortoiseshell Senior Buck that he had bred, with 4,278 rabbits in the open competition. That is a record that has never been set before. That same year the Holland Lop Rabbit Specialty Club was founded with 25 charter members. The breed has become known as "The Hallmark Breed."

LIONHEAD LOP

Lionhead Lops have been created by a number of people, especially in England, when the erect eared Lionheads were mated to the Mini Lops of the UK (Holland or Dwarf Lops). This breed was easily created as the mane gene is a dominant trait for the Lionhead breed. Lionhead Lops are only recently recognized in a few countries, and the process is well underway to recognize them in the United Kingdom. This type of Lop will not be recognized in America, per the rules of our standards. Lionhead Lops have all the same features as the Lionhead, with the exception of ears. To this author, it sort of defeats the purpose of having a nice full mane of wool, as the lopped ears greatly interfere in showing the mane to its best advantage.

MEISSENER LOP

eissen, Germany is the home of the Meissener Lop, created at the end of the 19th century by a school teacher by the name of Leo Reck. Mr. Reck kept the breeding secrets to himself, but it is largely assumed he mated Silver and Champagne d'Argents to Lops to create the Meissener. This author is of the opinion that he used French Lops, although it could have been the English Lop, as the head of the Meissener is more elongated. Leo Reck showed this creation for the first time in 1906 as the Meissner Widder, but only in the black color. Other colors would appear in the years to follow: Agouti, Argente, Blue, Brown and Yellow. The silvering should be evenly distributed over the entire body, but more often than not, the

Meissener Lop. Photos courtesy Interessensgemeinschaft Meissner Widder, Germany.

head, ears, feet and tail are normally always darker. Meisseners are mostly kept in Germany, but are beginning to appear in other countries, including England. As with all the silver breeds of the world, the silvering does not begin to appear for approximately five weeks. The breed is calm natured and weigh in at 3.5 to 5.5 kg (7 lb. 12 oz. to 12 lb. 2 oz.).

MINI LOP

he Mini Lop was developed in Germany and given the name of Deutsche Klein Widder or German Little Hanging Ear. While several German fanciers started the development of the Klein Widder at the same time, it is Mr. Erhard Kiener of Bischmisheini and Mr. Johannes Geerds of Neumunster who received the greatest credit. Several breeds were being used with the addition of French Lop blood, namely, English Lops, New Zealand, Hermine (Polish), Chinchilla and the newly developed Dwarf Lop. Breeding began in the mid-1950s, with Erhard Kiener showing them off to his club for the first time in 1957. There were seven Agouti colored ones exhibited in the "New Creations Class" at Saarbruken in 1960, and Johannes Geerds showed off his

Klein Widders in 1965. The breed was officially recognized into the German Standard in 1973, and quickly spread throughout Germany as a popular new breed. The colors at the time were bred only in solid colors, and in only the Agouti and White.

Holland imported the breed in 1972, as did an American fancier and judge by the name of Robert "Bob" Herschbach, of Watsonville, California. Herschbach attended the German National Rabbit Show in Essen, Germany, and saw the cute little Klein Widder. The late Bob Herschbach purchased a trio: a pair of Agoutis and a White doe, and had them shipped to California. It was also at this time that he reintroduced the Rhinelander breed back to the U.S., importing two pairs.

Herschbach was a master breeder, in my opinion, as he raised outstanding Netherland Dwarfs from the beginning in this country, worked heavily with the French and English Lops, when they were picking up keen interest by fanciers in the early 1970s. He wrote of the development of the broken variety in 1985, "The broken color Mini Lops were bred in America by mating a Standard Chinchilla to a broken French Lop. However, it takes a good many generations and selections to get them down to mini weights. Size is very difficult to control as it takes a good deal of inbreeding, which can cause trouble."

At the 1974 ARBA Convention and Show held in Ventura, California,

Bob entered a pair of Klein Widders for display only. Oddly enough, the new little Lop did not create much interest amongst the people. Was the name so strange, or was it the size? Still to this day no one is quite sure of the reason. One thing for sure, this author liked them, and at the close of the convention, Bob Herschbach said, "Bob,

The late Robert Herschbach of California introduced the German Klein Widders to the United States in 1972.

248

you take them home with you and have a play."

Herschbach changed the name to Mini Lop right after the convention and sought the help of Lorna Anderson and Bobbie Meyers, both of California, to raise, perfect and promote the breed. The real turning

Mini Lop. *Photo courtesy American Rabbit Breeders Association.*

point for the promotion of the Mini Lop would begin in 1977, when the sponsorship was given to the late Herb Dyck, of Sepulveda, California. Herb was quick to carry the torch and gathered a dozen interested individuals, who formed the Mini Lop Rabbit Club of America on December 19, 1978, with Herb sitting in the president's chair.

Herb Dyck's beloved Mini Lops were approved for their third showing at the 1980 Milwaukee, Wisconsin ARBA Convention and became an official recognized breed on January 17, 1981, and a chartered club with well over 700 members.

MINI PLUSH LOP

he Mini Plush Lop is a fairly recent creation for the United States and was created by Devie L. D'Anniballe of North Lawrence, Ohio. She liked the personality of the Holland Lops and the wonderful disposition and the plush coat of the Mini Rex, so in 1995 Devie D'Anniballe mated the two breeds together. After two years, she realized this cross would not work. Other breeders who joined in on the program would give up, saying that it was impossible and just too much work. D'Anniballe continued; this time she mated a three-pound Mini Rex with an excellent coat to a Mini Lop. This coupling proved far better; offspring had the body type she was looking for, ears fell properly, but the size was still too large. Does from this cross were mated back to the bucks of the Holland Lop x Mini Rex. Only does were kept from these crosses, then again bred back to bucks of the Holland cross. After several years, other breeds had been introduced: Jersey Woolies and American Fuzzy Lops. Finally a three-and-a-half-pound Mini Plush Lop was produced called

Dillion, which became the foundation for the breed. It does not appear that the Mini Plush Lop will ever be accepted into the American standards under their current rulings.

ROYAL SATIN LOP

Royal Satin Lops are a very recent American creation, which began in the late 1990s. There was a time when you would see several breeders presenting information on them through various web sites, but for some reason, they are no longer seen. It would be a shame if fanciers who love a small lop-eared rabbit with a satin coat would give up perfecting this breed. Royal Satin Lops were mainly bred in the red, and are the size of the Mini Lop. These are a cross of the normal Satin and the Mini Lop.

VELVETEEN LOP

elveteen Lops are not of the story book that bears the same name, but a miniature English Lop with a Rex coat of fur, which is an American creation first conceived by Virginia Menden, of California. During the 1980s, Virginia Menden began mating Mini Rex to English Lops. Although putting a rex coat of fur on a breed is not a difficult task for any rabbit fancier to achieve, putting those long ears and a good mandolin type is. In 1994, Virginia gave up on the project and passed the breed presentation rights to a Paul Lewis of New Mexico. Lewis was to present the Velveteen Lops for the first time in 1998 at the Portland, Oregon ARBA Convention, but was unable to do so. Paul Lewis passed the presentation rights to Mary Crawford of Texas, who did present the breed in Louisville, Kentucky at the 1999 ARBA Convention. Mary's next two presentations were not successful, and presentation rights went to another Texan by the name of David Kabela. David has managed to secure one accepted showing in each group: broken pattern and solid.

Velveteen Lops are bred in all the patterns and colors of the English Lop breed. Weights have been set at 5 to 6.5 pounds (2.26 or 2.94 kg) for both bucks and does. Ears under 14 inches in length are to disqualify the rabbit, but one cannot expect to obtain the remarkable ear length of the English Lops. The Velveteen Lop has quite a following forming in the United States, and has also begun to make its way into other countries.

LUTINO

 enmark is the original home of this most unique rabbit called Lutino, and although it has been recognized as a new variety of Netherland Dwarf, I personally feel, because of the unique features, it could certainly be well classified as its own breed.

In February 1984, Mr. Gerner Rasmussen purchased his first Harlequin Netherland Dwarfs. In 1985 a doe with the ear number of E399 produced the Orange rabbit with red eyes. This first Lutino was nearly destroyed by Rasmussen, as he did not want to be breeding Harlequin Dwarfs

Lutino rabbit. Photo by Carl Aage Sorenson and courtesy of Anton Dam Nielsen, Denmark.

without markings. It appears in Denmark that it is not at all uncommon for a Harlequin Dwarf to be produced which does not show the Harlequin pattern.

In a third mating another Lutino appeared. These two Lutinos had the same mother, but different fathers, which happened to be brothers. At no time has any combination of

Harlequin Dwarfs been known to produce the Lutino rabbit. Both of the Lutinos that Gerner Rasmussen had in his shed were does, which were mated back to their respective fathers. Gerner reports that one doe was a rather bad breeder, but the other doe in her first litter produced four youngsters, all being Lutinos. In a second litter of four, she produced one

Dedicated to Gerner Rasmussen of Denmark, who had the foresight to maintain and develop this unique new rabbit and saw it recognized. Photo by Bent Knudsen, Denmark.

Harlequin and three Lutinos, which became the grounds for the breed. In the beginning, Gerner believed that the Lutino genes were dominant, but later realized that Lutinos were actually a recessive.

The Lutino rabbit was officially recognized in October 1988 in both the Orange and a Blue Tortoiseshell, known as Shadow, which had been developed in Norway. This amazing little rabbit is fairly rare, being maintained by only a handful of breeders in Denmark and a couple of fanciers in Norway.

LUTTERBACH ERMINE

 rom France comes this brand new breed, truly unique in its pattern, an all-white rabbit with pink eyes, but with colored or mottled ears. There are no further markings anywhere on the body extremities. The new breed was created by Mr. Jacques Czeschan, who named it for the region in which it was created.

For years Jacques Czeschan worked with breeding Dwarfs in many different experiments; fixing the Papillon markings on Dwarfs, reproducing the Hotot as had supposedly been done by Mrs. Bernhard, and working on the depth of color on the Himalayan Dwarfs. Czechan further worked with Martens, Siamese and Chinchilla Dwarfs. He knew that many of these colors were already in Europe and didn't want to bother his fellow fanciers by exhibiting them, so decided to stop.

During judge training courses, he suggested to his colleagues that they should make a difference grouping between hairs which are heat sensitive and those that are not of the Himalayan type. He received less than favorable remarks from some of the people, therefore decided he would produce animals to show them his theory.

He has an old five-year-old gray blue agouti Marten buck, that he mated to a Ruby-Eyed White Hermine doe. The buck died by the time the doe had kindled her two pale colored babies, which were slightly larger than normal. By the time they left the nest box they were still pale, but gradually the ears began to color, yet nowhere else on the body. The two youngsters were a pair, and at eight months the buck

Dedicated to Jacques Czeschan of France who developed this uniquely patterned breed. Photo courtesy Pierre Periquet, France.

weighed 1.7 kg (3.75 lb) and the doe 1.8 kg (4 lb), which was much larger than the parents. The ears were a gray blue with white mottling.

When one mates two Lutterbachs together, the offspring will be Ruby-Eyed Whites, Lutterbach Ermine and Himalayan. When you mate the Ruby-Eyed White to the Lutterbach, you can expect 50% of each, and the same can be expected when using the Himalayan to a Lutterbach. The genes of Jacques Czeschan's amazing new rabbit called Hermine de Lutterbach (Lutterbach Ermine) have been fixed, so larger breeds are likely to be created in the future. The breed will become recognized in France at the end of 2004 in both solid colored ears and mottled.

Lutterbach Ermine showing the mottled ear.
Photo courtesy Jacques Czechan, France.

LUX

Lux or Lynx rabbits are a product of Germany and were created by Karl Hoffmans of Dusseldorf. Hoffmans, who is also the creator of the Perlfee breed, used Tans, Sables, Marburgers and Perlfees in the genetic makeup of the Lux rabbit. The breed was shown for the first time in 1919 and admitted to the breed standards of Germany in 1922. Lux rabbits are popular throughout Europe and the Scandinavian countries, and recently have been brought into England. The beautiful Lux breed is similar in build to the Havana, and weigh in at 2 kg. to 3.5 kg. (4 lb 6 oz to 7 lb). The color is very near the same as the Lynx variety of the Palomino rabbit in America.

Lux rabbit. *Photo courtesy Federation Francaise de Cuniculiculture, France.*

MAGPIE

Magpie Harlequins were first produced in England during the early 1940s, when the normal Chinchilla was mated to the Black/Orange Harlequins known as Japanese (see Harle-

A beautifully marked Magpie, showing clear and distinct banding.

quins) and recognized by the British Rabbit Council in their 1946 Book of Standards. Within some countries, the Magpies are considered their own breed, but in America and the United Kingdom they are recognized as a Group, with four varieties: Black, Blue, Chocolate and Lilac in conjunction with white. The Japanese form the second Group of the Harlequin breed.

MARTEN SABLE

Marten Sables are recognized in many countries; some will group them as part of the Sable breed, and some keep them separate. The British Rabbit Council further breaks the breed down to various shades: Light Marten Sable, Medium Marten Sable and Dark Marten Sable. Americans place them with the Silver Martens, regardless they are all from the same product having originated as sports from the original Chinchilla of France, (see Sable).

MECKLENBURGER SCHECK

ermany is the original home of this beautiful tuxedo patterned breed. The creator of this race is Mr. Rudolf Wulf, from Goldenbow in the state of Mecklenburg, which gave the breed its name. Rudolf Wulf began creating his Checkered of Mecklenburger in 1973, by crossing the broken pattern German Lops with Blue Viennas and the black breed known as Alaska. The breed was given full recognition by the National Rabbit governing body of Germany in 1981. These beautifully sticking rabbits are bred in black, blue, red and a new color, the thuringer (chamois or tortoiseshell) in conjunction with white. It is a large breed, weighing in at 4.5 to 5.5 kg or 10 to 12.25 lbs. Mecklenburger Checkers are finding their way into other European coun-

tries, and have been ac-
cepted into Scandinavia.
The breed has a truly unique
pattern for the rabbit world
to enjoy. They were bred to
resemble the markings of a
cow, no doubt the Holstein.

MINI SATIN

ini Satin are an American creation, which began in the late
1970s by a Mrs. Ariel Hayes, of Troy, Michigan, and she called
her small Satins "Satinettes." To create the breed, the normal
Satin breed was mated to Polish, and when she gave up on her
breeding program in 1982, Hayes had the size down to 4.5 pounds. Ariel
Hayes disposed of the all her Satinettes for pets or the dinner table.

During the late 1980s a Netherland Dwarf breeder by the name of B.
Pettit began working on putting a satin coat to the Dwarfs. He would be
joined by Sue and Verle Castle in 1990, when they purchased some of his
stock. Pettit created his small Satins by the normal Satin and Netherland
Dwarf crosses. Later in 1990 a Michigan man was located who was breeding a Satinette, who said that he started in
1983, but would not divulge his methods,
or if they were purchased from Ariel
Hayes. He said that he created the Satinette
name. This man was not able to attend the
National Rabbit Conventions to present
the new breed, due to his work schedule

Dedicated to J. Leo Collins of Ohio, who has
worked on perfecting the Mini Satin breed for
a number of years and is currently going
through the process of having them recognized
by the American Rabbit Breeders Association.

255

during that time of the year, so by agreement with the Castles, it was decided that they would apply for the Development Certificate and present the new breed as Satinettes.

Sue and Verle Castle wrote up a standard for the Satinettes, and with agreement of the Michigan man, nine colors were chosen, which was then presented to the ARBA Standards Committee. The committee did not care for the col-

Red Mini Satin buck. Photo courtesy Loretta Ann Bowman, USA.

ors chosen for the development of the breed, and assisted the parties with color selection and re-writing the standard. Colors now to be worked on were: Copper, Red, Ruby-Eyed White, Sable and Siamese. The Michigan breeder was less than happy with the changes made, and demanded that the Castles stop using the Satinette name, which they did not do, but were forced to give up the development of the breed in January 1994.

In February 1994, a Jim Krahulec purchased all of the Castle's Satinettes and began to develop the breed, but went to a larger version, as they were too much like a satin coated Netherland Dwarf, which gave rise to a new name and a new direction to follow in creating a breed called the Mini Satin. Krahulec obtained three underweight normal Satin bucks and began to breed these with the Satinette does in the spring of 1994. By autumn of 1994 the normal Satins were disposed of in the breeding program, and the youngsters from those crosses were further mated to Mini Satin bucks. Jim Krahulec submitted a proposed standard and five varieties: Black, Chocolate, Copper, Himalayan and Red to the ARBA's Standard Committee on June 30, 1995, and a Certificate of Development for the Mini Satin was granted in September of the same year. Jim presented the Mini Satin at the 1998 ARBA Convention and Show in Portland, Oregon, and again in Louisville, Kentucky in 1999; however, the Mini Satins were failed by the Standards Committee.

J. Leo Collins, of Salem, Ohio, was granted a Certificate of Development for the Mini Satins, which were presented for the first time at the Wichita, Kansas ARBA Convention and Show in 2003, where two varieties, Ruby-Eyed White and Red, were accepted by the committee for a first showing, thereby completing one leg of their journey in becoming a recognized breed in America. Mini Satins are not to be found in Europe, as they prefer the Satin Netherland Dwarfs. This little sparkling rabbit weighs in at 3.25 to 4.75 lb. or 1.5 to 2.15 kg.

In the "Land Down Under," an Australian by the name of Warren Hill developed the Mini Satin, starting in 1999. Hill mated a normal size Satin with a Mini Rex. A working standard was approved by the Western Australia Rabbit Council in 2000, with the breed receiving full recognition in 2002, with a total of 60 colors and 14 patterns, as recognized by the British Rabbit Council.

MORAVIAN WHITE

I have been able to locate little information on the Moravian White rabbit, which comes from the Czech Republic. The breed was created by a cooperative of rabbit breeders from southern Moravia, and they began in 1971. After 13 years, in 1984 the breed was recognized. It is a white rabbit with extremely suppressed black-tipped hairs. The breed has brown eyes and weighs in at 3 kg. to 4 kg.

MORAVIEN BLUE

Moravien Blues are a creation from the Czech Republic, having made their appearance to the rabbit world in 1906 when they were first recognized. The breed was created through years of selection within the Blue Vienna breed. This all Blue rabbit is mostly bred for its meat-producing qualities, and is often crossed with New Zealand Whites, Giant Chinchilla and Champagne d'Argents. The breed is rather dumpy in shape and flat over the hindquarters. Dewlaps are not permitted in either bucks or does, and the Moravien Blue weighs in at 5.5 kg or 12.25 pounds.

NETHERLAND DWARF

 olland is the true home of the Netherland Dwarf rabbit, but to better understand their history, one needs to study the history of the Polish and Hermelin of Germany. In 1903, largely through the efforts of Otto Lippolt, the Hermelin was given a standard

Dedicated to the late Darrell Bramhall of Arizona, who along with his wife, Joy, did much to promote the "Gem of the Fancy." Photo courtesy ARBA's Domestic Rabbits.

in Germany. These little white gems found their way into Holland and were recognized by the Netherlands Bond Konynenfokkers in 1907. Up until the later part of the 1930s, only the Ruby-Eyed and Blue-Eyed Whites were known. The famous Dutch fancier, Jan Meyering from Opheusden, along with some close associates, H. Andrea, J.A. Schippers, C. Calcar, and Hoefman, began to cross these white rabbits with small wild rabbits, and the large rabbit breeds, in an attempt to produce colored dwarfs. These gentlemen worked many years in perfecting these rainbows of color, but would be justly rewarded when they were given a standard in Holland on May 1, 1940, just mere days before the occupation and war during World War II.

Years of work in the development of the Netherland Dwarf would go down the drain, as many rabbits had been eaten or destroyed due to the bombing. By the time the war ended, just 17 Netherland Dwarfs remained in the whole of the Netherlands. In 1947, a group of British Rex fanciers took some standard Rex to Holland to help the Dutch breeders re-establish their herds during a show in Amsterdam. A lady by the name of Joyce Taylor was part of this British group. At one end of the exhibition hall Taylor and the rest of the party saw these tiny, bold-headed, big-eyed, tiny-eared rabbits, in Black, Blue and White. They were told they were called Dwarfs, and, oh, how they wanted to own some. The Dutch fanciers would show the British their appreciation for helping them with the Rex, and sent nine Dwarfs to London in 1949. These nine Dwarfs included: one agouti, two

Netherland Dwarf. Photo courtesy American Rabbit Breeders Association.

blacks, two blues, one sable, one blue-eyed white and two ruby-eyed whites.

Joyce Taylor, along with three other fanciers, founded the Netherland Dwarf Club on October 13th, 1949, and the breed was recognized by the British Rabbit Council in early 1950. It took years to build up stock in England to meet the ever-growing demand for the little rabbits.

The Netherland Dwarf would arrive in America and Canada first in 1965, to improve on the Polish breed. A British fellow living in the United States for a time due to his job had raise Netherland Dwarfs in England. Jack Turnbull met Darrell Bramhall of Iowa at the Fort Worth Livestock Show in Texas during January of 1969, and they were talking about his Netherland Dwarfs. Darrell became quite interested in the breed, and Jack told him that he planned to bring some Dwarfs over to the States. By June of 1969, Jack Trunbull had imported the Netherland Dwarfs, and Darrell was able to acquire some of these. The two men set out to get them recognized as a breed by the American Rabbit Breeders Association. The British standard, with some mortifications, was to be the American standard used. During the Calgary, Canada ARBA Convention and Show in September 1969, Jack Trunbull exhibited a pair of Ruby-Eyed Whites, a Black and a Siamese Sable. Bert Ruers, of Listowel, Ontario, Canada, also showed a pair of the Ruby-Eyed Whites. I was at this convention, and believe you me, the Netherland Dwarfs were a sensation. The "Gem of the Fancy" became a recognized breed in America in 1969.

No other breed of rabbit, since the boom days of the Belgian Hare and Chinchilla, have seen such massive importing from England and Europe as have the Netherland Dwarfs, which continues today, especially from Holland. Netherland Dwarfs are recognized the world over by all national rabbit governing bodies, and it is one of the leading show rabbits today, winning more than their fair share of Best in Shows.

Joy Bramhall with her Netherland Dwarf that won Best in Show at the 2001 National Convention of the American Rabbit Breeders Association. Photo courtesy Heinold Feeds.

NEW ZEALAND

The land of the Kiwi has nothing to do with the origin of the New Zealand rabbit. The breed was not brought to the west coast of America by a sailor returning from New Zealand at the beginning of the twentieth century as some people have reported. New Zealands are as American as apple pie, with the first variety to appear being the Red. New Zealand Reds were developed in California and elsewhere, from what is said to be a cross of an extinct breed called the Golden Fawn, perhaps back crossed to Belgian Hares to deepen the red color. From the early boom days of the Belgian Hare, off-colored red and fawn rabbits would appear out of the Hares. These sports could have well been mated back to the Flemish Giants of the time, as Flemish were first brought to this country in the late 1800s, which would explain the rise of the Golden Fawn. In 1924 Alfred Zimmerman, of Mobile, Alabama, writes: "The New Zealand is strictly an American breed, though some maintain that it was originally introduced from New Zealand, and Australia, while others have considered it a variety of Golden Fawn, a sport of the Belgian." Regardless, Red New Zealands were advertised as early as 1908. The New Zealand Red standard was written by C. P. Gilmore and Charles S. Gibson and adopted by the National New Zealand Red Club and the National Pet Stock Association in July 1916.

C.P. Gilmore wrote a small book on the breed called, *The New Zealand Red Rabbit,* 1918, and gives this rather glamorous picture of the history of the breed. "WHAT WE KNOW OF ITS ORIGIN — The first New Zealands

we have record of in this country were imported by John Henry Snyder of San Francisco in 1906. When he returned from New Zealand, he brought four does and a buck with him. Later we learned of a Mr. Henry in Los Angeles who also imported a large number.

Dedicated to Eabert "Fibber" McGehee of Oklahoma, America's premier showman. Fibber has raised some of the finest New Zealand Whites this country has ever seen, winning no less than three Best in Shows at the American Rabbit Breeders Association National Conventions.

C.P. Gilmore, circa 1915.

"When we first introduced this rabbit to the fancy, we were met with the usual opposition that always greets anything new; in the April 1915, number of *Domestic Pets,* a Mr. M. H. Branning, who had taken up the breeding of the New Zealands, wrote an article about them and incidentally mentioned that the first specimens were imported into California in 1906. This article drew forth considerable comment from those who acquainted with the Sport Belgian and Golden Fawn, which are of a buff color. They were want to believe that they were all one and the same rabbit. Some of these parties wrote Mr. Branning, stating flatly that he was mistaken. Mr. Branning then sat down and wrote to Mr. Jas. Duncan, acting director of the Department of Agriculture of the Dominion of New Zealand and the following reply he received:

In His Majesty's Service —
   Dominion of New Zealand, Department of Agriculture, Industries, and Commerce. Advice on Field Corps - Inspection of Rabbits.
      Wellington, June 17, 1915
Mr. M. H. Branning, Los Angeles, Cal.
            The New Zealand Red Rabbit
   I am in receipt of your letter of the 7th ultimo with reference to the above.
   The description you give of the rabbit coincides with the rabbit known in the southern part of this Dominion as the Otago rabbit. It is largely exported in a frozen state to Great Britain. Last year there were 105,752 crates of rabbits shipped away from here. In addition to this, there are two tinning factories that make up the flesh of the rabbit. This rabbit was originally imported into this country in the early days from Scotland and was known as the Scotch rabbit."

(He then goes on to tell how they breed and so forth and signs himself) Jas. Duncan, Acting Director.

This letter is in my possession and can be seen by anyone at any time.

The first or original New Zealands were of a much lighter color than are the ones we have today; in fact, there are almost four shades between the ones of four years ago and the ones of to-day. They also weighed about seven pounds, but were extremely hardy and healthy.

As you will note, Mr. Duncan states that the original specimens were imported from Scotland to New Zealand. Now just what cross the Scotlanders made to produce this

Gilmore's Pride, one of the early prize-winning New Zealand Reds, which sure shows off more like a Belgian Hare, circa 1916.

rabbit we could not say, but it is very evident that the cross was well established, for the pure bred New Zealands never throw 'sports' as do our other crossed or made rabbits."

While this is an interesting story recorded long ago, it is simply false. There were but two types of rabbits known to exist in New Zealand during this time period. The European wild rabbit, *Oryctolagus cuniculus,* and the English Silver Greys, which had been set out to cross with the wild rabbits. For Mr. Duncan to say that these were exported to England as frozen or canned rabbit meat tells us that it was the European wild rabbit, and not one of a domesticated sort.

The late great American rabbit pioneer, John C. Fehr, wrote of the origin of the New Zealand in 1930, which would confirm this author's research; "The origin of the New Zealand breed is not shrouded in mystery like some of the writers would have you believe; neither was it originated in one certain locality. I well remember an incident at Ft. Wayne, Indiana, in 1913, when one of our prominent judges was to attend one of the first table shows held in this country. Breeders from miles around came with rabbits of all descriptions, to be passed upon by the Judge. One breeder from Anderson, Indiana brought some fawn colored rabbits. They were more blocky that the Belgian and did not have the color our New Zealands now have. The judge looked them over and said, "They will never amount to much." A short time after this, the same judge made a trip to the Coast and saw more of these same fawn colored rabbits, and at once saw the possibility of a good breed for both meat, fur and fancy. Thus they were given a boost, and soon became one of the most popular breeds.

"I know of one strain of New Zealands that was originated in Indiana, and the fourth generation back was pure bred Belgian Hares. Now these were not culls, but were put in the show room, and they were consistent winners in some of the largest and best shows in the country.

"At one time there were a number of Belgian Hare breeders in Ohio who were getting these so-called sports out of their Belgians. They had good red color, as good or better than we now have in our New Zealand, but they had Belgian type. They became so enthusiastic, that they wanted to change the name of New Zealands, to American Reds, and a split in the association was narrowly averted.

"I only mention these facts to show that the New Zealand was not originated in any particular locality, but that different strains were being started in numerous sections of the country at one and the same time.

"I notice some of the California breeders advertising them now as California Reds. California has no more claim on them than any other state; if the name must be changed, then my personal opinion is that it should be called American Red, for it is truly an American rabbit. I do give California credit for developing some of the best New Zealands in the country, and at one time Oregon and Washington were right up in front with their New Zealands.

"Our greatest trouble with our original Whites was a short stiff coat. Some crosses with Angora were made with good results, for now we have some New Zealand White skins with ideal fur as to length and density. The only bad features in the crosses made with Angora, some breeders did not test out the offspring; consequently many were sold for breeders that carried Angora. Consequently if two normals carrying Angora were mated, they produced Angoras." This author has seen this occurring in New Zealand White litters as late as the early 1970s.

"Personally I have always felt they should be called American Reds and Whites, for they are truly an American rabbit."

Charles S. Gibson, who was the founding father of the National Pet Stock Association, wrote of the New Zealand Red in 1917, "The New Zealand had made the greatest improvement in type and color of any rabbit ever seen in America. During the winters of 1915 and 1916, certain fanciers conceived that the name should be changed to American Reds, and without a vote or any authority whatever, they were entered at a certain show as "American Reds," "Formerly New Zealands." This proved the best thing that ever happened to the New Zealand rabbit, for the real fanciers banded together and called for elections in both the New Zealand Club and the National Association. The elections were held during the summer of 1916, and proved to be a great victory for the name New Zealand. The New Zealand Club voted about "ten to one" not to change the name to "American Reds." The vote of the National Association was 18 for "American Reds" and 144 for "New Zealand." This vote clearly showed "New Zealand" was the name desired by the old fanciers. The agitation over the name created such a demand for stock that the large breeders were soon sold out; hence it proved to be a good thing for the New Zealand."

With the passing of the "Boom" of the Belgian Hare days, the New Zealand Red quickly filled the bill as a truly dual purpose animal for meat, fur and show. New Zealands soon spread throughout the United States. Then in 1917 appeared the White New Zealand, once again in California, created by a Mr. William S. Preshaw, who resided in the town of Ripon. Preshaw wrote on the subject in *Rabbits and Dollars,* "THE NEW FUR-BEARING RABBIT, ORIGIN." In 1917 the writer, who at the time was raising New Zealand Reds, in examining a nest of young, found that four of them were pure white and three were red. Three of the whites were does and one buck.

"Believing that a white New Zealand would be a profitable and popular breed, I thought I would see what would be the outcome of line breeding. One of the does I lost by heat before she was old enough to breed. The other two does were bred to the white buck. Not knowing what the outcome would be, I did not attempt to sell or exhibit them until I had the third generation.

The first ad for New Zealand Whites by the originator, January 1920.

W.S. Preshaw
Originator and Breeder of Pure White New Zealand Rabbits. The best fur-bearing Rabbit on the market. Fine Foundation stock for sale.

264

"In October 1919, I exhibited them at the Stockton, California Fair, as White New Zealands. They have been exhibited at six different shows and fairs in the last year and have always attracted a great deal of attention. At the big Championship Show in San

New Zealand White doe. Photo courtesy American Rabbit Breeders Association.

Francisco, January 29 to February 1, 1920, there were 21 entries. Judge C. S. Gibson, in commenting on them at this show, said that they were of the true New Zealand type, and with their pure white fur they were bound to become popular. Judge Salisbury, in commenting on them at the State Fair at Sacramento, said that they were absolutely perfect in New Zealand type.

"FROM A FANCIER'S POINT OF VIEW, there is nothing that can beat the White New Zealand for beauty, fur or meat. I have raised several hundred, and not one of them has been off in color."

The first club for the bred was the National New Zealand Rabbit Club, which was organized in 1914. In November 1918, a group of New Zealand breeders met at Convention Hall, at Kansas City, Missouri, during the Heart of America Poultry and Pet Stock Clubs Show at the suggestion of Ray W. Harris. There were 14 breeders at that meeting who became charter members, and at the suggestion of a Mr. L.A. Lee, the new club was named the Heart of America New Zealand Club, in honor of the Heart of America Show going on at this time. Although some wanted to keep the club as a local one, membership in the new organization had spread to nearly every state in the union. On December 27, 1919, at a meeting in Kansas City, the name was changed to American Federation of New Zealand Breeders. The club maintained their own registration system until December 1925, when it decided to abolish it and become an affiliate of what is known as the American Rabbit Breeders Association today. During the Omaha, Nebraska Convention in 1921, a standard was presented and adopted for Preshaw's New Zealand White. Little did anyone ever know just how this new variety would impact the world of

The late Dr. Alfred DeCastro, who rallied the acceptance of the New Zealand Black.

rabbits in such a global way.

Black New Zealands were written of as far back as 1924, but the Blacks we have today are the creation of Californian breeders once again, and the late Dr. Alfred DeCastro, of New Cannaan, Connecticut, who presented them in 1956 at the St. Paul, Minnesota Convention, with final approval as a recognized variety in 1958 at Springfield, Illinois Convention. Blacks were created by a marriage of the Red and White varieties. The New Zealand Blue has been worked on for many years, but is yet to be recognized in this country, although it is accepted by the British Rabbit Council. Oddly enough, the Red variety in the UK is treated as a totally separate breed.

England was the first country to take up the breed, with a Mrs. E. Shirley Grant importing the Reds from California in 1917, but since that time, New Zealands, especially the White variety, have found their way all over the world. The breed has greatly given a life to the people of numerous developing countries, through rabbit breeding farms. However, no country can boost the extreme perfection attained in the New Zealand breed today, other than the Americans. It is a first class animal in all properties.

NIL

Tax-Xiber is the local name given for the Nil rabbit of Malta, which is a blending of many local rabbits on this island. The breed was officially recognized in 1985 by the Malta Rabbit Club. Nils weigh on average 2.80 kg. and are solidly built and bred in gray agouti, gray hare, black and blue butterfly patterns. This breed's main uses are for meat, by the local population. Does are known for their large litters of 7 to 10 kits, and the breed is well adapted to the hot climates of its native Malta.

NORMAND

very old breed from France, with a history somewhat shrouded in mystery, and also known as the Giant Normand or Picard. In *Life in the Countryside,* 1920, disputes that a historical version of the breed's origin by Naudin, saying, "The Norman one would derive from the remote crossings of wild rabbit domesticated with the rabbit Patagonian (Giant of Flanders) imported in 1809, to tell the truth, it does not have there exclusively of Norman Giant, but a large rabbit, extremely well built, not having neither the form nor the weight of the Giant. In all Normandy, mainly in the area of Rouen, one meets a large gray rabbit, of variable intensity, short and broad forms, the thick and brilliant fur, the sharp eye. It weighs approximately from three to four kilograms, but the case is rather rare. This rabbit always reproducing of the same form, of the same color and of the same weight, appears well to be an indigenous type, and nothing to have of its many qualities (quality and delicious flesh, fast ultra development, rusticity with any test) with currents of foreign blood ..."

In the *Books of the Academy,* February 1, 1983, Jacques Arnold writes, "It is a very old race of which it is difficult to date the appearance, at least under its current type. For some, its origin would come from a gray rabbit which one met in a significant number in Normandy, cradle of the race. For others, like Professor Cornevin, it would be the result of the crossing between ordinary rabbit and the Giant of Flanders. This race, rather rare today in France, however, was well adapted to its area."

Normand. Photo courtesy Federation de Cuniculiculture.

The Normand was admitted to the Book of Standards in 1919. Now having read all of this, this author is of the opinion that the Normand rabbit is one in the same as the Steenkonijn or Stone Rabbit of neighboring Belgium, as the weights, color and type are the same.

ORANGE

Sweden is the original home of the Orange rabbit, which was developed by Nils Jonsson from Vintrie. The Orange rabbit was fully recognized to the breed standards book in 1966. The color of the Orange rabbit is to be truly an orange, and the rabbit weighs 2.5 to 3.2 kg or 5.5 to 7.25 lbs. The breed is recognized in all of the Scandinavian countries.

ORESTAD

The Orestad rabbit was developed in Sweden by Gunnar Carlsson from Malmo, and was shown for the first time in 1970. Orestads are another of the Ruby-Eyed White breeds, which weigh 2.5 to 3.2 kg or 5.5 to 7.25 lbs. The breed is only found in the Scandinavian countries: Sweden, Norway, Denmark and Sweden.

PALOMINO

 alominos are an American creation, developed by Mark Young, of Coulee Dam in Washington state, during the 1940s and early 1950s. We will never know what breeds flow through the blood of the Palomino rabbit; in fact, Mark Young didn't know himself. Young began raising rabbits in 1910, and always had the vision and a desire to create a new breed of rabbit. For many years he purchased meat rabbits from the youngsters of the area. These were mostly from non 4-H or Future Farmers of America children, and according to Young, the rabbits were typically black or brown ones. Mark Young selected what appeared to be sport rabbits from some of these live fryers, and

Dedicated to the late Mark Young of Washington who developed the Palomino rabbit over many years starting in the 1940s. Photo courtesy American Rabbit Breeders Association.

Golden Palomino. *Photo courtesy American Rabbit Breeders Association.*

would mate them together, and on occasion he would obtain in some of the litters buckskin skin or light yellow-brown youngsters. These off yellow-brown rabbits were all saved and interbred, with the introduction of blood from other sources. Mark Young wrote in March 1965, "It was a great day in my life when I got a 100% litter of these new colored rabbits. Future generations from then on would run 100% or nearly so. By this stage, their coloring had developed into what one would call a beige, and in 1952 I was listed in our Inland Empire Rabbit Breeders Association as the raiser of a new breed called 'The American Beige.' This color was actually the Lynx Palomino we know today. Future generations would produce a fawn or golden colored rabbit.

Mark Young and his wife, Mabel, showed the new breed for the first time at the 1952 ARBA Convention and Show at Portland, Oregon, and dubbed the breed "Washingtonian'; however, not overly pleased with their choice of a name for the new breed, a coffee can was placed next to the cages holding the rabbits, as a suggestion box for naming the breed. The winning suggestion was Palomino.

Palominos were presented at the 1953 Amarillo, Texas ARBA Convention, and at the 1954 York, Pennsylvania Convention the Fawn color was introduced to the rabbit world. The Fawn variety was changed to Lynx, at the suggestion of the Standards Committee in Columbus, Ohio at the 1955 Convention. At the St. Paul, Minnesota Convention in 1956, the Standards Committee did not approve the breed, as they felt it needed further improvement. Little Rock, Arkansas Convention in 1957 would see the Palomino recognized as a new breed in America, with one variety, the Lynx. The most popular color of the breed is the Golden, which received final approval in 1958 at the Springfield, Illinois Convention and Show.

Mark Young's Palominos are an outstanding addition to the breeds of America, with outstanding hardiness, excellent production and growth. It is a fine breed for either meat production or the show table. The breed has been introduced into Europe and even South Africa, and at one time was accepted in the 1972 French standards, yet are no longer found. Adult weights are 8 to 11 pounds or 3.6 to 5 kg.

Palominos are sponsored by the Palomino Rabbit Co-Breeders' Association which was founded in 1958.

PANI

The Pani rabbit comes from Japan, typically in the area of Nowapan. It is an important livestock animal for both meat and fur. It is said to be raised by the millions by the local people; yet oddly enough, little to no information has been found about this Japanese breed, other than it is a larger rabbit than most Western breeds, approaching a hare in size.

PANNON WHITE

ungary is the native home of the Pannon White rabbit, which was developed by Professors Zsoit Szendra, Biro Nemeth and I. Radnai of the Pannon University of Agriculture. The Pannon White rabbit was created using New Zealand Whites and Californians through the procedure of selection for weight gains. The selection program began in 1988.

Between the years 1988 and 1990, progeny tests were performed on a breeding population of 100 New Zealand White does on a breeding farm in Kornye. The only material to this site from external sources was sperm, which was used for artificial insemination of the does. Careful studies were made on the basis of weight gain and dress-out percentage. Sperm from the progeny of the best bucks judge for their goals was collected and again used

Pannon White. *Photo courtesy Professor Zsoit Szendra, Hungary.*

to artificially inseminate the does.

In 1991, the Pannon White rabbit developers initiated their own genetic program. For the purpose of producing a synthetic line, comparisons were made of the weight gain and dress-out percentage in Californians and New Zealand Whites at the Kornye breeding farm, also reciprocally bred rabbits, and the progeny of bucks from known and previously proven breeding sites. These breeding combinations proved the most favorable, that would form the synthetic line.

Since 1992, a stock of 250 does and 60 bucks of the Pannon White breed has been bred in a closed population, without the introduction of any other genetic material. Selection continues to this day on rapid weight gains and dress-out percentages. Pannon Whites at 10 weeks of age will weigh 4.75 to 5.25 pounds (2.13 to 2.31).

The Pannon White rabbit has begun to spread to other countries, which are developing rabbit breeding farms, to put a high protein meat on the dinner table. On an interesting note, Pannonia was the old name of Hungary, when it was a province of the Roman Empire.

PERLFEE

he Perlfee rabbit with its unusual coloration originated in Germany in the early 1900s. There are two notable breeders who created the Perlfee with very similar results. Mr. Karl Hoffmans of Dusseldorf used Havana and the Fee De Marbourg breeds to create his new breed which he called Dusseldorfer Perlfee. Hoffmans' objective was to produce a coat color that resembled the Siberian squirrel which was in such great demand by the furriers of the time. It should be noted that Mr. Karl Hoffmans is also the creator of the Lux rabbit (Lynx) which he created by using his new Dusseldorfer Perlfee, Fee De Marbourg, Tans and Sable which was officially recognized in Germany in 1922.

Another breeder by the name of Deiniger, from Augsburg, Germany crossed Havanas with agouti colored rabbits. Mr. Deiniger, named

Perlfee. Photo by author.

271

his new breed Augsburger Perlfee. The two different Perlfees creations were eventually combined into one breed simply known today as Perlfee. In Switzerland a Mr. Charles Weber discovered in a litter of four youngsters, produced by a wild agouti doe which he had mated to a Silver gray buck, two rabbits (a pair) which had light blue gray fur very similar to the Perlfee, but he named his Little Gray Swiss.

The unique feature of this breed is the fact that the tips of the guard hairs are both light and dark gray, giving the coat a pearling effect. As you walk around the animal before you, it seems to change colors.

PETIT PAPILLON TRICOLOR

Switzerland is the home and the native land of this beautiful little tricolor rabbit called Petit Papillon Tricolor. The breed was created by Harberli Anton during the early 1960s and were shown for the first time in 1967. The Petit Papillon Tricolor was officially recognized and given a standard in 1984. Anton used Harlequins and the Petit Papillons to create the breed, which does not resemble the breed we call Rhinelander. Since the breed's appearance, it has developed quite a following as they are fairly small, weighing in at 2.3 to 3.3 kg or 5 to 7.25 pounds.

POINTED BEVEREN

 ointed Beverens originated in England, probably some time in the early 1930s, and were formerly called the Pointed Fox; however, there appeared to be little interest in the animals at the time, and they would become extinct. During the early 1970s, Derek Medlock and Harry Nicholson set out to recreate this extinct breed. The gentlemen introduced the Argente Noir from Europe, which was mated to a Black Beveren, and by careful selection the breed was reborn. Unsure what to call the creation, animals were shown to Miss Meg Brown of Scotland. She suggested, since Black Beveren was in the breed's genetic makeup, that they call it Pointed Beveren.

Pointed Beverens are recognized as their own breed by the British Rabbit Council, and not as a variety of the Beveren, although the standard for the Pointed Beveren is the same as the Beveren, with weights upwards of 3.17 kg or 7 pounds. The breed is recognized in four varieties: Black, being the most popular, followed by the Blue Pointed, Brown and Lilac. The fur is to be soft, silky and very dense, with an ideal length of 3.81 cm or 1.5 inches long. Ticking is to be moderate and evenly distributed of the entire body, including the head, ears, feet and tail. The white ticking is not just white hairs, but white tipped. Pointed Beverens are rather uncommon in the British showrooms, but are maintained by a handful of dedicated fanciers.

POLISH

 oland could be the native home of the little Polish rabbit, but this is quite doubtful, as the breed was not even heard of in Poland, when the Polish breed began to emerge in English writings in the last quarter of the 19th century. It has been well documented that 17 Polish were exhibited at a show in Hull, England, in 1884 under that name. Germany imported some of these that same year, where they were named Pole and later given the title of Hermelin (Ermine). The Polish rabbit may well have been the Prussian rabbit, when a pair of small white rabbits with pink eyes was shown in January 1858, at Nottingham, England. By 1860, the name Polish was firmly fixed in England, although some authors haven't painted a very pretty picture of the little white rabbit. Cuniculus wrote of the breed in his *The Practical Rabbit Keeper,* 1880, "The Polish rabbit is one of the most pointless, and one of the most delicate animals of the whole tribe. Little wonder then that it has been gradually dying out for the last few years, and that now its presence either in the rabbitry or show-pen is quite the exception. This was not formerly the case, and at one time considerable interest was taken in it, and this must be our apology for devoting a few lines to its consideration.

"It is believed to have come from Poland, and we have no evidence to the contrary. An old fancier once said in answer to a query on the point, 'Come from Roosha? Not it. It's only the common hutch rabbit, and some fools have bred whites in-and-in till they've made a regular breed of them. They're poor sickly things at the best of times.' We would hardly go so far as this, but there is certainly some possibility that the aspersion may have more truth in

Dedicated to the late William H. Kennedy of Pennsylvania, who bred an outstanding strain of Ruby-Eyed White Polish for many years and did much to promote the breed.

A prize-winning Polish doe from 1888. This is also the oldest known illustration of a Polish from England.

it than may appear at first sight.

"The Polish rabbit is white and of a peculiarly milky colour, perhaps of the purest white known in the rabbitry, beating even the Angora in this respect. It is a very small, compact little animal, seldom weighing more than 4 lbs., and looking even smaller owing to its very delicate organization generally. The back has no rise at all, and from the head there seems a gradual fall to the hips. The legs, the hind ones especially, are weak and diminutive, and the animal quickly tires of using them, the most common position being a reclining one. The ears are short but not very erect, being of somewhat delicate construction. They, however, should not lop, but generally lie down at full length down the back.

"It is of a very timid nature, and runs away very rapidly on seeing anyone approach the hutch. The doe is not a good breeder. Hence, there is but little to recommend Polish rabbits to the general fancier. They have no prizes at shows, except in the Any Variety class, where we think they stand but little chance. The only good that can be gained from the Polish rabbits is the very pretty fur, which is valuable for tanning purposes. We are afraid we have not drawn a very inviting picture of the puny breed called the Polish, but we certainly do not recommend it as a profitable breed to keep."

The first standard drawn up for the breed was by a Mr. H.E. Gilbert of England in the 1880s.

SCALE OF POINTS FOR THE EXHIBITION POLISH RABBIT

1. Shape .... 20 points
2. Coat .... 15 points
3. Condition .... 10 points
4. Eyes .... 5 points

Total = 50 points

British Polish doe, circa 1905.

Mr. Enoch Hutton, of Pudsey, England, wrote of the breed in the 1880s in Kempster W. Knight's work, *The Book of the Rabbit,* "This is one of the most common of domesticated rabbits, its principal characteristic being the purity of its snowy whiteness of coat. It is known in all rabbitries, and is quite common in most warrens; or I may, perhaps, best explain myself by saying that the ordinary albino of the common warren answers all the points required of this breed for successful prize-taking, considering that it is most of all removed from its primitive state in colour, &c. Upwards of 30 years ago I had them in large quantities, the does frequently producing as many as eleven at birth, very few being lost in rearing, and seldom or never any deviation or sport from the parental colour. Many are not more than about 3 lb. in weight, and these, as a rule, are at the present day the best in other points. I have seen then them quite up to 10 lb., but seldom one of more than 8 lb. that was fit to win, so that I should say about 8 lb. as the standard weight, allowing fifteen points for it."

British Polish buck. We can start seeing the elevated stance, circa 1905.

It would appear to me that the Polish was indeed bred from the common white hutch rabbit, as there is a considerable difference in the weights. The earliest picture of the Polish rabbit that I have been able to obtain was of a doe belonging to Mr. A. Outhwaite, which had been awarded second prize at Driffield, England in 1888.

POLISH IN AMERICA

 olish arrived from England to the United States in 1912, having been imported by Mr. W.Endicott Dexter of Boston, Massachu- setts shortly after the National Pet Stock Association was

An American Polish, circa 1924.

founded on January 10, 1910 and recognized as a breed, although they were seldom seen in the showrooms, until after 1925. By 1930, the breed had become quite popular amongst fanciers.

First American Standard for Polish

Color: Pure white 14
Shape: Short (3 pounds) 14
Coat 26
Ears: Short, set close together, erect, well furred 16
Eyes: Large, bold and blood-red 16
Condition: Flesh solid, fur fairly short, good fine,
    thick, soft, silky 14
                       Total = 100 points

    The Ruby-Eyed White Polish was the only variety recognized for many years. The Blue-Eyed Whites were the brain child of Samuel E. Rice of Saugus, Massachusetts. Rice mated two White Beveren does to a 2-1/2 pound Polish buck. The offspring were anything but Blue-Eyed Whites; yet Rice mated the half-brother and sisters together, and by the third gen- eration he was producing about 50 per cent Ruby-Eyed White and Blue- Eyed Whites. His biggest problem with the new variety was selecting for size and ear length. Rice showed the Blue-Eyed Whites for the first time at a show in Mineola, when his animal won Best Polish out of 60 animals entered. He then sent a display of them to the Columbus, Ohio American Rabbit & Cavy Breeders Association Convention and Show in 1938. It was at this convention that the Standards Committee voted to admit the Blue-Eyed Whites to the standards.

    Samuel E. Rice would also be credited with the development of the

Black and Chocolate varieties. He mated a Havana doe to a Ruby-Eyed White Polish buck and a small Black Rex buck. The matings produced both Blacks and Chocolates, which he mated together. The Blue Polish were recognized in 1982, and finally the Broken pattern being accepted.

James Blyth obtained Polish during the early 1930s, and called a small group of breeders together to form the National Polish Federation at the New Haven, Connecticut Convention in 1935. Blyth was the elected president, and a Douglas Clarke of Long Island, New York as the first secretary. James Blyth gave up the Polish breed after becoming ill in 1939, giving his Polish to William H. Kennedy. Interest in Polish waned and the organization regrouped in 1943, changing the name to the American Polish Rabbit Club and rechartered in January 1944 by the ARBA.

POLISH IN THE UNITED KINGDOM

 he Polish recognized by the British Rabbit Council is indeed a much different creature than found in the United States. The Polish, of the United Kingdom, is the same breed as the Britannia Petite of America. Just as to when British fanciers began to style their Polish to look like a small hare type is not known. Many members of the British Belgian Hare Club were also breeders of Polish, before the 1920s, which was the time that the Belgian Hare was losing out popularity in England among fanciers. It is believed that it was at this time the Polish started being bred to a stand-up arched breed. For many years the only

A Champion Polish from England, 1935.

known variety was the Ruby-Eyed White; Blue-Eyed Whites were introduced after World War II. Other colored Polish began making their appearance in the early 1950s, thanks to the introduction of Netherland Dwarfs to England. Today the Polish of England is an outstanding show animal, with very high levels of perfection. It is recognized in no less than some 35 possible varieties.

The British Polish of today.

The British Polish has just been imported into Holland and the Scandinavian countries where it is the picking up a dedicated following of fanciers, and is known as the Dwarf Hare.

PRAT

Prat rabbits are the product of Spain, and have been bred for their meat-producing qualities. In 1992, 178 crossbred animals (146 does and 32 bucks) were being mated and selected at an experimental farm in El Prat del Llobregat (Barcelona, Spain). These rabbits are mainly used as grand-dams in a three-way crossbreeding program. Crossbred daughters are then mated with males from a specialized sire strain, to produce an ideal meat animal which holds up well to the Mediterranean climates. It is an all white rabbit with pink eyes, and differs from the Caldes by its more compact form.

REX BREEDS

ASTREX

strex, or sometimes called Astrakhan Rex, first appeared in England in 1931 in the stud of Mrs. A. De Ville Mather of Yorkshire. Mrs. Mather said the first Astrex mutation occurred when she bred a Blue Rex buck to a White Pointed Lilac Rex. Neither parents nor grandparents carried this unusual water-wave or curly coat; in fact, the first Astrex did not carry the complete curled coat until the rabbits reached six months of age, when the rabbits had their adult molt. That first litter only one Astrex appeared, and all Astrex could be traced back to it.

Dr. J. N. Pickard made an intensive study of the Astrex mutation at the Institute of Animal Genetics in Edinburgh, Scotland, beginning in 1932. He would report his findings in the *Journal of Genetics,* April, 1941. Dr. Pickard, described the mutation as a simple autonomic monogenic recessive to Rex. In a later report in the *Year Book of the British Rabbit Council,* 1943, he said that he believed

Dedicated to Loretta Ann Bowman of Louisiana, who has worked for a number of years to re-establish the Astrex rabbit and keep it from extinction.

that the Astrex factor is closely related with the Angora, but can only appear when combined with the fine-coated genes of that breed.

Astrex pelt, circa early 1930s.

Mrs. A. De Ville Mather offered a limited number of this new Rex breed in 1935. At that time in England, though the breed was uncommon, stud fees ranged from $5 to $10, and show specimens were valued as high as $350. Astrex were imported from England to the United States in 1946 from the shed of a Mrs. E. Fearon of Thaxted in Essex. These rabbits were imported by Marcellus Meek, of Chicago, Illinois, and these animals were in all the colors known in England at the time: White, Blue, Lilac, Lynx, Havana, Sable and Black. Though not recognized by the America Rabbit and Cavy Breeders Association, Inc., the breed was permitted to be judged by the British Standard. The adult weights were set at 5 to 7 pounds.

It is said that the pelts did not hold up well to tanning, and the breed became extinct in England, although curly coated Rex appears in a number of breeds of rabbits still to this day. A small band of fanciers are trying to bring the Astrex back here in the United States, with the most enthusiastic of them being Loretta Ann Bowman of Louisiana. This author has produced a number of them from one strain of Blue Lionheads, imported from England in 2001. Each litter would typically contain one blue curly-ripple coated bunny, always Blue, and always a buck.

Astrex youngsters, showing the curly, wavy coat, circa 1935.

DWARF REX

There appears to be a move by rabbit fanciers to make Lops of many types, and the Rexing of other breeds is no different. In the Netherlands, it is believed that the first Dwarf Rex were created, but the Germans can be created with the best of the Dwarf Rex to be found. It is common knowledge that putting a Rex coat on a rabbit is not too difficult; simply breed a normal coated rabbit with a Rex. From their offspring (the F1 generation) you mate together, producing the F2 generation. By this crossing, the breeder can expect 25% to have the Rex coat, and the balance to be normal coated rabbits.

Blue Dwarf Rex. Photo courtesy Jean-Claude Periquet, France.

Dwarf Rex were first shown in Germany at Baden in 1974. It appears that these were all the Dalmatian marked. In 1980, at the great German National in Hanover, there were no Dwarf Rex exhibited, but in 1982 at the Stuttgart exhibition, one could find 10 Dwarf Rex. While the fur is good on these little fellows, much improvement is needed to bring out the true type of the Dwarf, especially in the head structure. Dwarf Rex have a dedicated following in Germany, and have since spread to France, the original home of the Rex rabbit. The breed is recognized in all the same varieties as Rex breed.

MICRO REX

Micro Rex are a breed being developed in the United States, mostly by Loretta Ann Bowman of Louisiana. Beginning in 2000, Bowman began to select the smallest animals of the Mini Rex breed, which she named Micro Rex. Her desire is to develop a "Pocket Size" rabbit with the wonderful plush and soft fur of the Rex breeds. Micro Rex have not been crossed with the Netherland Dwarfs to achieve her goal. Bowman has set the maximum weight

A two-pound Himalayan Micro Rex. Photo courtesy Loretta Ann Bowman, U.S.A.

for does at 2.25 lb (1.02 kg) and bucks at 2 lb (0.90 kg). The body type is very refined, over that of the Mini Rex. This author has seen and handled these cute little teacup-size rabbits, and just as Mini Rex are a pleasure to behold, so are the little Micro Rex, which should become popular pets for both young and old.

MINI REX

 o breed of rabbit has taken the rabbit world by storm in recent times, than has the Mini Rex. To touch one is to hold one, and to want one of these velvety plush little rabbits, which were first created by Mona Berryhill of Texas and presented for the first time at the Columbus, Ohio ARBA Convention in 1986. Mona Berryhill began her Mini Rex breeding program after winning a pair of Dwarf Rex at the Research and Development Raffle at the Orlando, Florida ARBA Convention in 1984, which had been donated by Marylouise Cowan of Maine. The little doe died soon after, but the buck named Zoro was crossed to a small standard Rex Lynx doe named Cotton. That mating produced a litter of seven, with three does from the litter becoming the foundation stock of the Mini Rex we know today. Two does, named Bashful and Happy, were sent to Linda Thompson and Gloria Middleton, both of Sarasota, Florida, and the other doe, Dopey, stayed with Berryhill. A single variety, Castor Mini Rex, was presented to the Standards Committee in 1986 at Columbus, by Mona Berryhill, when the new breed was approved and given a working standard.

Many colors of Mini Rex were cropping up throughout the U.S., because of the Netherland Dwarf genes of the Dwarf Rex. Sable, Smoke Pearl and Tortoise appeared the first year. Breeders further crossed their Mini Rex with all the standard Rex colors to improve on fur and body type, and this mixing gave rise to many additional varieties: Beige, Blue, Black, Broken, Californian (later named Hima-

Dedicated to Mona Berryhill of Texas who developed for the rabbit world the ever-popular Mini Rex. This photo was taken at the moment Mona learned that the breed had been officially recognized. Photo courtesy Mona Berryhill, USA.

Zorro, the little Dwarf Rex that was the foundation of the Mini Rex development. Photo courtesy Mona Berryhill, USA.

layan), Chinchilla, Chocolate, Lynx, Opal, Red, Seal and Ruby-Eyed White.

Portland, Oregon was the site of the 1987 ARBA Convention, and others joined in on the presentation of additional colors in the Mini Rex. Virginia Minden of California presented Beige, Blue, Black, Californian, Chocolate, Chinchilla and Seal, while Laurie and Bill Turner from Arizona presented the Reds. Smoke Pearls and Tortoise were presented by Linda Thompson, with Gloria Middleton presenting Otter and Sable. Mona Berryhill continued with the Castor, but also added in her presentation Broken, Lynx and Opal. After being reviewed by the Standards Committee, all colors, with the exception of Beige, Sable, Smoke Pearl and Otters, had passed.

In 1988 at the ARBA Convention in Madison, Wisconsin would be the final showing of the Mini Rex breed, and the Standards Committee, with ARBA Board approval, had agreed that if the Mini Rex passed, they would allow the other colors to be accepted with just two showing, provided those colors were worthy of recognition at the time. Mini Rex were indeed recognized as a new breed, but two colors failed, the Blacks and Chocolates. Both colors again failed in Tulsa, Oklahoma the following year, with Eric Brennan taking over the Black presentation and Chocolates going to the hands of Freda Kraus.

Linda Thompson presented the beautiful Tricolor Mini Rex at Pomona, California in 1991, in Black, Blue, Chocolate and Lilac, and received final recognition in 1994. Freda Kraus saw the acceptance of her Chocolates in

Castor Mini Rex senior doe, bred and owned by Lou and Anne Lassen of California, won Best Rabbit in Show at the 1995 ARBA National Convention. Photo courtesy ARBA's Domestic Rabbits.

1992, with Eric Brennan's Blacks winning recognition in 1993. Judy Ball presented the Lilac Mini Rex in 1992, and gained approval in 1995. Jan Coffelt began presenting the Blue-Eyed Whites in 2001, and Armando Carberra presented the Otters in 2003.

Mini Rex have become a very highly perfected breed. Show entries of them are quite high throughout the United States, and they have certainly won more than their fair share of Best Rabbit in Show. In fact, Anne and Lou Lassen's Castor Mini Rex have won Open Best in Show at two ARBA National Conventions in 1994 and 1995.

MINI SATIN REX

Australia is the native home of this rather recent creation, having been developed by Warren Hill, beginning in 1999. Warren says that he mated the normal size Satin to a Mini Rex, and after the first progeny were born,

he separated the two lines from one another. Actually in the process he was also developing a Mini Satin as well through his breeding program.

The Western Australian Rabbit Council approved a working standard for the Mini Satin

White Mini Satin Rex. Photo courtesy Warren Hill, Australia.

Rex in 2000, with full recognition of the breed taking place in 2003. Mini Satin Rex should weigh 3.5 to 4.5 pounds (1.587 to 2.041 kg) and are recognized in all the colors and pat-

Dedicated to Warren Hill of Western Australia, who developed the Mini Satin Rex and was able to get the breed recognized. Photo courtesy Warren Hill, Australia.

283

terns as listed in the standards for the British Rabbit Council, which is no less than 60 colors and 14 patterns; therefore the combinations are almost limitless. It does not appear that this breed is recognized in any other country outside of Australia.

The scale of points is rather short: Color – 50 points; Color and/or Pattern – 30 points; Type – 20 points; Total = 100 points.

OPOSSUM REX

Opossum Rex were created in three different countries. In Europe it was discovered when breeders attempted to create a breed to imitate the Blue Silver Fox, by using Silver Fox (Silver Martens) crossed with Rex. This took place in Switzerland, at the hands of Mr. H. Reiler. The Opossums appeared as a sport or mutation in Germany in 1925, in the rabbitry of the famous judge and authority, Frederick Joppich, who was of the opinion that the breed was a Rexed Fox (Swiss Fox). In England, Thomas I. Leaver produced them during the late 1930s. In a general description, the Opossum is like a rexed Angora, with a shorter coat, but the hair are tipped with silver and the hair is 1-1/2 inches long and carried over the entire body at right angles. The head, ear, feet and tail are not silvered. Weights were set at 6 to 8 pounds. The breed is still recognized in the standards book of the British Rabbit Council. This strange coated rabbit appears to be nearly extinct in Europe, and only one known breeder of them is left in Scotland.

STANDARD REX

ex are, of course, from France, and the early history of the breed is very well documented. Of course, when I speak here of Rex, I am talking about the true original Rex which was first discovered in 1919. A French peasant, who used to purchase rabbits in his countryside, found a curious rabbit in a batch of rabbits which a country man named Desire Caillon, from the village of Louche-Primge, had just sold him. The rabbit was quite deformed, yet it was very different, as it possessed no guard hairs. The peasant's son was a servant to Monsieur l'AbbeGillet, the cure of Coulonge (Sarthe) in France. His servant gave him the deformed rabbit. The Monsieur was extremely interested in this rabbit, and requested that the fellow to locate another specimen just like it if at all

Chinchilla Rex. From the Wippell Collection. Reproduced from a Fur & Feather colour plate first issued 24 January 1930.

possible. He managed to secure another one from the same source, which gave the priest a pair. It was reported that no other rabbit of this nature was produced again at the Caillon farm. So that one pair would be the foundation for all the Rex. I must confess here that this is the generally accepted history of the Rex breed, at least in the English language. However, it is not quite exactly true to form, as told by Alex Wiltzer, former president of the French Rabbit Federation, who I'm quite certain is the first person to ever obtain Rex rabbits from the Abbot in 1924. This is a rather interesting article that Wiltzer wrote in an old issue of *Avicolous Review.*

Dedicated to the late Alex Wiltzer of France, who fortunately recorded the early history of the Rex rabbit. Wiltzer was past president of the Federation Francaise de Cuniculiculture, worked many years to improve the breed, developed new varieties and distributed animals throughout Europe and to America. Photo *courtesy Pierre Periquet, France.*

The Church of Coulounge.

The home of Abbot Gillet.

Below: Diagram showing the placement of the buildings, which formed a court-yard where the Abbot built many cages which were lined up end to end.

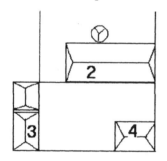

The old Presbytery with the Abbot's home behind.

The old Masonry where many of the rabbits were kept.

Another old Masonry where rabbits were kept.

Photos and diagram provided by two dedicated Rex fanciers, Jean-Claude Periquet and his son Pierre, France.

"Coulonge is a small town, about 1200 inhabitants, especially of farmers. The Abbot Gillet was the priest of this village, whose peasants were very anti-clerical and did not call the priest. Abbot Gillet explained to me that he could not speak to them about religion. To live with the population and to spend his time, they attended the bars on the corner where all went, but they will not speak of religion. Sunday, at the church he officiated with of the people going down to hear his word and the child choir, which had his servant boy of 12 years old and he also helped look after the rabbits. He told me that he did not see people with a birth, for baptism, and anything else, but saw all for the burial.

"The Abbot Gillet was a man very frustrated and worked to keep the operation going each year. He lived in the old presbytery which greatly need repairs; yet this was not the goal of the town council, which were also anti-clerical , any repairs were obviously excluded. He cleaned the church himself, sounded the bells and was certainly poor. Following the separation of Church and State, the priests were not paid since 1905." One can only envision a very sad, sad picture for this priest.

"The Abbot Gillet told me that he met one of the farmers, Desire Caillon, and that he had told him that he had very naked rabbits. Normal, the priest answered that all rabbits were born naked, then Mr. Caillon said: 'Goal these rabbits are already adult, they are very unpleasant besides since they have cuts that wrinkled and curlied skin.' The Abbot answered that he wanted to see them. He said that Mr. Caillon was not a rabbit breeder, but a drunk, he had some common rabbits which ran under the cows to eat the hay that was being wasted. Caillon's rabbits were naturally intended for slaughter. Now we know it wasn't a lady farmer, but a man.

"Desire Caillon gave the Abbot two of these naked rabbits, which just happened to be a pair. The priest who did not keep rabbits had to build a rabbit borrow for them. The rabbit flourished

A typical specimen of the very first Rex rabbit; little wonder many people called them WRECKS. Circa 1925.

better with the priest than they had done with the peasant farmer, and to the great astonishment of the priest, started to push tufts of very silky hairs to them. That occurred in 1919. Progressively, the Abbot Gillet starts to build hutches of about a meter in size. Then the Abbot told me that he started crossing his rabbit with ordinary rabbits and that did not do anything. He actually showed me his barn in which there were about 50 Gray rabbits of normal fur. He thus said to me that it was useless to make similar crossings, that was to be a waste of his time."

Alex Wiltzer further states that the Abbot had no concept of the laws of genetics, of selection and was not even curious enough to gather information and learn. Wiltzer knew that the Gray cross-bred rabbits carried the genes to produce Rex breed without having to introduce any additional blood. From 1919 to 1924, the Abbot Gillet had bred many, many rabbits, but did not have the numbers that he had hoped for with the Rex coat. When Alex Wiltzer visited the Abbot for the first time in 1924, after they were first shown at the Paris exhibition, he said that vast majority of rabbits, about 150 in total, had major signs of degeneration, long crooked feet and legs, wry tails, very chopped-off hindquarters, and they simply looked as though they had rickets. Many of the animals were sterile, and those that did carry a Rex coat had large patches which appeared stripped especially along the side, nape of neck and on the thighs.

The Abbot contacted a couple of businessmen to help him finance a commercial breeding operation, as the priest certainly could not afford it, and he saw major money signs in the Rex breed. They too had no idea of the genetics involved, nor did they know anything about rabbit keeping. These gentlemen were of no help, as each one of them was pocketing the money from the early sales of any of the rabbits.

Alex Wiltzer was able to purchase a nice Castor Rex buck from the Abbot for the unheard-of price of 6000 francs (just over $1,000) and two does, both

Rex of the 1930s, a great improvement from the 1920s, but still a long road ahead.

Gray, one from a Red doe and the other from a Black and Tan doe. Wiltzer befriended a Professor Kohler, who taught Spanish at the University of Strasbourg where Wilzer was also studying. They saw each other daily and teamed together on developing the Rex rabbit, along with a third person, an old Alsation judge by the name of Mr. Ruos, whose specialty was the recently developed Chinchilla rabbit breed. Ruos, who could not afford the expensive Rex, mated several of his Chinchilla does to the Castor Rex buck and is given credit with producing the first Chinchilla Rex. Professor Kohler is given credit for producing the first White and Blue Rex, and Alex Wiltzer bred the first Lynx Rex, followed by the Fawn Rex.

Then tragedy struck. Wiltzer found his Castor Rex dead one morning, with no signs of illness or disease. Wiltzer's father saw great possibilities in the commercial aspects of this new breed and told his son to go to the Abbot and purchase a pair, this time with both animals having the Rex coat. Alex Wiltzer returned to the Abbot Gillet on an gray afternoon in November, who was waiting for him at the station. The Abbot said the pair would cost 10,000 francs each ($1,950) to a shocked Wiltzer, so he chose his pair of rabbits carefully, and later said that the rabbits appeared to have scale, because the way they pulled. Gillet's young boy servant nailed the pair of rabbits up into the box for the journey home. With an hour left before Wiltzer had to depart from the station, the Abbot invited him in for tea. Upon returning home, Alex Wiltzer opened the box to his disgust, and found that the pair of rabbits had been switched. Since the Abbot had been with him the entire time of the tea, the boy switched the animals, per the orders of Abbot Gillet. Wiltzer was furious and wrote the Abbot a scandalous letter. The Abbot Gillet replied that it could not have been possible, and he wanted proof that the rabbits were indeed switched, because he wouldn't do it, as he was a representative of God. It turns out that Professor Kohler had a similar experience with the Abbot, as the buck he purchased from him did not sire any litters, so he took the buck to the veterinary, only to learn that the rabbit had been castrated. Kohler regarded the Abbot as a swindler. The Abbot took Kohler to court for slander, and the professor was fined.

Beaver was to have been the first chosen name for the Rex breed. Beaver in French is called Castor. Monsieur Gillet intended to call the breed Castor, but was advised that a variety of Havana rabbit was being called Beaver in England, which could well cause confusion if the Beavers were brought into France. Abbot Gillet then christened the new mutation as Castorrex, Castor for Beaver in French and Rex is the Latin word for King in English.

Monsieur Gillet first showed a Castorrex pelt to the Societe Centrale d'Aviculture, at Paris, in the year 1923, and they exclaimed, "Why, it's a dressed pelt." But when Gillet brought in a living animal, there certainly was no denying that the rabbit world was to be faced with an entirely new thing, and such as no fancier had ever thought of being remotely possible.

Gillet exhibited six of his Castorrex for the first time in February 1924 at the International Show in Paris. They were an instant sensation. The breed was awarded a prize of honor, first, second and third prizes, as well as two "very honorable mentions."

Abbot Gillet did finally consent to sell a few Castorrex in 1924, not 1925 as has been recorded in the history books, but did not really begin to sell the breed until 1926, after seven years of trying to perfect them. It should be noted that he was obviously dedicated to the breed, we believe, as some of offers were incredibly high. The British offered Gillet one million "fancs," or $195,000, for his entire lot of rabbits, which was approximately 150 animals in 1924. Gillet was the only person in the world to have this amazing rabbit; yet within two years the breed had spread rapidly over Belgium, Germany, Switzerland, Holland, and into England in 1927. Some fanciers scoffed at those early Rex and proclaimed that they should be called "Wrecks" in-

C.A. Gelbke, Sr. of Appleton, Wisconsin imported many Rex from Germany during the late 1920s.

stead, as they were indeed nothing like the Rex of today.

A furrier from Leipzig, German wrote in the *Leipzig Kaninchenzuchter*, "Up to the present time we doubted the existence of this breed, the possibility of the thing. We are satisfied now, and marvel at it. We never saw anything so beautiful."

It should be noted that the Rex mutation had also occurred in other European countries: in Lubeck, Germany, 1924; Chartes, again in France, 1927 and at Schoonhoven, Holland in 1938.

Rex were introduced to the United States by one of America's rabbit pioneers, John C. Fehr, and his rabbit partner, Alfred Zimmerman, in 1924, who paid $350 for

John Fehr's Ermine King was in the first shipment of Rex brought to the U.S. in 1924.

a pair of Castor Rex. It should be noted that these gentlemen did not buy from the Abbot Gillet. Many additional imports were coming into the United States over the next five years; another "Boom" was taking place in America, with prices going as high as $1,500 for a pair of Rex rabbits.

A working standard was adopted for the Castor Rex variety only during the Fort Worth, Texas Convention, December 9-13, 1929. By 1932 there was Rex mania taking place in the United States, everything was becoming Rexed. These are the following breeds which were accepted by the American Rabbit and Cavy Breeders Association: Beveren Rex in Black, Blue and White; Flemish Giant Rex, in all the accepted colors of the time; Standard Havana Rex; Heavyweight Havana Rex; Black and Blue Silver Marten Rex, plus Sable Rex with the nor-

Dr. C.F. Friend, with some of his Rex. Friend was the first secretary of the National Rex Club in the U.S. Circa 1930.

mal Rex colors of Castor and Ermine. Working standards were granted for New Zealand Red and White Rex. All of the Rex breeds which had a normal fur counterpart were recognized by their various National Specialty Clubs, until 1935 when the AR&CBA, Inc. voted to pull the Rex and place them with the Rex Specialty Club. Now by 1944, Blue Vienna Rex, Standard, American and Giant Chinchilla Rex, Himalayan Rex, Lilac Rex and Polish Rex had been added to the growing breed list. These were all Rexed

End of a Rex hair follicle enlarged 200 times. Note the brush-like appearance. Circa 1935.

counterparts of the normal fur breeds. Colors recognized were: Castor, Opal, Lynx, Beaver, Ermine, Blue and Black.

The Rex breed today has been so finely tuned from the crippled wrecks of yesteryear. In their native France, the breed is found in 20 colors, plus they have also bred Rex in a Dalmatian pattern, Dutch, Hotot, Rhinelander, Tan, Brown Silver, Rhoen and Tricolor.

Above: A beautiful Dalmatian Rex.

Right: One of the more novel Rex of France, a Dutch marked.

Photos courtesy Jean-Claude Periquet, France.

STANDARD SATIN REX

atin Rex were first an American creation which began in the mid-1940s, by, of course, crossing Satins with the Rex. This new breed was shown for the first time at the Long Beach, California Convention of the American Rabbit & Cavy Breeders Association in November 1949, but would have to make two additional showings before being recognized. It would appear that the Standards Committee of the time had little interest in the breed, with the late Vern Ashton, chairman of the committee, writing of the breed, "Do the Satin Rex belong to the Rex Federation or to the Satin Association? It's the opinion of our Standard Committee that we and the breeders at large devote more time to improving our recognized breeds before trying to create new breeds. Experimentations along these creative lines should be confined to genetic students, and until firmly established and pure breeding, no breed can be accepted as a Standard AR&CBA recognized breed." Well, the breed was never recognized in the United States, but is officially accepted by the British Rabbit Council for quite a number of

years. The breed is extremely rare in England, with perhaps only three to five fanciers keeping them. I have had the pleasure of seeing and handling the breed, and they are uniquely different, though they do have a ways to go on improving the density of coat, but the satin sheen is quite good.

Dedicated to Stephanie Davies of England, who for many years has kept the Satin Rex alive in England.
Photo by the author.

RHINELANDER

he Rhinelander, as the name implies, hails from Germany, having made its appearance in the rabbit world at a show in 1902. The breed was developed by a postman and rabbit fancier in the person of Mr. Josef Heintz, of Grevenbroich, in North Rhine-Westphalia, which would explain Heintz's choice for the breed's name. To

create the Rhinelander, which began in 1901, Josef Heintz, crossed a Japanese (Harlequin) buck to a common gray colored checkered type doe. In this litter there were four young, one resembling the mother, one of the father, one solid gray, and the fourth, the first Rhinelander. This particular rabbit was a buck, and though the chain, ears and butterfly marking had the desirable combination of orange and black markings, the spots on one side were only orange and the other side all black.

Mr. Heintz then took a Black Papillon (Checkered Giant) doe and mated her to a Japanese buck, which gave him a nice specimen in a doe from that litter. Crossing these back and forth with each other and keeping the best specimen does to cross with Japanese bucks, Heintz finally produced the somewhat ideal Rhinelander. The Rhinelander was given a standard in 1905 in Germany.

Rhinelander buck imported to America in 1923.

In 1908 at the West German Rabbit Association exposition, 17 rabbits were exhibited.

Rhinelanders were brought to United States from Germany in 1923, and accepted to the Standards of the National Breeders and Fanciers Association of America in 1924, but were called the Rhineland instead of Rhinelander. Mr. E.W.C. Arnold who owned Oknok Rabbitry in Babylon, Long Island, New York, imported the first Rhinelanders. By the time the 1930 Book of Standards was published, the breed was called Rhinelander. The standard for the breed in the US for 1924 reads:

The color must be white ground with yellow and black markings, the white very clean, the yellow from a creamy yellow to intense golden yellow of bricky red.

BODY well knitted together, not too slender, and weight 7 pounds to 9
   pounds.

COAT thick, soft, set close and the shorter the hair the better.

EYES large clear chestnut brown in color.

EARS V-shaped and not longer than 4-3/4 inches and no white.

MARKINGS are creamy yellow to brick red, butterfly nose, one-half smut black, other half red, reverse color for eye circles; again reverse color for cheek spots; reverse for ears.

SADDLE must be without interruption, herring boned, and at least 9-1/2 inches long, black, red and yellow and no white.

EARS striped with same colors, well defined edge and no white.

MARKINGS on sides for show purposes, should be as well defined as possible in regular formation.

SCALE FOR JUDGING

Build of body and ears	20 Points
Regular marking of spots	30 Points
Size	10 Points
Hair and Color	30 Points
Condition	10 Points
Total	= 100 Points

GRAVE FAULTS

Absence of butterfly	Eyes different color
White in butterfly	Madagascar color
Irregular marking	Presence of chain
Irregularities in upper part of ear	

The Rhinelander would vanish from our American soil by 1932. It is not known whether the standard set for the breed was too difficult to achieve, or the breed died out due to lack of interest by the fanciers of the day, because of the much more popular and massive Checkered Giant which at the time was accepted in all known colors. I am more inclined to believe that the ever-popular Checkered Giants, caused the downfall of the Rhinelanders in the early days.

In February 1972, Robert "Bob" Herschbach, of Watsonville, California, was in Germany to attend the Tenth Annual Bundeskaninchen Show held at Essen-Grugahaollen, West Germany. There he saw the beautiful Rhinelanders and purchased four of the prize-winning animals to bring back to his rabbitry in Watsonville, California. This author coined the slogan, "The Calico of the Fancy," and called all interested parties together to form the Rhinelander Rabbit Club of America in 1974. The Rhinelanders were once again given breed recognition by the American Rabbit Breeders Association when they

One of the original Rhinelander does imported to America in 1972. Photo courtesy Robert Herschbach.

were accepted into the Book of Standards in 1975.

Rhinelanders are only accepted in the black and orange markings in the U.S., but they can be found in Germany and Sweden in the blue and fawn combination.

There is no doubt that it is just a matter of time that this new variety will be recognized in America, as a breeding program is currently underway in California.

RHOEN

This is a fairly recent breed of rabbit developed in Germany by Mr. Karl Becker, and named Rhoen for where he began his program in 1969.

Rhoen is located in Thuringe at the borders of Hesse and Bavaria. Karl Becker first mated a Chinchilla buck to a Black and Orange Japanese Harlequin. The resulting offspring were further bred with the Alaska and Silver Marten breeds. The Chinchilla factor masked the orange pigmentation of the Harlequin, just

Rhoen rabbit. Photo courtesy Zentralverband Deutscher Rassekaninchenzuecher, Germany.

as in our Magpie Harlequins today. The Rhoen rabbit, although it does resemble the Magpie Harlequin in many respects, is severely faulted in having the checkerboard pattern. The dark spots, which shade to gray on the dominant white background, are to resemble the bark pattern of the white birch tree. This nearly impossible to breed show rabbit is basically only found in its native Germany. Since the appearance of the Rhoen rabbit, breeders have since combined it with the large Rex and have created the Rhoen Rex of Germany.

SABLE

 ables are strictly throwbacks from the original Chinchillas of France. Black and Tan blood had been introduced, to improve the quality of the fur in the Chinchilla breed which had been imported into England from Mr. J.J. Dybowski of France who originated the breed. Credit for the first Sables to appear was in the Sunnyside Fur Farm of Mr. David W. Irving, near Liverpool. Irving wrote many years ago: "The very earliest specimens of the Sable rabbit made their appearance in this country (England) amongst a few litters bred in my own rabbitry from imported French Chinchilla rabbits; my old champion, Ivor Ideal, being the sire of the original Sables. As far back as 1919, I produced several Sables in this way, but little attention was paid to this brown-shaded rabbit, as at the time Chinchillas were all the rage. However, one or two breeders mated these brown rabbits together, and found that they would produce their like under certain conditions. Thus, in course of time, by careful breeding, the Sable rabbit was established as a variety which could be relied upon to breed comparatively true to type and colour." The early Sables were given the name of Maraaka. The first Sables to appear were the Martens, which, of course, is a tan pattern rabbit, but with white bellies, and from the Martens came the Siamese. This would be the first time that we would hear of

David W. Irving, of Liverpool, England, produced the first Sables in 1919 and would be responsible for their distribution throughout Europe.

Light Marten Sable Buck, circa 1925.

a variety called Siamese, which was named for the Siamese cat, and also the term Marten, for the wild Stone Marten.

The British Fur Rabbit Society, which was formerly known as the Beveren Club, would adopt the Sable as a Fur Breed, issue a standard of perfection for the breed, and remain under this governing body until 1927. Sables were becoming very popular in Britain, and it was felt that the time had come to establish the British Sable Rabbit Club, when a meeting was called on November 25, 1927 at Leicester. This new club quickly revamped the standards, which were approved by the British Fur Rabbit Society. Sables would be recognized in two varieties: Marten and Siamese, with light, medium and dark shades being acceptable in the showroom.

Sables were first found in litters of pure bred Chinchillas in the rabbitry of Otto Brock, of San Gabriel, California, in 1924. The American Sable Rabbit Association was formed in early 1929, with Judge C.F. Dickinson of Albion, Michigan as the secretary. A working standard was adopted at the Forth Worth, Texas Convention on December 9, 1929 for the American Sable, and called for a medium-colored variety. The Marten Sable and the Siamese Sable would be left in limbo for the time being. By 1931, the American Sable was recognized by the American Rabbit and Cavy Breeders Association. It was in this same standard that a working standard was presented, as adopted by the American Sable Rabbit Association for the Siamese Sable. Sable Martens would be taken up under the Silver Marten standard, being called Silver Sable Martens.

The popularity of

British Light Sable, circa 1925.

298

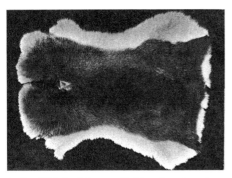

Pelt of Light Marten Sable, showing de-
sired graduation of shading, circa 1925.

Pelt of Light Marten Sable, showing de-
sired graduation of shading, circa 1925.

the Sable rabbit began to wane considerably. Siamese Sable would be dropped from the Book of Standards in 1976, and the American Sable was strictly called the Sable. In 1981, only one Sable was shown at the ARBA Convention in Syracuse, New York, by the late Al Roerdanz of Kingsville, Ohio, which appeared doom for the breed. Taking the lead, Roerdanz managed to locate seven purebred Sables, which he bred together, as well as crossed with Sable Silver Martens, Sable Rex, Havanas, Californians and Standard Chinchilla. Al even imported a trio of Sables from England to strengthen the gene pool. With the help of Marg and Jay Lawton, offspring was distributed to interested parties. Further crossings would be made with Tortoise Mini Lops, New Zealand Whites, Palominos and even Harlequins. It would be in 1982 that a group of Sable fanciers were called together with Al Roerdanz at the helm to form the American Sable Rabbit Club with 13 charter members. Twelve Sables were exhibited at the 1982 ARBA Convention in Seattle, Washington, and the following year at Colorado Springs, Colorado Convention the Sable breed had easily reached the required quota of animals needing to be shown, per ARBA rules, thereby saving the breed in America from extinction.

SABLE DE VOSGES

This French breed is a rather recent addition to the world of rabbit breeds and was created by a Mr. A Fritsch, a retired school teacher of Barr in Alasce. Fritsch was also the founder in 1912 of the Trade Union for Poultry Farming in Barr. He was one of the first men to keep the Rex rabbit once they were released and carried out a number of experiments accord-

ing the laws of genet-
ics as established by
Gregory Mendel to pro-
duce other varieties of
Rex. A. Fritsch crossed
Sable Rex, Thuringer,
Angoras and Sables,
and continued for six
years when he stablized
the lighten brown shade
seen in the Sable De
Vosges today. This new
coloration excited the

Sable de Vosges. Photo courtesy Meg Brown, Scotland.

furriers of the time, as the color was near Pastel Mink or Palomino Mink
as it is called today. This new breed was shown first at Barr, then Belfort,
Metz and Strasbourg, where they always created excitement. The Sable De
Vosges was officially recognized in 1964, after completing the required
three showings at the Paris Nationals. This breed, although fairly new, is
considered rare today in its native France.

SACHSENGOLD

his deep orange-red rabbit is the product of Germany and was
created by Richard Bennack from Rohrsdorf. In 1925, Bennack
decided he wanted to create a golden rabbit of Saxony, with a
shape and size of the Chinchilla. He first took a common fawn-
colored male, which he mated to a black and orange Japanese Harlequin,
which would give him the dominant yellow he was working with. He then
tested the offspring to what is believed to be an Argente Cream. However,
it could have been a Silver Fawn, although the Argente would be more
likely the breed, because of the type. This test mating would hardly prove
ideal, as Richard Bennack was now faced with the difficult problems of
the silvering. He continued to further cross with Havana, Chinchilla, New
Zealand Red and Black and Tan. World War II would see an end to Bennack's
work with the new breed, and much of the stock would be lost.

In 1945, his son took up the torch for the breed and continued to develop them for another eight years, when he showed his father's Gilded of
Saxony, Saxon Gold or Sachsengold for the first time in the former East

German town of Leipzig in 1953. The new breed would be recognized by the National German Rabbit Governing body in 1961.

It should be noted that a very similar breed called the Thrianta was developed in Holland and recognized there in May of 1940. The Thriantas would be crossed into the Sachsengold by a Mr. Kissener to help improve the color. Although the two breeds

Sachsengold rabbit.
Photo courtesy Zentralverband Deutscher Rassekaninchenzuecher, Germany.

are very close twins, Thriantas are somewhat smaller and the color a good bit more intense.

SALLANDER

Sallenders or Salland rabbits are a fairly recent addition to the rabbit breeds, and were developed in the Salland region of Holland by a well-known rabbit judge, Mr. D. J. Kuiper, from Ost. Kuiper crossed Thuringers with Chinchillas to create the Sallanders. The Chinchilla genes masked the russet color of the Thuringer, giving the beautiful shadings of the Sallanders. The breed was recognized in the Netherlands in 1975, and became quite popular in Holland. England imported the breed in the early 1990s, and it was recognized there in 1994 to their breed standards. The Sallander color is not found in any other rabbit breed. Rabbits are good natured and weigh 3 to 4 kg. (6 lb 10 oz to 8 lb 12 oz).

SAN JUAN

Off the coast of Washington State in the United States there is an island called San Juan, and it is here that the San Juan rabbit makes its home. Originally the European wild rabbit was introduced to the island by the early settlers during the 1880s, and by 1895 the rabbit had become well established, especially in an area called the American Camp. The rabbit is believed to have been further crossed by the local population using Belgian Hare, Flemish Giant and New Zealand blood added. San Juan rabbits, although living wild, have been easily domesticated and have gotten the attention of some laboratories as a lab animal. San Juans have been brought as far south as Louisiana, which were used to train hunting dogs. They are a rather small breed, which weigh between 3.5 to 5.5 pounds or 1.58 to 2.5 kg and are a light to dark shaded brown coloration or the wild chestnut agouti.

SATIN

 atins were a major mutation which occurred in the United States in the rabbitry of Walter Huey of Pendleton, Indiana. Huey was a dedicated breeder of Havanas, and in trying to improve their brown color and fur, he began to inbreed his stock. During this process, the first Satin mutation occurred in 1934. Walter Huey sent animals to Harvard University, where geneticists determined that this new mutation was a simple recessive gene for the shine and texture of the coat, but not length. When Huey showed these Havanas with the brilliant sheen against the normal Havanas, a storm of protest ensued; therefore the rabbits were given the name of Satin Havanas, and recognized by the National Havana Club.

Sadly, Walter Huey would pass away on Friday, August 15, 1937, at the age of just 53 years of heart failure.

Since the Satin mutation was a recessive gene, like that of the popular

Dedicated to Al Lunde of Wisconsin who began raising Satins as a 4-H project in 1965 and continues today. Al has raised all the varieties, with the exception of the Chocolates. He was recognized as "Mr. Satin" in 1984 for his many years of dedication to the breed. Al developed, presented and saw the acceptance of the Broken Satin in 1985, and his Otter Satin was recognized in 2000. He was the first person to ever win a Best in Show title with a Satin at an ARBA Convention. This was with a White doe in Tucson, Arizona in 1979.

Rex breed, breeders quickly began to Satinize many of the breeds of the day. Professor Castle, a famous American geneticist of the time, wrote of the mutation, "The Satin mutation, like the Rex, is an interesting plaything for the fancier." A National Satin Club was first formed in 1936, by Walter Huey and John C. Fehr, but soon folded. It was announced in 1942 that at Akron, Ohio show on March 5 to 8, the American Federation of Havana Breeders voted to sponsor the Satin breed in the various colors. By 1939, Satin colors could be found in: Brown, Black, Blue, White and Orange. John C. Fehr was very keen on the breed, and was breeding all these colors, plus working on the development of the Chinchilla Satin. Fehr even created the Satin Angora, but said that the wool was so fine that it was worthless as a commercial venture.

In 1946, another club was organized for the breed, the American Satin Rabbit Breeders Association, with two colors recognized, Ruby-eyed White and Chinchillas, but with two different sets of points for the two varieties, as the emphasis on type was placed on the White, which were developed from New Zealand Whites, and on color for the Chinchilla variety. By 1950, a number of proposed standards were being suggested to the American Rabbit & Cavy Breeders Association to get Lilac, Orange, Black, Copper, as well as a few other colors recognized. However, these had to be presented at three National Convention Shows. In 1956, eight varieties were recognized for the breed. Siamese Satin were accepted in 1965, and in this same year one standard set of points for all the varieties was established. Wesley W. Dixon of California developed the Californian Satin, as well as the ever-popular Siamese. The Siamese were produced from a Black Satin doe that Dixon had purchased from the late George Sutherland. Through a Black to Black pairing, the Siamese were produced, to the amazement of both gentlemen, who perfected the variety over three years. The beautiful Broken Satins were finally recognized in 1985, which gave a huge boost to the breed. Otter Satins were recognized in 2000.

From the shinny babies found in the nest box of Walter Huey in 1934, the Satin breed has been recognized throughout the world by every national rabbit governing body, but credit must be given to the Americans for perfecting this beautiful breed as an outstanding dual purpose rabbit, for meat, fur and show. Satins weigh in at 8.5 to 11 pounds, or 3.85 to 5 kg. Walter Huey would be very proud of his rabbits today.

SATIN DWARF

Satin Dwarfs were being created in Germany, France and the United States all about the same time in the 1990s. American breeders then decided to breed a larger version, called the Mini Satin (the Dwarf form were to be called Satinettes), while Germany and France continued with the true Dwarf version. A true Satin Dwarf is to be exactly the same as the Netherland Dwarf, but with a satin coat. Of course, the breeds used to create the Satin Dwarfs are Satins and Netherland Dwarfs.

SCHWARZGRANNEN

 chwarzgrannens are an old breed which have been extinct for many years in eastern Europe, but a small population of them were being maintained in Eastern sector of Germany. However, because of Russian control and their laws, the Schwarzgrannens could not be brought back into the West. Willy Schopf first saw the breed in 1991, and because he couldn't have some for himself, set out to recreate the breed.

To create the breed, he would need a Chinchilla and a Red rabbit, but because of their size, he quickly ruled out the New Zealand Red and the Giant Chinchilla. Schopf then chose the small Chinchilla (Standard Chinchilla) and Sachsengold. To begin his breeding program, he obtained all from different breeders, to have a broad gene pool: one Chinchilla doe, two Sachsengold does, four Sachsengold bucks and two Chinchilla bucks.

Schwarzgrannen rabbit. Photo courtesy Willy Schopf, Germany.

The body type and fur were the most important goals in Willy Schopf's program. By December 1993, he would have the first generation crosses, nice size litter, good bodies, and the youngsters resembled the Deilenaar breed. At the age of seven weeks he culled, just keeping those with great bodies and fur, with the rest of the offspring tagged for fryers. When the

F1 generation was ready to breed, these were mated up, but at the same time he kept the original parents in production to have a broader base to work with. With the F2 generation arriving, he produced the first Schwarzgrannen: snow white fur with black tips to the hair and brown eyes. Schopf entered into the age of computers, having written up a program to trace his every move on the breed's development. Further back crossing with the original rabbits was producing some rabbits which had red tips to the hairs, which he considered a fault. I would think that this red-tipped hair to the coat would be rather beautiful. Schwarzgrannens are fully recognized now in several European countries, which weigh in at 2 to 3.5 kg or 4.5 to 7.75 lbs.

SEPARATOR

Czechoslovakia is the native home of the Separator rabbit or Black Guard Haired Rabbit. It is the Czech National Breed, and was created by Mr. Frantisek Provaznik of Holice. To create the Separator, he used the Chinchilla and small yellow Silvers. He kept choosing offspring with various intensity to the guard hairs, giving the results of a rabbit that actually had a coat combination that resembled the true Fox.

The breed was recognized in 1975. It is a rather small rabbit weighing from 2 kg. to 3.25 kg., is rather thick set, and of a meaty type. Eyes are dark brown, and the nails are a dark horn color. The rabbit is totally white, with the guard hairs tipped in black over the entire body.

Separator rabbit. Photo courtesy Lenka Kadeoabkova, Czechoslovakia.

SIAMESE SABLE

Siamese Sables are recognized in a number of countries. In the United Kingdom, they are recognized in three shades: Light Siamese Sable, Medium Siamese Sable and Dark Siamese Sable. Of course, when we refer to the Siamese name, it is the cat of that breed where the rabbit gets their name. Siamese Sables were at one time recognized in the United States,

Siamese Sable. From the Wippell Collection. Reproduced from a Fur & Feather colour plate first issued 25 January 1929.

but that has been dropped and Americans have simply Sables. All Sables, whether Siamese or Marten, originated as sports from the original Chinchillas brought out of France (see Sable).

SIBERIAN

The new or modern Siberian, as it is often called, was created in 1930 by Mr. Charles Banfield and Mr. C. Pope of England, in the brown color. Their goal was to produce a quality fur rabbit, in which the pelts were easy to match. The breed's fur is a roll-back coat; when stroked in the opposite direction, the fur must have a sheared or pulled appearance, showing as few guard hairs as possible, with an extremely dense, glossy sheen and a unique colored flecking to the coat. Oddly enough, self-colored English (Spots) were largely used to develop the breed. It was quite popular during World War II, but is kept alive in the United Kingdom where it can only be found, by a small band of dedicated fanciers. Siberians are bred in black, blue, brown and lilac. The Lilac Siberian was the last variety to be developed in 1946 by Ron Crowther, from Wores, England. Weights are 5 to 7 lb (2.68 to 3.175 kg).

SICHUAN WHITE

Sichuan Province of China is the home of the Sichuan White rabbit, which may have been for many decades, or centuries for that matter, kept by the local population on the many scattered farms and villages of the region. Sichuan Whites are not a large rabbit, just weighing approximately 6 pounds or 2.68 kg, which is all white with pink eyes. This rabbit is probably kept more into the interior than in the more modern cities, where commercial meat rabbits have been developed in large-scale rabbit production.

SILVER

 ou shall not, as in other cattell, looke to their shape, but to their richnesse, onely elect your buckes, the largest and goodliest conies you can get; and for the richnesse of the skin, that is accounted the richest which hath the equal lest mixture of blacke and white haire together, yet the blacke rather shadowing the white; the furre should be thicke, deepe, smooth, and shining; … they are of body much fatter and larger, and, when another skin is worth two or three pence, they are worth two shillings." This was written by Gervaise Markham, in 1631, for his *A Way To Wealth — The English Hus-wife,* and is believed to be the first true accounting that the Silver rabbit existed in England; yet of another importance, he also speaks of the selection of proper breeding stock.

Many of the early authors say that the Silver Grey rabbit was found in the greatest abundance in Siam, where it was brought to Portugal by sailors, then to the ports of England and Europe. This author is of the belief that the first Silvers appeared in England in 1592, having been introduced by Sir Walter Ralegh, also spelled Raleigh, (1552-1618). This theory is just as imaginable as

Earliest known drawing which is titled Silver-Grey or Riche, circa 1865.

Silver Grey. *From the Wippell Collection. Reproduced from a Fur & Feather colour plate first issued 14 September 1928.*

Silver Fawn buck. *From the Wippell Collection. Reproduced from a Fur & Feather colour plate first issued 15 March 1912.*

Sir Walter throwing down his cloak to cover a mud puddle for Queen Elizabeth I, to walk over and not dirty her royal feet. It was in 1592 that Ralegh sailed to Portugal and brought goods back to England, so it is quite likely that he also introduced the first Silver Greys to England.

In *The Wild Rabbit in a New Aspect or Rabbit-Warrens That Pay,* by J. Simpson, 1895, "The nearest approach to the wild rabbit, among tame kinds, is the dark 'silver-grey,' a beautiful variety, differing in no respect from the wild type except in colour, and said to be as good for warren purposes, and more valuable on account of its skin. Eighty or ninety

Sir Walter Raleigh, circa 1600.

years ago, many warrens of silver-greys existed. Parkinson mentions one warren of 700 acres demanding a capital 1400 (pounds).

"How or when the silver-grey rabbit originated, I have not been able to learn, but it appears to be as distinct and quite as old a breed in this country as the common gray kind. There are still some warrens of silver-greys in existence. One of the oldest and most extensive is that belonging to Captain Vyner at Askrigg, in north Yorkshire. Captain Vyner informs me that 'Sir Walter Raleigh brought the silver-grey rabbits to Nappa warren at Askrigg, and that the rabbits were turned down in a 60-acre warren, surrounded by a wall, and have been there ever since.' Also, that until the last Chinese war they were very valuable, the skins being used for a particular class of mandarins, and commanding a high price. Since then, however, that market has been closed. Captain Vyner describes the silver-grey as a short thick rabbit, of no more value now than the ordinary one, but with beautiful fur. It is not improbable that the warrens of silver-greys in Lincolnshire and elsewhere originated from Askrigg. It is stated that the skins from these warrens were likewise exported to China. Lord Walsingham has, I understand, also a warren of silver-greys on his Norfolk estate. Pure black rabbits (sports) are common, and are often produced in warrens of the common wild rabbit."

Now this is the only mention of Sir Walter Ralegh having introduced the Silver Grey into England that I have been able to locate. A bit more about Sir Walter; he, of course, was executed for treason, by beheading, in 1618. At his execution, he asked to be able to see the axe and exclaimed, "This is a sharp Medicine, but it is a Physician for all Diseases." It was common practice at the time to embalm the head and present it to the family. Indeed, Sir Walter's head went to his wife, and it is said that she carried it with her at all times until she finally died, 29 years later at the ripe old age of 82 years. The head was finally buried with their son Carew, to the south side of the altar at St. Margaret's Church, founded in the 12th century, which serves as the parish church for the House of Parliament, right next to Westminster Abby.

From *Cyclopaedia,* Rees, 1819, under the heading of "Rabbit in Agriculture," according to a Mr. Chaplin of that day, in the "Agricultural Survey of Lincolnshire," "from Louth to Castor, eighteen miles, ten of them were warrens, chiefly silvers. The average price for ten years was 10 pounds per 100; silver skins from 15s to 21s per dozen." It was at Lincolnshire, where the greatest concentration of Silver Grey were kept in warrens, until the time that warrens became extinct.

On the 13th of May, 1778, under the command of Captain Arthur Philip, a fleet of 11 ships left Portsmouth, England to colonize Australia. It was a 15,000-mile voyage, which would take over eight months. The lead ships arrived on January 18, 1788. Among the list of livestock aboard the store ships were five rabbits, which in all likelihood were Silver Greys, as wild rabbits were not introduced until many years later.

In 1859, the British Silver Grey is well documented in New Zealand. "In 1859 the Keene Brothers of Swyncombe sheep station released one pair of 'precious' Silver Grey rabbits onto their property — jealously guarding their offspring from poachers. Within 10 years the Keenes were ruined and had to abandon their land because of the depredations of the Silver Greys which were branded as 'outlaws.' Ten thousand were trapped on Swyncombe in six months in 1869." This flood of Silver Greys prompted the following poem in the *Marlborough Express,* of this time.

> Away they went, on pleasure bent,
> With freedom quite transported;
> And very soon. Nay! Ev'ry moon,
> Proved buck and doe had courted.

In years a few, the rabbits grew
And multiplied tremendous,
Till everywhere was heard the prayer,
From "Silver Greys" defend us.

It has also been well documented that a gift of Silver Grey rabbits was given to the Acclimatisation Society of Victoria, Australia, founded in 1861. On Monday, October 18, 1865, 12 Silver Grey rabbits were released on the sub-Antarctic Island known as Enderby, which would become their own breed and the purest breed of rabbit known genetically, having been left to breed through natural selection during a course of 127 years (see Enderby Island).

From the Enderby Island rabbits, we can see exactly what the Silvers of yesteryear looked like, nothing at all like the finely bred show animals of today. Charles Darwin, in his *The Variation of Animals and Plants Under Domestication,* 1868, did extensive studies on the domestic rabbit, including the Silver Greys (see Himalayan).

Silvers were known by a variety of names in the early days. Charles Darwin referred to the hutch-raised rabbits as Chinchilla and the wild ones of the warrens as Silver-Grey. Other names for the breed have included Millers, Silver Sprig, Lincoln Silver, Lincolnshire Silver-Grey and Riche (French for valuable). The furriers of the time called them the Lincolnshire Silver-Grey or Silver Sprig. Lincoln was the center for the hat-making industry, and many a Silver was used to produce felt, taking no less than 40 pelts to produce a single hat.

People became seriously interested in showing the Silver as a breed around 1874. Originally they were all shown together, but because of the varying degrees of silvering, protests were common place. Then there was a period of the Light, Medium and Dark groupings, with buck and does competing together. At the All-England Show, held at Walworth in 1886, a fur-

Silver-Grey, illustrated in 1880.

ther innovation was tried, classes being provided for bucks and does, their idea being that this would do away with the question of shades.

There were three different standards for the various shades. A Mr. J. H. Roberts, of Bramley, a leading judge and breeder of the Silvers on a large scale during the 1880s, offered his standard in *The Book of the Rabbit,* 2nd Edition, 1889.

POINTS OF THE SILVER-GREY, &c

	No. of Points		
	Light	Medium	Dark
1. Colour blue grey, clear and bright	30	25	20
2. Evenness of silvering and sharpness of ticking	20	25	30
3. Shape with condition	15	15	15
4. Fur fine, soft, short and close	15	15	15
5. Ears short, carried well together	10	10	10
6. Eye large, full and bright	5	5	5
7. Weight between 5 lb. and 9 lb	5	5	5
Totals =	100	100	100

"The same points also apply to a Silver-Cream and Fawn, and also to Silver Browns."

A Mr. H. E. Gilbert, writing in the same book on the origin of the Silver-Cream or Silver-Fawn, " I am told that a pair of this variety was first exhibited at York Show about the year 1871 or 1872, the same variety having been bred by the same exhibitor three or four years previously, the judge at this show passing them over in ignorance, but at the following show awarding the same pair a prize."

Upon further investigation, actually at the Crystal Palace Poultry Show in October, 1863, first honors were awarded in the foreign class to a

First illustration of the Silver-Cream, December 1883.

buff Silver-Grey doe exhibited by Mr. J. de la S. Simmonds. There was much said regarding the Silver-Fawn during the 1880s as to its exact origin. Some said they were produced from the Silver-Greys; others claim they were crossed. Well, if 12 Silver-Greys can be let loose on Enderby Island in 1865,

Silver Brown, Crystal Palace winner of 1887.

and then found 127 years later, both Blues and Creams, then it is all very likely that the original Fawns were sports of the Silver-Greys (see Crème D'Argent).

The history of the Silver Brown is well recorded, having been developed by George Johnson, of Kettering, England, who crossed a Belgian Hare buck to a Silver-Fawn doe. By the late 1880s this new variety was very popular on the English show bench.

The fourth Silver variety is the Silver-Blue, having been developed by a Mr. Entwisle of Bawtry. In 1887, a large class of them appeared at the big Saltaire, Bradford show; yet for some reason the color never quite caught on. Silver-Blues became extinct, but were recreated by Alan Reice and standardized in 1989 by the British Rabbit Council. Reice mated Silver Greys with the small Argente Bleu; however, they are very scarce in England.

First talk of a Silver Club was in 1885, by a Mr. A. Whittam, when he wrote a letter in *Poultry,* which was the best paper at the time for rabbit fanciers. It would not be until August 10, 1889 that the first meeting was called at the Potoven Show, near Wakefield, which was reported as having a large attendance. An-

Silver Grey, Crystal Palace winner of 1887.

other meeting was held at Morley, on August 31, 1889, where rules were passed and the first election of officers took place, showing Mr. A. Outhwaite as president and Mr. T. Gilpin as secretary.

The impressive awards offered by the National Silver Club of England. Photo by author.

The first club show was held on the 24th of January, 1891, in Leeds. Oddly enough, the Silver Fawns were divided into classes called Cream and Fawn. The entries for that first show would be: Greys had 62 entries, Fawn 72, and Browns 59. The total of 15 classes provided a total of 224 entries.

Silvers would arrive in America during the Belgian Hare boom days at the beginning of the 20th century and were among the first breeds recognized by the National Pet Stock Association, founded in 1910. They were recognized in all four varieties, although the Fawn, Brown and Blues were extremely rare.

Silvers are recognized the world over; however, the Silvers of America and the United Kingdom are the same breed, while those of Europe are a night and day difference, in particular the type and coat (see Little Silver).

SILVER FOX

he Silver Fox of America is totally different than the Silver Fox of England, which is known as the Silver Marten in the states. The Silver Fox has its roots in America, as the third breed developed here, that is still recognized by the American Rabbit Breeders Association. What is certainly known is that the breed was created by Walter B. Garland, who owned Vema Rose Rabbit Farm in North Canton, Ohio. The breed was first recognized and a standard approved at the Colorado Springs, Colorado Convention in 1925, as the American Heavyweight Silver, but in 1929 at the Fort Worth, Texas Convention the name was changed to American Silver Fox. The breed was recognized in two varieties: black and blue from the very beginning. Garland was a breeder of Checkered Giants; he was also the founder and first president of the Checkered Giant Club in America.

Now as to the history of the development of the breed. Considering Walter Garland never divulged, at least in writing, what the genetic make-up of the breed was, some enterpris-

Walter B. Garland, in the center, was one of the judges for the 1929 National Convention in Fort Worth, Texas.

ing person has painted this picture of the history of the Silver Fox for the National Silver Fox Rabbit Club guide book, which I will share. It has been stated that Walter Garland, during the 1920s, had a Black self Checkered Giant doe, which had an unusual amount of white hairs in the coat, and that he also bred the English Silvers (can't find any record of this). Silvers at the time had a weight limit of six pounds for showing. Garland wanted the Silver fur on a Checkered Giant size rabbit. He mated the Checkered Giant doe to a Silver buck; after considerable difficulty, a litter was produced. A buck from this cross was mated back to the Checkered doe, and does from the first cross were mated back to their father. Garland had about 40 cages tied up in his experiment, and after 14 years of culling, had a rabbit breeding true to type and color. Now, if the breed was recognized in 1925, and he had 14 years into their development, then Garland would have had to start the creation process sometime around 1911, and not during the 1920s. Using the English Silver is highly unlikely because of the snappy, close-lying fur structure of the coat.

This author is far more inclined to believe what has been recorded by Mr. Marcellus W. Meek, a noted rabbit authority, who wrote, *The Standard of Perfection for American Domestic*

Black Silver Fox. *Photo courtesy American Rabbit Breeders Association.*

Rabbits, 1928, "In America, the nearest approach to the dark Silver-Grey, which combines the lustrous black underwool and silver ticking so desirable for the fur purposes with the medium utility size of the American Blue, is the product

Known first as the American Heavyweight Silver, then renamed American Silver Fox in 1929, circa 1929.

of a first generation cross with the light Champagne D'Argent and a deeply colored American Blue. The size is a blend between the two breeds, and the color "just exactly like silver fox," according to many feminine admirers of living specimens. As a fur animal, it has many possibilities, and as a meat producer, it ranks with both the American Blue and the French Silver, its progenitors. One California breeder has succeeded in producing these dark silvers of exquisite coat and excellent utility value."

During the early 1920s, Walter B. Garland advertised for sale Champagnes, so it is recorded that he did keep this breed, but there is no record of him ever keeping the American Blues, nor the English Silvers.

Oren Reynolds tells of another story of breeding Silver Fox rabbits. Some years back, when Oren was breeding his noted strain of Champagne D'Argents, he was brought a Self-Tortoiseshell English Spot doe owned by Ivan Miller. Ivan had been breeding Spots for many years, but had this idea to produce Silver Foxes. They mated this Self-Tortoiseshell doe up to a Champagne buck, with the resulting progeny all being black. As the offspring matured, it was obvious that some were far under weight, while other were not, but Oren noted that they all had good quality Silver Fox fur. Ivan Miller showed some of these animals at the Illinois State Fair as Silver Fox and walked away with Best of Breed and Best Opposite Sex of Breed.

It is for certain that Walter B. Garland did develop an Alaska Red Fox, which was given a working standard in October of 1931, at the St. Louis, Missouri Convention. Garland's Silver Fox was the first breed of rabbit to dress out a pound and a half under the rabbit's live weight. The breed was in great danger of becoming extinct in America, until a group of 18 people gathered and formed the National Silver Fox Rabbit Club, which was granted a charter on August 31, 1971. Today only the Black Silver Fox is recognized by the ARBA, as the Blue variety was dropped from the standards for lack of rabbits shown during a five-year period at ARBA Conventions.

Silver Fox are beautiful rabbits, as this author keeps them in both colors. Does are excellent mothers, rear large litters, which make weight in short order, and the breed is extremely docile. Bucks top out at 11 pounds and does at 12 pounds. The most unique feature of this breed is the fur, which is longer than your normal coated rabbits and should ideally be 1-1/2 inches, and when the coat is stroked slowly from rump to head should remain upright. This breed is not found in any countries other than the U.S. and Canada, and is strictly known as the Silver Fox today.

SILVER MARTEN

 ilver Martens are sports from the original Chinchilla breed, which had been created in France. The sports occurred about the same time in Europe, England and the United States during the early 1920s. To improve the fur of the Chinchilla, Black and Tan blood had been introduced. The breed is, in fact, a Black and Tan rabbit minus the yellow factor, which has been masked by the Chinchilla genes. England named the new breed Silver Fox, and indeed, many Americans referred to the breed under the same name during the early days.

When these sports first appeared in 1921 in the United States, many

Chinchilla breeders were most disgusted at seeing black rabbits appearing in their purebred litters, thinking their breeding stock must have been of inferior quality. Some of the very finest Chinchillas imported from abroad in those early days were known to produce these sports. A few

Dedicated to Tex Thomas of Missouri, without a doubt the greatest breeder of Silver Martens of all time. He has won no less than two Best in Shows with his Silver Martens at the ARBA National Conventions, and a number of Best of Group winners at the same event. A showman, par excellence. Photo courtesy Heinold Feeds.

Labeled as a Black and Tan throwback, this is believed to be the first photo of a Silver Marten in America, circa 1921.

enterprising fanciers mated the black sports together, and they almost invariably would breed true to type and color; seldom would a Chinchilla appear in the litters. However, when Silver Marten was bred to Chinchilla, the probability was that all the young would be Chinchilla.

In France the Silver Martens were shown for the first time in 1926 by Mlle. Foucault, at Pithiviers, and were named Noir Argente, meaning Black Silver.

In the 1930-1931 *Guide Book and Standard* of the American Rabbit and Cavy Breeders Association, Inc., it was announced, "Arrangements are now being made for the Silver Marten Specialty Club to affiliate with the American Rabbit and Cavy Breeders Association, and it is probable that the standard will then go into effect for the Blue Silver Marten. Standard for the Black adopted at Forth Worth Convention, Dec. 9-13, 1929." Oddly enough, the Black and Blue Silver Martens were the only colors for a few years, but were even joined by the Black and Blue Silver Marten Rex. Sable Silver Martens would appear in the Book of Standard in 1934, followed by the last variety, the Chocolate Silver Marten, which was first known as the Silver Beaver.

England recognizes the Black, Blue, Chocolate and Lilac varieties within their Silver Fox breed, and places the Marten Sable under the Sable breed, which allows for three variations: Light, Medium and Dark Marten Sable. There is also the beautiful Smoke Pearl Marten, which is placed under the Smoke Pearl breed.

The modern Silver Marten. Photo courtesy American Rabbit Breeders Association.

SMOKE PEARL

Scotland is not known for many breeds of rabbits which they may call their own; however, to that country goes the credit for the Smoke Pearl. It is believed to have been bred by a Mr. Lawrie Stenhouse, using Sables and probably Blue

Smoke Pearl. Photo courtesy Meg Brown, Scotland.

Beverens, making its appearance in 1926 under the name of Smoke Beige. It was known as the Smoke Beige until 1932, when the name was changed to Smoke Pearl. The breed is bred in two varieties: Marten pattern and the Siamese type. This 5 to 7 lb. breed is very beautiful, but sadly it is pretty much restricted to the British Isles.

SPANISH GIANT

s the name would imply, the Spanish Giant rabbit comes from Spain. The breed's exact origin is unknown, but the generally accepted theory is that Flemish Giant males were crossed with a breed known as Lebrel Espanol females. These cross-bred females were there mated to Belier (Lops) and then only selecting rabbits with erect ear carriage. Spanish Giants were created at the beginning of the 1900s in the region of Valencia. The breed soon spread throughout Spain, and would become the basic breed for commercial rabbit breeding farms, and especially for the family-owned small-scale farms. It was said that the Spanish Giants were exported to other countries.

With the introduction of the Californian and New Zealand breeds and later hybrids of the two, commercial rabbit keeping blossomed in Spain, but to the unfortunate decline of the Spanish Giants (Gigante de Espana) to near extinction. A rescue program was quickly established in 1984 to save the mammoth Spanish Giant rabbit. The breed shows a great resistance to digestive diseases, with only one reported case since 1984 with a youngster. Reproductive problems are also reported to be rare. The Spanish government is studying the possibility of conserving frozen semen, since the purebred breeding population is between 250 and 300 does.

SQUIRREL

Squirrel rabbits are what we call a Blue Chinchilla and were created about the same time in Scotland and the Netherlands. Lawrie Stenhouse of Scotland created the breed in 1930 using Chinchilla, Polish and Sables. The Dutch version was created by D. Vogel from Apeldoorn, by crossing Silver Fox (Silver Martens) with Chinchilla and the Argente Bleu. It is a coby rabbit, with blue eyes and weighs 2.5 to 3 kg or 5.5 to 6.5 lb. The fur of the Squirrel is extremely dense, and of a rather long length of 1.5 inches. The bred is all but extinct in both countries; however, it is still recognized today by the British Rabbit Council, because a mere handful of fanciers remain steadfast in keeping this beautiful breed alive.

ST. NICHOLAS BLUE

 elgium is the native home of the St. Nicholas Blue or Blue of Sint-Niklass, which appeared at the beginning of the 20th century, and was said to have Flemish Giant in its background, but came about as a mutation, according to Belgian sources. The breed originated around the city of Sint-Niklaas, in the Waas region. Belgian authors considered the breed of the early days the same as the Blue Beveren, which also comes from the same area, but of that I cannot be sure. The original St. Nicholas Blues had a white blaze, with the point finishing between the eyes and carried down to encircle the lips. Many of

the early specimens also carried white feet and spots, but these were eliminated in the breeding programs. The breed was quite large at 11 pounds, and the color is the lightest shade of sky blue. In fact, this breed is the lightest of all the blue rabbits known, truly beautiful with a mandolin type. The Standards Commission ruled that the breed must be a uniform color without the blaze

Dedicated to Reginald Deyaert of Belgium who continues a dedicated effort to keep the rare St. Nicholas Blue from extinction.

The old world St. Nicholas Blue, showing the white blaze, circa 1910.

in 1917, so today this extremely rare breed is only bred in a solid color. Standard weights have been set at 4.5 to 6 kg or 10 to 13.25 lb. St. Nicholas Blues are in critical danger of becoming extinct, but are being maintained by a very small handful of breeders, in particular a Mr. Reginald Deyaert.

STEENKONIJN

he Steenkonijn, or more literally translated as the "Stone Rabbit," is a very ancient breed from the Flanders region of Belgium. Oddly enough, the breed was given its name as a former measure of Belgian weight called a "stone" which equaled 3.5 kilograms or 7 lbs. 11 oz. which also equaled the British equivalent of one stone. This weight measurement was used because this was the live weight size that the rabbits were to be for shipments to the markets of London. Dressed weights would typically equal 1.5 to 1.75 kilos. Stone rabbits are the direct descendants of the true European wild rabbit, and are the basis for many of our other breeds of domestic rabbits, in particular, the Belgian Hare and Flemish Giants. Many thousands of this breed were raised for the markets, but it would be the Australian wild rabbit that nearly caused the extinction of the breed by late 1800s. Australia, having been plagued by the introduction of the wild rabbit with no known biological control at the time, simply shot or trapped the rabbits. The new invention of refrigerated transport by ship ended the rabbit meat markets of Europe, at least as far as British were con-

Steenkonijn or Stone Rabbit, circa 1900.

321

Stone Rabbit. *Photo courtesy Willy Kreydt, Belgium.*

cerned. The Australian colonies could easily supply the millions of pounds of rabbit required by that country.

Stone rabbits owe their salvation to a Mr. Delounois in Belgium, who saw the breed at the very verge of extinction, and was able to locate a male that very closely resembled the Stone rabbit at a show in Hornu. Mr. Delounois then managed to locate a doe that somewhat looked like the breed. By careful selection of this single pair, Delounois showed off his recreation of the Steenkonijn at a show in 1932 to much praise by his fellow rabbit fanciers, who also greatly encouraged him to continue. On June 12, 1934, Mr. Delounois was justly rewarded when the Stone rabbit was adopted to the Belgian breed standards. Delounois would further be rewarded for his hard work when one of his Steenkonijns was given Champion status in 1969 after 37 years of specialization.

Stone rabbits are still rather rare today even in their native Belgium, and have been downsized considerably from the originals, as they currently weigh in at 2.5 kilos or 5 lb. 8 oz. being the ideal. They are bred in three colors: the original Chestnut Agouti, Steel Gray, Red Agouti, much like the Belgian Hare color.

STOR EGERN

Stor Egern is one of the Scandinavian breeds, and is nothing more that a very large form of Lilac, yet the color is a bit darker. The rabbit weighs in at a hefty 4.6 kg or 10.25 pounds. The Stor Egern is not one of the more common breeds of the north.

STORA HAVANA

Sweden is the native home of the Stora Havana, having been created there at the early part of the 20th century. In all respects, the Stora Havana is just a very large Havana, which weighs in at 4.6 kg or 10.25 pounds. The breed is very rare today, and few are seen in the shows of the north.

SUSSEX

ussex County in England is the home to a number of animals which carry the Sussex name: Sussex cattle, Sussex foul, Sussex Spaniel, and now the latest, the Sussex rabbit, created by Judy Le Marchant, formerly of Crawley in Sussex. When Judy began breeding rabbits, she chose the Californian breed, which at the time was recognized in the normal black points and in chocolate. For a time she would campaign for two additional varieties to be standardized by the British Rabbit Council: blue and lilac, which they did in late 1986. According to Judy, the Blue Californians were a beautiful slate blue, but the Lilac variety was mudding in color, and not the pinkish dove that the standards called for. Le Marchant gladly accepted a normal Lilac doe, to apply her new knowledge of rabbit genetics, in hopes of improving the Lilac Californian.

The Lilac doe was mated to her lightest Chocolate Point Californian buck. From this pairing, two colors of chocolate appeared in the litter. The normal chocolate and an unusually light reddish brown color. On the idea that she might have produced a new color mutation, Judy took one of these light reds to the renowned geneticist, Roy Robinson, for an opinion.

Robinson suggested that it appeared to be a tortoiseshell point. Upon the arrival of the first actually Sussex, it was apparent that Robinson was correct, as Judy was breeding Chocolate Tortoiseshell Californians.

From the F1 offspring, which were all self chocolates,

Dedicated to Judy Le Marchant of England, who developed the Sussex breed strictly by accident, but has greatly perfected it over the years for others to enjoy.

she chose a buck with good type and coat for the breed she called Chocky, which she mated to his aunt, a light red Californian, with the hopes of obtaining Lilac and Chocolate Californians. The doe gave birth to a mixed lot of self colored, pointed and one baby which looked like a fresh apricot, the first Sussex, a chocolate tortoiseshell doe. Her features com-

Sussex doe. The baby on the right is the first Sussex Cream ever born. Photo by John Daniels and courtesy Judy Le Marchant, England.

bined the best of both parents: type, coat, color and temperament. After several more attempts, it was apparent that she would have just this one unusual doe to work with, which she named Oakwood Golden Girl. Judy reported that she couldn't even obtain a decent Californian that she had been trying all along for in the first place.

Goldie, as she was dubbed, was shown around to several people, who delighted in the new color and wanted to purchase some. The new color was actually named by Judy in April 1987 when she showed the rabbit off at the Sussex Coast Fanciers Show as a joke, because at the time so many new breeds had been imported from Europe by a Hugh Halliday and were still under quarantine. Judy Le Marchant began to realize she was going to have to turn this one doe into a new breed. Goldie was mated back to her father to found the breed. The two rabbits during their lifetime produced a total of seven really good F1 Sussex colored offspring, which would create seven producing Sussex lines. Each of these seven rabbits were mated back to either Lilacs or Californians to give self F2s. Further matings of the F2s would produce some mixed lots, with Judy selecting the best Sussex colored F3s. These were again outcrossed, so alternate litters were inbred to procure the unique Sussex coloration and type, and further outcrossed to allow for a broader gene pool for the future of the Sussex breed. With a fair number of Sussex rabbits in Judy Le Marchant's hutches that were fairly consistent in their breeding, she began to distribute the new breed in England. The British Rabbit Council, in 1991, approved the Sussex rabbit as a breed, and admitted it into their book of standards.

The Sussex rabbit is found in two varieties, Gold and Cream, and the weights have been set at 7.5 to 8.5 lb or 3.39 to 3.84 kg. At this time Sussex are only recognized in the United Kingdom and in Malta.

SWISS FOX

 wiss Fox were being created about the same time in two different countries. An engineer by the name of Muller, from Zug, Switzerland, began to cross Chinchillas and Angoras in 1920, and produced a Blue Fox which was recognized in 1925. A Mr. Hermann Leifer of Germany saw a pelt of the Artic Blue Fox and decided to try and create a breed of rabbit for the fur trade. Leifer mated Angora and Chinchillas; further crossing the brothers and sisters, produced blacks with short coats and two Chinchilla does which had the long desirable coat. He then mated these does to a Havana buck, which gave him some nice blacks with long coats. Further crossing of the progeny produced the first Blue Fox that he had so desired in 1926. In the following years, Whites, Blacks, Blues, Yellows, Browns and Chinchillas were presented to rabbit fanciers. The two gentlemen shared rabbits, and the two lines were bred together, which greatly improved the men's objective. Swiss Fox, or Fox as they are sometimes known, were shown in 1928 in Berlin and again in Leiptzig in 1930. The furriers of the time were quite excited by the new creation; however, it was just a rabbit with a long coat, and not the true fox of the Artic. Swiss Fox are well represented in Europe and the Scandinavian countries. It has recently been imported into England and recognized there, but is not found in the United States. Swiss Fox weigh from 2.5 to 4 kg. (5 lb 8 oz to 8 lb 13 oz.) with an ideal coat length of 2-1/2 inches.

Havana Brown Swiss Fox. Photo courtesy Schweizerscher Rassekaninchenzucht Verband, Switzerland.

TADLA

orocco is the home of the Tadla rabbit. At the beginning of 1994, extensive field work was being carried out in order to gather information of the dominant population of rabbits in the Beni Mellal re-

Tadla rabbits of Morocco.

gion, in order to develop rabbit farming in this province. No information could be located as to whether the native stock of rabbits had been crossed with exotic species brought in from Europe during the colonization of Morocco by Spain and France in 1912.

Experimental work was carried out at the Institute Technique Agricole of Fkih Ben Salah in 1995, to further evaluate the parameters of the Tadla rabbit populations. The Tadla breed is small to medium is size and is raised for meat. The breed is a rather nervous one, but is very well adapted to the climates of Morocco.

TAN

ritain is the native home of the Tan rabbit, which first appeared in 1887 in the warren at Culland Hall, near Brailsford, in the county of Derbyshire. It seems that the Reverend William Cox, who resided at Culland Hall at the time, released some Dutch rabbits, along with common hutch rabbits to his warren which, of course, carried the European wild rabbit. These sports attracted a great deal of atten-

Dedicated to Joseph Kim of Oregon, who has developed an outstanding strain of Tans, more than winning his fair share of Best in Shows with his beautiful animals, including the prestigious Best Rabbit in Show at the ARBA National Convention in 2003. Photo courtesy Heinold Feeds.

tion with their jet black color and pale yellow bellies. The rabbits were quickly dubbed Black and Tans and shown for the first time in 1888. These early Tans were stocky in build, yet small and of a very flighty nature. In fact, when first exhibited, the early Tans spent all their time hiding in the hay. The breed

This is the earliest known photograph of the original Black and Tans, circa 1900.

soon spread to other parts of England, especially in the London area, Kent, Bedfordshire, the Midland and in Durham. The town of Cheltenham, which was noted for its rabbit fanciers, began to specialize in the new breed. In an effort to deepen the Tan's yellow coloration, it is said that Belgian Hare blood was introduced by a Mr. Purnell. This became known as the "Cheltenham Strain," which was a much larger Tan and more racy than those original ones from Derbyshire.

In the year 1890, the first Black and Tan Club was formed in England, which favored the Derbyshire type. Then came the British Black and Tan Rabbit Club shortly after, which favored the Cheltenham type. Both clubs began to resort to cross-breeding to improve the breed, using chiefly Gray and Brown Silvers.

The Black and Tan Club soon dissolved, but the British Black and Tan Rabbit Club continued on improving the breed by blending the two types, until eventually the type was fixed that we know today.

Black and Tans were soon taken up by the French people, having been exhibited for the first time in 1894 at the Concours de Caen Show, where it created a sensation.

The Blue and Tan would be the next variety developed at the turn of the 20th century, which

A group of prize-winning Tans in England, circa 1901.

British illustration of a Black and Tan, circa 1912.

was created by Albert Atkinson, of Huddersfield, England. He mated a sooty fawn doe, believed to have been produced from a Tortoiseshell Dutch, to a Black and Tan. The progeny was then inbred to get them established. The Blue and Tan became extremely popular almost overnight, and were true rivals against the Black variety.

For a number of years, there were only the two varieties. However, after World War I ended in 1918, the Chocolate and Tan came upon the scene through the efforts of a Mr. Childs of Cambridge, in about 1920. It can be assumed that Childs created the new variety by crossing with Havanas. However, he insisted that they came about as sports from his Black and Tans, but this is doubtful. Chocolates became very popular, which for

Beautiful Black and Tan. Photo courtesy American Rabbit Breeders Association.

a period of time caused the Blue variety to suffer. It should be noted that about the same time that the Chocolates were created in England, Belgium had also created them.

In about 1927, the Lilac and Tan came upon the scene, of course, by the pairing of the Chocolates and Blues, and mating the progeny together.

Tans reached America prior to 1908, having been imported by Fred Miller of Detroit, Michigan. The wealthy Mrs. Margaret M. Guggenheim of Long Island, New York imported more in 1917. Further importations

Tans. From the Wippell Collection. Reproduced from a Fur & Feather colour plate first issued 9 December 1921.

were made by Marcellus W. Meek during the years of 1918-1920. Tans were among the handful of rabbit breeds first recognized by the National Pet Stock Association.

In the Netherlands, another variety of Tan was developed by a Mr. Deurloo. Beginning in 1935, Deurloo crossed Silver Grays (Black) with Black and Tan. The Silver and Tan variety was breeding true by the year 1938; however, it found little favor with the Dutch fanciers.

While Tans have won many Best in Show awards over the years, none can quite equal a little Black Junior doe called Malibu Go Go Dancer, bred and owned by Joseph Kim of Oregon. This particular doe beat out no less that 12,566 rabbits to take the coveted title of Best Rabbit in Show at the 80th ARBA Convention and Show held in 2003, in Wichita, Kansas.

THO NOI

Viet Nam is the country of origin for this rabbit breed. I have been able to locate very little data on the Tho Noi rabbit, other that it is a indigenous breed of gray and black, which is kept in the villages and farms for local consumption. Data collected in 1997 showed a population of upwards of a million rabbits, with 100,000 breeding females and 2,000 bucks used in the breeding programs. The Tho Noi rabbit breeds 100% pure. One of the odd features of the breed is the males are considerably larger than the females, with bucks weighing in at 3.5 kg. and the does at 2 kg. Litter size is six to nine kits, and does begin to breed at 4-1/2 months.

THRIANTA

 he Thrianta (pronounced TREE-AAN-TA) rabbit is no doubt the most orange-red colored rabbit that you'll ever see. The breed was developed in the Netherlands by a Mr. H. Andrea, of Assen, Holland. To achieve his goal, he bred Tans, Havanas and a self-colored Tortoise Papillion (English Spot). Mr. Andrea's goal was to produce a totally deep orange breed of rabbit, perhaps to honor the Dutch royal family whose accepted color is orange. The Thrianta, named after the province of its birth, was recognized on May 1, 1940, just mere days before the war broke in the Netherlands.

It is unfortunate that there was little interest in the breed after the war. While the intense color was very good, the rabbit's build was rather coarse, plus the standard that the Dutch national rabbit breeders association laid down for the breed was rather difficult to achieve. The Thrianta was soon withdrawn from the list of recognized breeds in the Netherlands.

In former East Germany, a breeder by the name of Mr. Bennack from Rohrsdorf created a similar breed of orange-red rabbit called the Sachsengold (Saxon Gold). To achieve his goal, Bennack mated Chinchilla, Havana, Harlequin,

Dedicated to Glen Carr of Illinois for carrying the torch to seeing the Thrianta rabbit recognized by the American Rabbit Breeders Association into the Book of Standards. Photo courtesy ARBA's Domestic Rabbits.

New Zealand Red and Tans. The build of the Sachsengold was much like that of the Thrianta; however, the color was not as deep. They were first shown in 1953 in Leipzig and accepted in 1961 to the German standards. The breed would soon spread to neighboring countries, but not to Holland.

The late Mr. H. Andrea of Assen, Holland, who developed the Thrianta breed, circa 1950. Photo courtesy Thrianta Specialty Club, Holland.

In order to improve the color of the Sachsengold, a German breeder by the name of Mr. Kissner imported the last of the remaining Thriantas from Holland. These were mated to the Sachsengold. By the late 1960s, the Dutch imported Sachsengold rabbits back into Holland from Mr. Kissner, and they were recognized under that name to the Dutch standards in 1971.

The Dutch decided to honor Mr. Andrea's efforts for producing this lovely, deep-colored rabbit, perhaps as a protest for the Nazi occupation of the Netherlands, and renamed the breed Thrianta in 1979.

Thriantas were imported into the British Isles in the early 1980s from Holland. The breed would reach American soil in 1996 also from Holland, with additional bloodlines imported again from Holland and England as late as 2003.

In both 2001 and 2002, Judith Oldenburg-Graf of Iowa presented the Thriantas before the ARBA Standards Committee, but unfortunately they did not pass due to errors in the paperwork and rabbits be-

Thrianta from Holland, circa 1985. Photo courtesy Thrianta Specialty Club, Holland.

ing over weight. The presentation rights then passed to ARBA secretary, Glen Carr.

During the mid-morning hours of November 5, 2003, at the 80th ARBA National Convention & Show, Mr. Glen Carr, of Bloomington, Illinois, presented four Thrinatas before the ARBA Standards Committee. When the vote was called, Carr's presentation was unanimously approved, and the idea for the American Thrianta Rabbit Breeders Association was born on January 1, 2004, and a slogan was adopted as "The Fire of the Fancy."

THURINGER

 huringers are from Germany and were created the later part of the 19th century by a local school teacher by the name of David Gartner, who lived in the village of Waltershausen in the Thuringer Wald in the eastern part of Germany which borders Czechoslovakia. David Gartner wrote of his creation, "I wanted, says it, to obtain rabbits Russian (Himalayan) and Argente (English Silvers) a strong size by helping me only of the selection, but my efforts gave only poor results; my subjects gained little weight. I have recourse then to use Giant of Flanders (Flemish Giants); immediately the size increased, but there was another disastrous counterpart, the marks of the Russian weakened and the uniformity of the fur of Argente disappeared. However, the unexpected result occurred: crossing of the Russian or Silver plated with the Giant, from the mixture perhaps even of these three races, was born a new rabbit with the yellowish dress, similar to that of the chamois, with brown colors on the nose, the ears, the legs, the tail, recalling in some kinds the marks of the Russian, or the dark ends of a good of Silver hair. This rabbit with

Thuringer rabbit. Photo courtesy Meg Brown, Scotland.

the abnormal dress was a male and it was easy for me, by crossing it with his mother, to obtain the small similar ones to itself. I actively selected them following long crossing continuously, I succeeded in fixing the variety."

David Gartner's actual goal was to produce a larger version of Himalayans and Silvers, but there was little interest shown in them, but the breed he actually named Chamois of Thuringe were a delight to fellow rabbit fanciers. The breed was recognized in Germany in 1907, but were of a slightly small size. Further crossings with Flemish Giants has given us a rabbit recognized throughout Europe and the Scandinavian countries of almost 9 pounds. Thuringers are very similar to the American breed known as Cinnamon.

TRONDER

Norway is the original home of the Tronder breed, which was developed during 1916 to 1918 by a T. Hannemo. The Tronder was originally known as the Norwegian Silver which is to weigh over 4 kg or 9 pounds. During both World Wars, when rabbit meat was in

Thronder rabbit. *Photo courtesy Mirjam Gille, Sweden.*

great demand as an alternative meat, the Tronders were further crossed with the Belgian Giants (Flemish Giants) to increase size of the fryers. Thronders are recognized in Norway, Denmark, Sweden and Finland.

VIENNA

ustria is the native home of the original Vienna breed, with the Blue variety being the first. Blue rabbits have existed in Europe for many years. Even as far back as the 1600s, blue rabbits were noted by the Dutch biologist known as Leuwenhock. H. Schwaab spoke frequently of blue rabbits being observed in Moravie during the year 1860, being heavily kept by the town's people of Heinzendorf and Zwittau.

Early German illustration of a Blue Vienna, circa 1910.

To Mr. J. K. Schultz goes the credit for creating the Vienna Blues, by using a mixture of the Belgian Giants (Flemish Giants), the extinct breed known as the Lorraine (Lotharinger Riesen) a blue-gray rabbit, and the blood of the Ram or French Lop, as we would know it. In 1895, Schultz showed 15 of these Blue Viennas under the title of Giant Blue of Vienna. The name "Giant" having been added would have been very fitting, as these specimens weighed in the neighborhood of 6 kg or 13.25 lb. It is said that Schultz was far more concerned with massive size, rather than the deep blue color the breed is known for today.

Blue Viennas reached Germany in 1903, and in Hamburg 30 of this new breed were exhibited in 1905. Further refinement of the breed took place by the Germany breeders, Weidner, Ehrentraut and Otteman, who would reduce the size somewhat to 4.5 kg with a maximum of 6 kg (10 to 13.25 lb), and the blue color was far more uniform than the original animals presented.

Controversy would begin to appear from other European countries, beginning in 1899, that the Blue Viennas were a crossing of Flemish Giant and the Champagne de Argente, according to Louis Van Der Snickt. The Belgian rabbit expert, Polydore de Keghel, con-

Blue Vienna. Photo courtesy Federation Francaise de Cuniculture, France.

sidered the breed was strictly made up of Flemish Giants, and authors from Belgian considered the Blue Viennas belonged to their country, as the original home. Carlos Blank de Breda was of the opinion that the Blue Viennas were nothing more than Blue French Lops, which were selected for an upright ear carriage. This would have certainly seemed impossible. There would be much confusion during the early 20th century with all the blue breeds, Beveren, Viennas, Flemish, St. Nicholas and the Blue Imperial, all which were known to more or less have a mandolin type during this period of time and, of course, all were blue. In Germany and the Netherlands, breeders fine-tuned the breed, greatly improving the intensity of color and fixing the Vienna type we know today.

The Gray Vienna was begun from a German breed known as Deutsches Manichean (German Rabbit), which was known as early as 1855 in Chemnitz. It was a rather small rabbit at 2 to 2.5 kg (4.5 to 5.5 lb) and was bred in many colors. After crossing it with "Giant" rabbits, it was renamed Neudeutsches Kaninchen or New German Rabbit, which increased the weight to 4 kg or nearly 9 lb. During the 1930s, a member of the Vienna Rabbit Club of Wurtemberg, by the name of Gustave Korn d' Eislingen, presented these gray rabbits as Gray Viennas. Although these were smaller than the Blue Viennas, they were recognized by the club. Korn was able to get the Standard recognized by the German governing body in 1936. In 1938, the Standards Commission recanted. In 1943, the Gray Vienna was reestablished as the German Rabbit.

The German Rabbit was further crossed with the Blue Vienna and Giant Chinchilla after World War I, and would be recognized as the Vienna Gray finally in 1962 and was presented a German Standard.

Black Viennas were created at the urging of furriers of the day in Germany, shortly after the end of World War I. The known black rabbit of the time was the Alaska, but the pelt was rather small, so through the German press in the early 1920s, rabbit breeders were asked to develop a large self black rabbit for the fur trade. The Blue Vienna Club took up the challenge by crossing Blue Viennas with the Alaska, and by 1925 the new variety was created.

Blue Gray Viennas are a fairly recent addition to the Vienna varieties, although during the development of the Blue Vienna by Schultz, blue gray rabbits were appearing in the litters. The color would be called decades later as the Large Feh (Lubeck) and Hinnefer Riesenfeh in Germany. During the 1930s the Blue Gray Vienna was accepted to the German Standards, but would be removed in 1961 for lack of animals being shown. It was allowed in the French Standards in 1989, although not widely kept in that country.

Blue Viennas were recognized in the United States as early as 1919 and were sponsored by the New Zealand Club for a time, but fell from favor during the late 1950s. The Blue Vienna was reinstated into the American standards through the efforts of Bert Reurs of Canada in 1976, but again failed to gain much of a following, and 10 years later in 1986 was dropped as a recognized breed for lack of numbers being shown at ARBA Conventions.

VIENNA WHITE

 iennas are from Austria, where the Blue Vienna would first appear in 1895. However, when the White Vienna was created, a Mr. Mucke, beginning in 1900, showed the two varieties together, bringing about great protest, as the Blue and Whites were greatly different in fur structure, type and size as well. It quickly became apparent that the two animals were indeed two different breeds, so today they are shown as White Vienna and Colored Vienna.

Rabbit keepers for a very long time wanted to produce a large white rabbit, but without the pink eyes. Hermann Ziemer began the project using Dutch, which in time Ziemer created the Husumer rabbit. Mr. W. Mucke, who worked for the railroad, continued on the same lines as Ziemer, by using Dutch rabbits in his crosses. Mucke finally reached his goal of an all white rabbit with blue eyes in 1907, and has been dubbed the father of the "White Vienna." Another fellow by the name of Schutze, from Ratingen, achieved the same results as did W. Mucke, just a short time later, but all of his stock would be destroyed during World War I.

White Viennas would

White Vienna. *Photo courtesy Federation de Cuniculiculture, France.*

Illustration of a White Vienna from Germany, circa 1910.

be introduced into Germany in 1910 by Ernest Ordel, from Tangermude. Much crossing of the White Viennas to other breeds to increase their size to match the Blue Viennas proved fruitless, as it just brought the two colors further apart.

Through the years, after carefully selected breeding, the White Viennas today have the same type as the Blues and other Vienna varieties, but the size is still smaller. The pale blue eyes and extremely soft and dense coat is a wonderful feature of these animals. Weights are 7 lb 11 oz to 11 lb 9 oz (3.5 to 5.25 kg).

VIT LAND

Vit Land rabbits, also called Hvid Land, are originally from Denmark, but are also recognized in Finland, Sweden and Norway. The breed was first shown in 1908 in Kopenhamn, and is one of the many Ruby-Eyed White breeds of the world. It is a large breed, weighing 3.8 to 4.6 kg or 8.5 to 10.25 lbs.

Vit Land or Hvid Land of Denmark.

WHEATEN

Wheatens are a British breed created by the late Hugh Halliday starting in the early 1980s. Halliday was responsible for importing the first examples of Beige, Deilenaar, Thrianta, Sallander, Swiss Fox and Blanc de Hotots from Europe. In 1981, Halliday was breeding Yellow Dutch, but was rather disappointed in their color, so decided he would make it his dream to create an all yellow rabbit. First crossing was a Blue Silver Marten (Silver Fox) with a Havana (Chocolate). For the next two years he crossed the rabbits back and forth, father to daughter, mother to son, and brother and sisters. Then he borrowed a light golden agouti-colored buck and mated it to a pinkish-colored agouti doe. The doe produced three offspring: a lynx, one opal and a straw-colored rabbit. Halliday then mated the lynx doe to the straw-colored brother, with the resulting offspring being just about the desired color the creator had been dreaming about.

Through selection for type and color, Hugh Halliday's rabbits were breeding fairly true by 1994 and were recognized as a breed by the British Rabbit Council. The first color was the original Wheaten, which was then followed by the Wheaten Lynx, by the introduction of Perlfee blood.

Wheatens weigh 5.5 to 7 pounds (2.49 to 3.17 kg). The breed was never very popular in the United Kingdom. They have not been seen at shows for a number of years and certainly could have fallen into the class known as "Extinction." However, the breed is still recognized in the book of standards.

WHITE OF DENDERMONDE

Belgium is the original home of the White of Dendermonde rabbit breed, also known as Blanc de Termode. Mr. W. Collier wrote in his book *Cuniculture Illustree,* 1928, that he could buy excellent white rabbits in 1918 of a large size from the region of Dendermonde. He further says that these white rabbits had blue eyes. Ten years later, Collier believed that he was wrong and that the breed was actually White Beverens, but the White of Dendermonde were a much larger animal. The breed was named by a Mr. M. Bobart, who was a well-known fancier of the day, and would later sell the breed to his best

White of Dendermonde. Photo courtesy Marc Vancayzeele, Belgium.

338

friend, a Mr. Omer, and he to a Mr. Dierickx. The White of Dendermondes were bred in large numbers and exported to fanciers in France and England for rather high prices. The breed did not remain for long in England, but in France it was said to have been developed into the Blanc de Vendee, but the creator of that breed, Mrs. Douillard, flatly denied this. Blue-eyed white rabbits of the time were high in demand and brought the best prices.

Rabbit breeders in Belgium were still not happy with the size of the White of Dendermonde. To increase weights, they were further crossed with White Flemish Giants, which first produced marked rabbits and of varying types. The blue eyes would be replaced with red. Ten animals were shown in 1919 at Hamme, Belgium, and by 1923 specimens were shown for the first time with uniform type. It is not a widely kept breed. Weights should be from 4 to 5.5 kg or 9 to 12.25 lb.

ZEMMOURI

 emmouri rabbits are a product of Morocco, which began in 1912, during the colonization of Morocco by France and Spain. Exotic breeds were brought from Europe by missionaries, which were naturally mated to the native stock in Azrou (middle of the Atlas mountains) and Temara (Rabat region). After many generations the resulting crosses had adapted to the local environmental conditions. Further inter-breeding of the two populations gave the origin of the Zemmouri breed.

During 1996 to 1998, experimental studies were carried out at the Skikima Station, in collaboration with Department of Avian Pathology and the National School of Agriculture. Their objective is to study the performance traits of the Zemmouri rabbit under controlled conditions of farming and management. Pelleted feed and all wire indoor cages are still being used. Trials are also being conducted in the pure breeding of the

Zemmouri rabbit has adapted to the harsh conditions of Morocco.

Zemmouri rabbits, along with crossbreeding experiments, using both Californian and New Zealand males to Zemmouri females. Zemmouri rabbits are bred for meat and fur. The breed is fairly well adapted to the hot climates of Morocco, and there is no danger of extinction with a breeding population of over 10,000 animals.

Leipzig, Germany, circa 1880.

CHAPTER III

OTHER HISTORICAL RABBIT TOPICS

RABBIT KEEPING CENTURIES PAST

abbit keeping in all wire hutches is more or less considered a modern method when one considers some of the earlier modes used by man over the centuries. You may be surprised to learn of some of the more popular facilities employed of yesteryear such as islands, warrens, courts and rabbit pits.

Rabbit Islands

Rabbit Islands have been in existence for hundreds of years. In Germany in 1407, an island in Lake Scheverin in the state of Mechlenburg was made home to rabbits in a treaty between the King of Sweden and the Duke of Mechlenburg. Near Berlin, an island now called Pfaunimsal was once known as Kaninchenwerder (Rabbit Island). Rabbit keeping here was started by the 18th century King of Prussia, Frederick the Great (Frederick Wilhelm). A rather famous lady who kept a rabbit island on the River Thames in England was none other than Queen Elizabeth I. The explorer Van Riebeck introduced eight rabbits to Robin Island, off the coast of Capetown, South Africa in 1652. The rabbits multiplied at such an alarming rate that the vegetation was destroyed and prisoners were placed there in 1658.

In 1418 or 1419, a J. Gonzales Zacro happened to have a female rabbit on board his ship which had produced young during their voyage, and he turned them out on the island of Porto Santa near Maderia, as written by Charles Darwin in his *The Variation of Animals and Plants Under*

Domestication, 1883. These animals soon increased so rapidly that they became a nuisance, and would actually cause the abandonment of the human settlement.

Most Rabbit Islands were created in the 13th and 14th centuries by early explorers and trading ships, especially those belonging to the Dutch East Indies Company. Islands along the main sea routes were populated with rabbits as a food source for shipwrecked sailors (see Enderby Island). Over the centuries, nearly every island of the world has had rabbits placed upon it at some time or another. Many populations flourished, while some indeed failed. Success stories of the European rabbit, *Oryctolagus cuniculus,* spread and survival have been well documented, especially in Australia and New Zealand, where this wild rabbit, the ancestor of all our domestic rabbits, has cost many millions of dollars to the vast landscapes of these island nations. Regardless of how romantic a Rabbit Island may sound, most people don't have the finances to afford such a unique method of keeping rabbits in this manner, so more reasonable modes would have to be found.

Rabbit Warrens

In its original sense of the word "warren," old French warenne and varenne, later to be used garenne, medieval English was wareine, and Low Latin warenna, signified a preserve in general, and came subsequently to be restricted to an enclosure especially set apart for coneys (rabbits) and hares. "Coney-close" had the same meaning, and "coney-garth" and "garth" was the term used in the north of England as a small enclosure adjoining a house. From *Promptorium Parvulorum* mentions "near to ancient dwelling-places the name 'Coneygare,' 'Conigree,' or 'Coneygarth' occurs, and from various conjectures have been

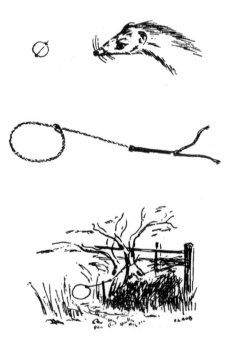

Rabbit Ferreting was only used when no young were about and rabbit snares would strangle the animals, circa 1880s.

342

A warrener of the olden days, circa late 1600s.

made respecting its derivation, which, however, is sufficiently obvious." From "warren" we get "warrener," Latin warinarius, corrupted into the surname, "Warner."

Rabbit warrens were quite commonplace in England until the later part of the 1800s. This system of rabbit keeping had been originally introduced to the British Isles by the Norman invaders. The Warrener with his ferrets would be employed to take care of the warrens, at least in the beginning. When the Romas introduced the rabbit into Italy, they also introduced the custom of hunting it with ferrets, and when they carried the same animal into Britain, they imported the same custom with it. The Britons adopted what the Romans practiced. It was known as the Roman-Spanish hunt, and the Roman-Spanish name for the animal employed it; denominating the later Viverra, in Welsh it was called Guivaer, and in Irish, Firead or Ferret.

The early use of ferrets is made apparent from several sources of information. They were employed by Genghis Khan in his imperial hunting circle at Termed in 1221, and are mentioned by the Emperor Frederick II of Germany in 1245, amongst the animals used to hunt rabbits.

So long ago as in 1390 in King Richard II's time, a statute was passed prohibiting anyone from keeping or using greyhounds and fyrets (ferrets) who had not the lands or tenements of the annual value of 40 shillings. Both the fychew and the fyret are mentioned in *Thystorye of Reynard the Foxe,* as printed by Caxton in 1481, and in the *Book of St. Albans,* in 1486. In the *Household Book of Lord William Howard of Naworth,* several entries occur which clearly indicate the employment of ferrets and nets for taking rabbits in Cumberland in 1621.

Warrens came under strict laws from the British Crown. Manwood, in his *Treatise and Discourse of the Laws of the Forest,* 1598, asserts that this expression included the hare, the coney, the pheasant and the partridge, "and none other," justifying this definition from the *Register of Writs,* and

Book of Entries, which show that in every case in which action was brought by any grantee of free warren against a trespasser, the statement of claim invariably ran "et lepores, cuniculos, phasianos, et perdices cepit et sportive." He was quite clear, therefore, that the beasts and fowls of the warren were limited to these four species. Typical warrens were huge areas of land, many 100 acres and up in mass. These warrens were surrounded by a natural moat, deep trench, fence, stone wall or hedgerow of thick brambles, so the escape of many rabbits was inevitable. In the *Survey of Lincolnshire,* where many warrens had become established, it is stated that the warren will have one buck to several hundred does. In a warren of 250 acres, 2,000 animals may be killed per year, leaving 700 to repopulate. Warrens would have to be rich in vegetation, and during the leaner times, especially winter, the rabbits would have to be fed usually with turnips, clover, hay and barley straw.

From E.S. Delamer's book, *Pigeons and Rabbits,* 1859: "Considerable expense too is incurred for warreners, for nets and traps, for the repair of fences, and for the destruction of different kinds of vermin, as well as for the protection from poachers, who, if not watched, would soon depopulate the place. Whoever becomes the proprietor of a warren must keep one or more warreners. These men make a regular profession of their business, which renders information here less necessary; they moreover are a peculiar set, and are not a little jealous of revealing the secrets relating to their modes of trapping and snaring. The best plan to get rabbits destroyed is to employ different and rival warreners at once. Of those officials there were seven, with dogs and implements in abundance. Besides wages, they were allowed all the rabbits they could eat, and bread, bacon, vegetables, beer, etc., from the farmhouse, to be consumed in their huts on the warren, where they cooked, in hermit-like solitude, for themselves. During the killing at about two in the morning, the catch was immediately "Bulked," or disemboweled, coupled, and sent off to London in regular vans. During the day, false burrows were dug in the portion of the warren to be worked in the evening which was afterwards partially encircled with a net. When the rabbits came out to feed, they were driven by the dogs and beaters into the enclosure. Taking refuge by droves in the false burrows, they were easily caught by the men; those that escaped thence were intercepted by the nets. The dogs not being allowed to touch them, very few rabbits indeed were mangled or torn. Stretching their necks was the mode of death."

Poaching was a serious problem for people who owned warrens. There were three type of poachers: the local men; the raiders who came in gangs from a distance; and the moochers, fellows who do not make precisely a profession of it, but who occasionally loiter along the roads and hedges, picking up whatever they can lay their hands on.

Illustration of a modern warren (right) and wire court (left) showing hutches. Oval items on shed are fur boards for stretching pelts. An American diagram, circa 1920.

Of the three, perhaps the largest amount of rabbits was taken by the local men. Poachers who used ferrets always preferred the white ones for night work, as they were easily seen and are not likely to be picked up by the poacher's dog in mistake of a rabbit, although the poacher's dogs as a rule were too well trained to make such mistakes. The keepers of the warren are all too glad to get hold of the poacher's ferrets when they could, for these animals were indeed well trained. Various laws were established to deal with poaching: Game Act, 1831, under King William IV; the Night Poachers' Act, 1828, under King George IV and modified in 1844; under Queen Victoria, the Larceny Act, 1861, and the Poaching Prevention Act, 1862, also under Victoria.

The history of the rabbit warrens of England is very well documented, far too lengthy to be included in any detail in this work, so I must move forward to bring about the time of a more confined method of rabbit keeping.

Rabbit Courts and Walled Gardens

With warrens, rabbits were still to be only found in the wild state. It was not until rabbit courts or walled gardens were employed that the European wild rabbit would become domesticated by man, and that selection would begin to take place as different colors and mutations occurred. Rabbits have been kept behind the walls of the monasteries well before the fifth century. Unborn and new born rabbits, which were called Laurices, were a favorite of the Romans, and it was Pope Gregory the Great who

rose to the throne of Saint Peter in 590 A.D., who issued the Papal Edict in 600 A.D., that rabbit was not considered meat, and could be served during Lent. It should be noted that Pope Gregory was the first monk to ever be chosen pope, and also, Pope Gregory was considered the last of the true Romans. It would appear only naturally that he would issue such a decree, as I'm sure he dined on unborn and newborn rabbits many times as a monk. It is believed that shortly after this Papal Edict was issued that rabbits actually became domesticated, and too, rabbits were the last breed of livestock domesticated by man. Records show that domestic rabbits were exchanged in 1194 between the monasteries of Germany and France, when the Abbot Carvey of Germany asked the Abbot of Solignac, France to send him two pairs of rabbits. It was in the walled areas that during the 16th century that the first white, black and piebald colored rabbits were discovered and reported by Atricola.

Cuniculus, in his *The Practical Rabbit Keeper,* 1880, gives an excellent description of the rabbit-courts, "The rabbit-court, which is a very profitable system of keeping hardy breeds, though it will not pay for Lops and other varieties requiring special care, a question we shall deal with anon. Several rabbit-courts in this country (England) are uncovered, but we believe such have not been found to pay very well, owing to the very wet seasons we are liable to. Covered ones are much preferable, and one of

Diagram of a Rabbit Court.
A. Door into court,
B. Does' hutches,
C. Bucks' hutches,
D. Mound of earth for borrows,
E. Feeding troughs. Circa 1880s.

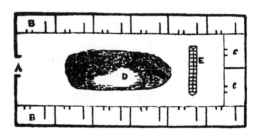

this kind we will now describe, with a few hints as to the best means of making it. If you have 'Hobson's choice,' of course, you must do the best you can; but if you have a selection of ground, select a corner built against by two houses, and having the south side open. By this means your labour will be greatly curtailed, and if a third side is also built against, so much the better. Dig out your foundations for the sides not already hemmed in by bricks and mortar, and go at least two feet below the surface. Lay your bricks nine inches thick — and it will be cheaper to employ a practical man for this part of the work — and let the wall be six feet high from inside at least. When this is completed, have the floor well laid. If it is on soft ground, it will be best to down flags (stone). If the ground is clay or hard, a cement floor will do better and be cheaper. If this be laid, the first thing to do is to level the ground carefully, and then cut a ditch six inches deep down one side, sloping to a corner, where an aperture should be left, carefully secured by iron bars about two inches apart. Then mix some Portland cement with sand — you can ascertain the proportions on purchasing — and mix the whole into the consistency of very thick cream. This done, lay the mixture on the floor, taking care to smooth very carefully with a board, and do it quickly, as the cement soon dries, and when dry it is as hard as a rock. Care should be taken to have the ditch or drain covered the same thickness as the rest of the floor, so that the depression is still apparent, as this is most essential for cleaning and scouring out the place. Further assistance will be provided by allowing the floor to slope very slightly towards this. A door must be made in the usual way, and a sliding board — such as is used for keeping young children within bounds — should be adopted, so that when the door is opened, any loose bunnies may not so readily make their exit.

"It is necessary next to make hutches of some sort or other round the sides. We shall describe a few pages further on hutches of various descriptions, but for a rabbit-court a set of apartments as described here will be not only sufficient, but will answer better than any other. The side opposite the door, or facing the person entering, can be first dealt with. Make a front of inch board for the whole length, about 18 inches high, and fix it on the ground nearly two feet from the wall. Before doing so, make as aperture every two or three feet, according to the length of the place and the size of the proposed hutches, say two feet in an average court. The holds should be circular, and the edges should be lined with tin, or the rabbits will gnaw them out of all shape. This done, divide the space into boxes, or

hutches, with a hole for each leading into the open court. Cover this with inch board; but let nine inches in width be fixed with hinges, so as to act as a door. One door for the whole is a clumsy way of doing the work, and it is not much more trouble to make one for each hutch. This, opening as it does on the top of the hutches, is very convenient for getting at the inmates, and for cleaning and feeding purposes. Each hole should be fitted with a sliding-door that can be closed at will, and each door should be fitted with a nut or bolt to fasten it down. These hutches will do very well for breeding hardy 'table' kinds of rabbits, though they would not do for delicate breeds. According

Italian etchings of Rabbit Courts or Walled Gardens, circa 1890s.

to the number you intend keeping, so large must be the accommodation provided for the young rabbits. A row along one of the other sides will generally be found sufficient. They need not be divided in hutches, and there need only be two or three holes cut, the whole forming a sleeping place which, with the timely addition of straw, will make all comfortable.

"A mound of earth in the centre of the court is sometimes recommended, and it undoubtedly affords the rabbits lots of amusement. Still it has its corresponding drawbacks, and is objectionable on the whole. It often falls in and

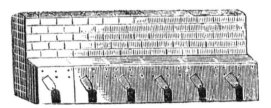

Wall inside of a Rabbit Court, showing the earliest of hutches, circa mid-1800s.

buries the frolickers, and as it cannot be properly cleansed, the dung and urine saturate it, and give out a nasty odour that is anything but agreeable or healthy. A good layer of clean sand, changed twice a week, is better. A tile or slate roof is desirable, or a good serviceable one may be made of asphalted tarpaulin. Circumstances must guide as to the construction, but in most instances a lean-to structure is found cheapest and most service-

Wall-mounted feeding trough for a Rabbit Court, circa 1800s.

able. It should be made to overlay the walls of the court at least a foot, but the aperture between it and the top of the wall need not be filled in; indeed, ample ventilation in this or some other way must be provided."

Rabbit Courts or Walled Gardens were usually employed by the city dwellers, and were fairly common during their day, but the farmers and country people, who were not within the confines of the packed cities, developed a much easier and far more cost-effective method, yet on a much smaller

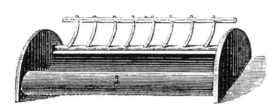

Movable feeding trough, in an open position, circa 1880.

scale. Their mode of rabbit keeping was in some cases just as grand as islands and walled courtyards, but called for some digging; these were known as Rabbit Pits, and were popular in the mid 19th century.

Rabbit Pits

A woodcut illustration appeared in *Farming for Ladies,* 1850, of an elaborate structure, which was the brain child of a man from Kent, England, and I quote; "who had arranged, in a paddock adjoining his house, a small rabbitry and pigeon house, solely for his family use and amusement, and enclosed it with post and chain, to prevent the access of his horses to the place. The enclosure was only about twelve feet in diameter, covering a pit six feet in depth, in which the rabbits were confined, and through the sandy sides of which they burrowed to the extent of from ten to fourteen feet to make their nests. The proprietor, however, it was said, intended to

An elaborate Rabbit Pit, circa 1850.

up three feet of the depth, as e thought that rabbits should be brought nearer to the air.

The mode of catching the rabbits in the pit was a long stick, forked at the end, which was hooked upon their neck when they came out to feed; or they were snared with a bit of wire fastened to the end of a stick."

Another Rabbit Pit design is from the same period, which appeared in the *Agricultural Gazette,* and was built on the Isle of Thanet, on the east coat of Kent, England. The owner oversaw the project and describes his design. "No. 1 represents a pit four feet on each side of the square. No. 2 is an oblong, four feet long, and about two feet broad. Both are dug to the depth of six feet, perfectly level at the bottom and sides, the latter so much wider than the wooden curbs, as to admit of a facing of four-inch brickwork, in cement, excepting the spaces to admit of about six arched openings (as marked) *(but he shows eight openings)* of dimensions sufficient for the passage of the largest rabbit. No. 2 is the feeding department. No. 3 is only an arched passage, tunneled at the ground level of the bottom of the two pits, about a foot wide and broad, to serve as a communication between the pits. This is also bricked and arched, but is not seen at the top. A covering of oilcloth is added to the curb of each pit, and the cloth extends over the frame several inches beyond the curb, in order to prevent the entry of the heaviest rain. At the place op., the arched passage is always open; and so it is also at the other extremity marked tr., excepting only when any of the rabbits are to be taken. Dryness is essential to the prosperity of this animal."

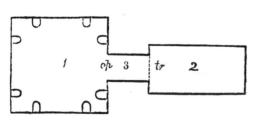

Plan of a Rabbit Pit, circa 1850.

350

Of special note; the rabbits which this gentleman kept in his double pit design were none other than the Silver Sprigs, our beautiful rabbit we call Silvers today.

It is quite remarkable how rabbit keeping has evolved over the many centuries; one can just close their eyes and envision these acres and facilities with hopping rabbits, but let's all be reasonable, nothing can replace the good old rabbit hutch, which is an evolution process in itself through the years.

EVOLUTION OF THE RABBIT HUTCH

h, the lowly bunny rabbit has endured just about every type of housing known to man. From the cardboard box, a vegetable crate from the local produce market, the simple all wooden box, bushel basket, chicken coop, wooden barrel, and even a claw-foot bathtub, I have seen rabbits kept in just about anything imaginable, as both permanent home or the quick fix temporary housing.

The rabbit hutch began to come into being during the time of the rabbit court method of keeping, typically this was started by the monks, which would lead to the domestication of the European Wild Rabbit. The monks would notice a particular trait not seen before and isolate the animal to a special quarters, which would become known throughout the world as the hutch.

There is indeed something very special about the wood and wire hutch, at least in the eyes of this author, because it brings back so many vivid

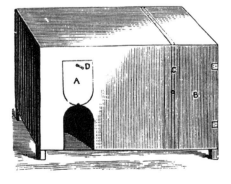

The first hutches were used in rabbit courts; however, just when is not known. Records do show that in the vicinity of London, England, individual hutches were being used in the rabbit courts of 1740. A Rabbit-Court Hutch of the mid-1800s was oftentimes made of "bacon boxes" used by provision dealers and lined up along the wall of the court.

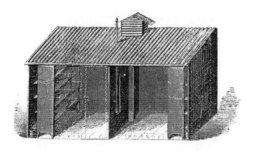

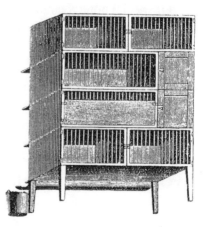

Because heat was believed to be extremely important to produce ear-length in the Lops during the mid-1800s, all-metal sheds were designed in which heats were placed to bring up the temperatures. A Lop shed and hutch unit for the shed.

memories as a five- to six-year-old, watching the rabbits hopping around in their cozy protected environment, eating hay from the manger, nibbling green foods scattered about the floor, or drinking from their earthenware crock. Those wonderful smells of freshly cut grass, or pine, cedar and redwood shavings, which typically made up the bedding. Yes, those were very memorial times, but memories they shall remain, as man always has improvements in mind to make a person's life easier, less labor-intensive and modernization. This has especially so taken place in the United States, where about 90 percent of all domestic rabbits are now kept in the all wire rabbit cage. What has happened to the word hutch? Typically Americans have passed that word aside, as we now use the term pen, hole or cage, when referring to hutches. It appears that only those people who do still raise rabbits in wooden and wire pens will call them hutches, certainly a dying term in America.

It is the Americans mostly, who have the fascination with the all wire rabbit quarters, which were first developed in the late 1920s, but it took many, many years for this type of system to be recognized by most rabbit breeders. It was at the Rabbit Experiment Station in Fontana, California, by the U.S. government, that extensive studies began, especially for commercial rabbit operations, that an all wire rabbit cage was developed, using a wire that was made for muskrat farming. The first individual who introduced the all wire cage into his private use was George West, the originator of the California breed. Very slowly this type of cage system spread east, but it was not until the late 1960s and early 1970s that it truly re-

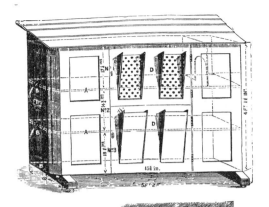

Stack of outdoor hutches for Lops, made completely out of metal. Note the only ventilation and light is from the holes made in the hay rack, which would be fitted with a pane of glass, circa mid-1800s.

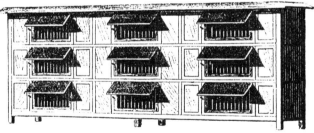

ceived wide acceptance by breeders and fanciers. The southern tier of the country was much quicker converting to the all wire cage, because of the temperate climate. Now this is America that I speak of, as the rest of the world is an entirely different story. In Europe and the United Kingdom where land is typically at a premium because of such dense populations, rabbits to this day are still maintained usually in an all wooden enclosure, with a wood and wire front, solid floors, and cages are normally stacked

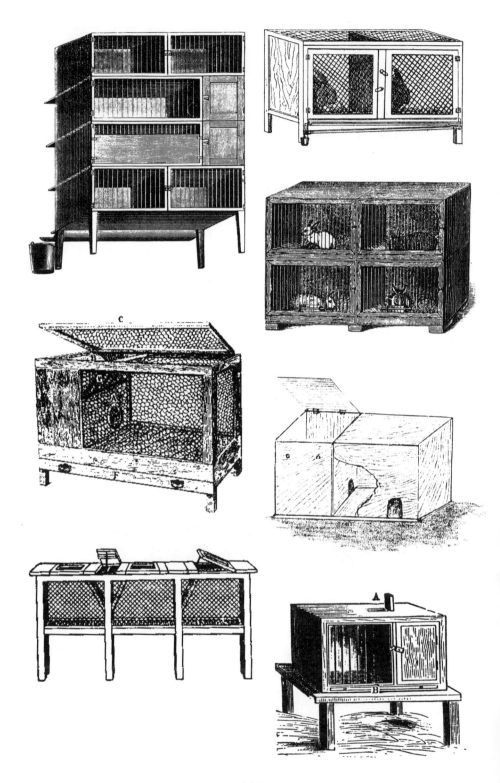

three tiered, and in some cases four high. A large Stud, as they normally call their rabbitries, would be 50 hutches. Most breeders have much less, as it is quite labor intensive to be fitted into the person's busy daily life. Only the large commercial operations use the all wire system in Europe today for rearing meat and laboratory animals. The huge commercial Angora wool operations of China have developed three-story concrete cubical quarters for their rabbit operations.

As I said in the beginning, the rabbit has endured all sorts of housing facilities, so a pictorial tour of rabbit housing and equipment from many lands would be appropriate and a feast for the eyes, and show just how far we have come in this rabbit hobby/industry.

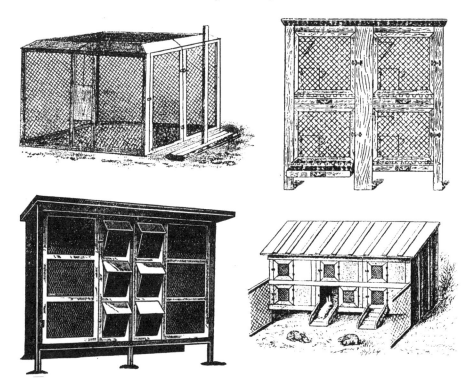

Major J.F. Morant of Essex, England developed the very popular Morant hutch in the early 1880s. It was a grazing hutch which could be moved about the yard. This hutch, although developed into many styles, was recognized the world over. Typically, it was built in a triangular fashion, but various flat tops were used as well.

355

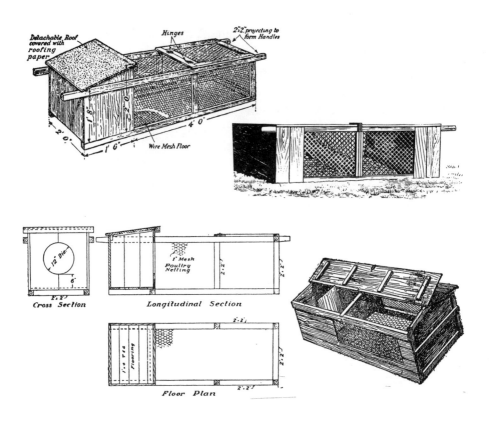

Three types of American Morant hutches, circa 1930.

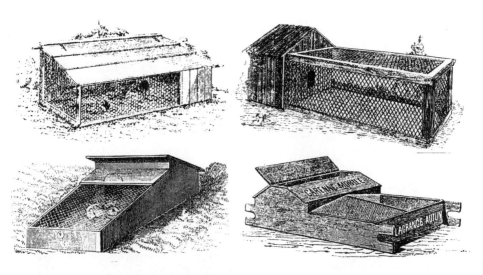

Four designs of Italian Morant hutches, circa 1910.

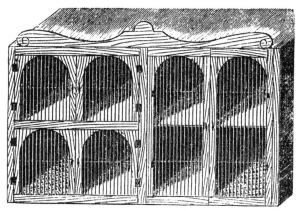

Many of the early rabbit hutches could be considered as fine furniture during the Victorian period of the 1800s.

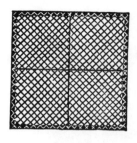

False bottoms of wire netting or wood, with holes drilled and channeled guttering, were already being employed in England as early as 1880.

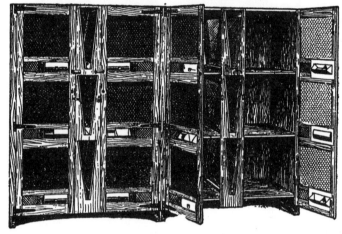

A typical British design from the 1920s was often used for Angoras, as they had a built-in V-shaped hay feeder, and specially built three-tier doors, having spaces for pivoted grain feeders, which could be filled without opening the door.

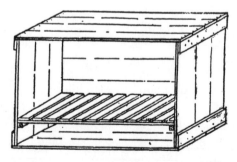

A rabbit hutch did not have to be expensive. Here is the simplest form made from a packing case. A wire-fronted door would be attached. Notice the slatted floor. These hutches normally would be stacked three high, with linoleum between each unit, circa 1920.

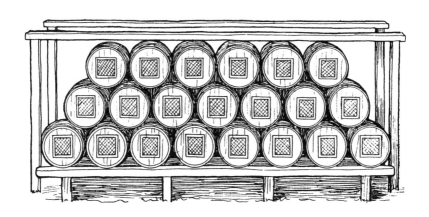

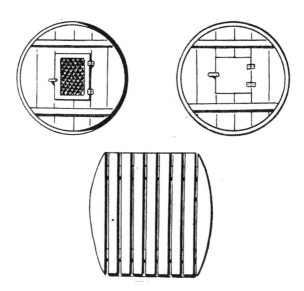

A remarkable bank of rabbit hutches made from wooden barrels was extremely popular throughout Europe and the Scandinavian countries at the beginning of the 20th century.

A single barrel hutch, which this author thinks is about the most unique of all the rabbit hutches ever designed.

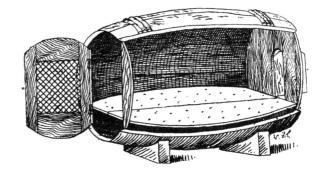

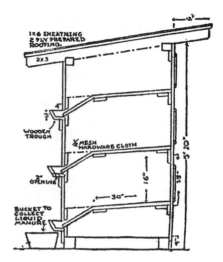

Cross-section of self-cleaning hutch, with solid floor in front and hardware cloth floor at rear, through which droppings fall, to be removed at rear.

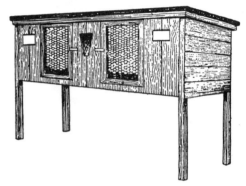

Various Americans designed a self-cleaning hutch as early as 1917. This design appeared in 1924 by Marcellus W. Meek.

Edward H. Stahl of Missouri designed this type of self-cleaning hutch in the early 1920s.

Earthen crocks are a staple that have endured the test of time for rabbit keeping throughout the world for better than 100 years.

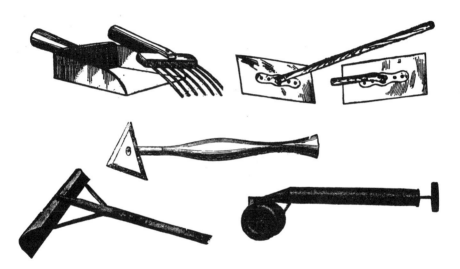

Important tools for the rabbit keeper to always have on hand: various hutch scrapers, cleaning fork and removal pan, as well as the pump sprayer for applying disinfectant.

A simple group of hutches in America which have been protected from thieves. Note the chain stretched across the doors and padlocks to protect the valuable Chinchilla rabbits, circa 1922.

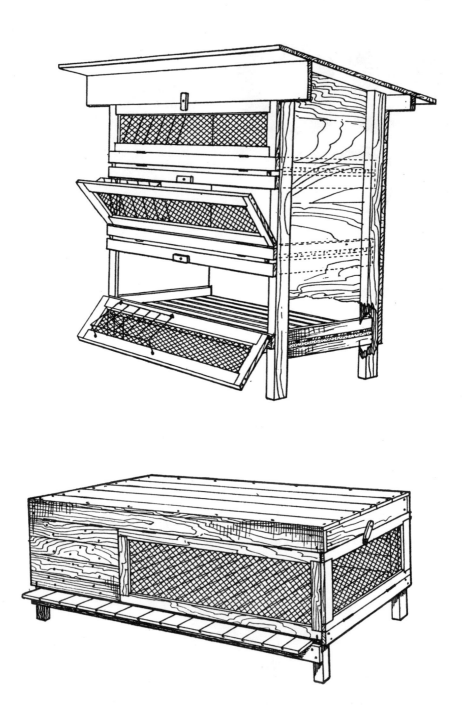

The United States Government issued bulletins on how to build a rbbit hutch. Here are two designs: the tiered slat-floored hutch and the single slant-floored hutch, circa 1930s.

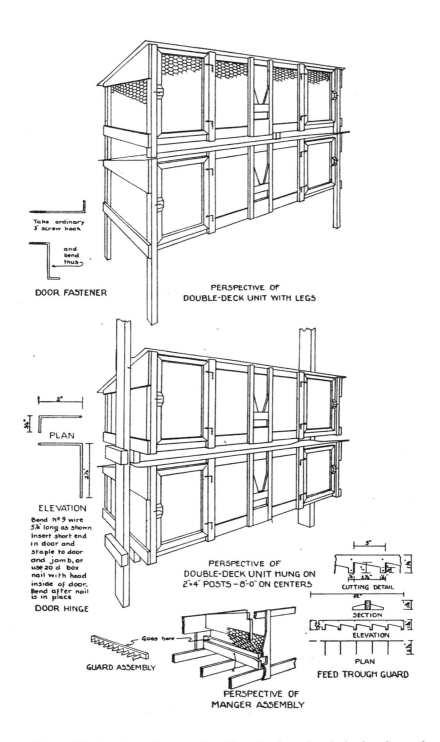

DOOR FASTENER
Take ordinary 5" screw hook and bend thus

PERSPECTIVE OF
DOUBLE-DECK UNIT WITH LEGS

PLAN

ELEVATION

Bend Nº 9 wire 5¾" long as shown. Insert short end in door and staple to door and jamb, or use 20 d box nail with head inside of door. Bend after nail is in place

DOOR HINGE

PERSPECTIVE OF
DOUBLE-DECK UNIT HUNG ON
2"x4" POSTS — 8'-0" ON CENTERS

CUTTING DETAIL

SECTION

ELEVATION

PLAN

FEED TROUGH GUARD

Goes here

GUARD ASSEMBLY

PERSPECTIVE OF
MANGER ASSEMBLY

Most living rabbit fanciers will remember this style of wood and wire hutch popular from the 1930s through the 1950s. From Farmers' Bulletin, #1730.

A large indoor rabbit facility for Chinchilla rabbit breeding in England. Note the round disk on the fronts for record keeping, circa 1920.

An artist's conception for the Premier Rabbitry, Inc. of Indianapolis, Indiana, where hutches outline massive gardening plots for growing crops for the animals, a processing plant, fur facilities, a shipping department, offices and a residence. This was the brain child of John C. Fehr, but his glamorous dream never came to pass, circa 1930s.

Huge rabbitries sprang up throughout the United States in the first half of the 20th century. This set-up had curtains that could be dropped to protect the animals from rain, wind and snow, circa 1930.

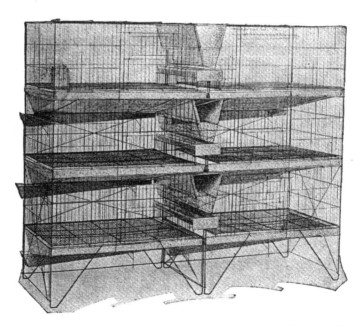

The first all-wire hutch in America was developed by the United Steel & Wire Company of Battle Creek, Michigan, and were called the United Hutch, appeared in 1929.

The Jax System from South Euclid, Ohio, for feeding and watering appeared at the 1931 National Convention in St. Louis, Missouri, and was unanimously approved as the most practical front feeder and water device on the market. A hundred hutches could be fed and watered in 20 minutes, without opening a single door.

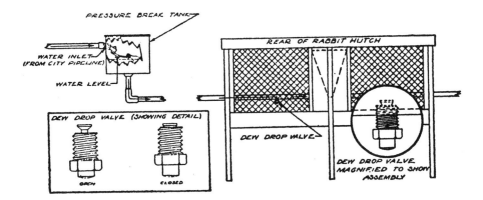

The Dew Drop Watering System made its appearance in America in the early 1940s.

The Quonset all-wire hutch was mainly used in California, Texas and Florida due to the mild climates, but was short-lived because of the tremendous waste of wire, circa 1950.

EVOLUTION OF RABBIT FEEDING

 et us be realistic in the fact that rabbit keeping today has never been easier, when one considers what our forefathers had to go through, in just keeping a small shed of rabbits in proper health and condition. Pelletized rabbit feeds became rather the norm for feeding rabbits only during the 1930s, and by the 1950s most would have thought one was crazy to be using anything other than a general ration of pellets with a bit of quality hay added to the rabbit's diet.

Rabbit keeping during the 1800s actually required a "Rabbit Garden" to be planted if one had any sizable number of rabbits. Certainly, for a few rabbits the family garden would have sufficed. From *The Practical Rabbit Keeper,* 1880, by Cuniculus, we gain an insight of just what it must have been like in those days of yesteryear, when it came to meal time.

"Bran and cabbage are the common food of a rabbit under the care of a beginner, and a viler compound can scarcely be imagined. Anyone who has seen cabbage boiled and smelt the broth can easily understand that the daily use of cabbages as rabbit food makes the hutch much more obnoxious in smell than it naturally is. Perhaps the very best green food for rabbits is hare parsley; not only does it contain a fair amount of moisture, but it has the extra advantage of being nutritious and flesh-forming. It is a wild plant, and grows very abundantly in most country districts. There are some difficulties in collecting wild herbage; and if a few square yards of land can be appropriated for the purpose, it is a very good plan to plant several roots of this valuable herb and cultivate it. By a pretty liberal use of your waste manure you may make it grow with extraordinary rapidity, and if it is cut with care it will yield several crops during the season. For young rabbits especially it is very valuable.

"Another excellent food is found in clover and its kindred species, including vetches, tares, trefoil, &c. These can be given pretty freely in the summer time, and form a splendid food, although, of course, none of them possess what may be termed strictly fattening qualities. Young shoots of all kinds of corn are also very good, but we feel somewhat diffident in recommending what we know can only be obtained at a great cost, and what is so often likely to be got with very light fingers. Chicory is very fine food; so is comfrey. For all round use, they almost rival hare parsley. Neither of the articles are very common, but they will pay for cultivation in the manner suggested above, especially in the case of a large rabbitry and

stock. The amount of time to be saved is very great, as perhaps for a week at a time there will be sufficient for all your rabbits. After a week a change is desirable, and if there are two or three beds of different sorts, variety can be easily studied. Chicory roots may be planted very closely together, and as they soon grow, good crops may be expected. Dandelion is also very good food, and few would imagine the improvement that may be effected in it by cultivation. A thickly covered area of a dozen yards will, if judiciously and freely manured, yield an enormous crop that will be exceedingly valuable. Marshmallows are good, as are the tops of carrots and turnips, the former especially. Grass is very good; we don't mean lawn cuttings, but soft juicy grass. The coarse and broad-leaved kinds are not relished, a fact that can scarcely be wondered at.

"There are several kinds of herbs that are only to be given under special circumstances. For instance, fennel and parsley are both what may be termed 'high food,' and should only be given as a treat, and for stimulating purposes. Lettuce, milk, sow thistles and endive all resemble one another in one particular: they all contain a quantity of vegetable milk, immensely palatable to the rabbit. It is very good food indeed, but, as we shall see anon, it is most useful for does with litters. In the spring and when the amount of milky juice is large, it should not be given in large quantities to young rabbits, as its effects are slightly too relaxing. Celery is rather stimulating, but is highly relished. On every rabbit fancier's brain should be written in letters of fire — 'Never on any occasion give green stuff wet, or without looking it over.'

Italian rabbit feeding platform, circa 1900.

"A great deal of success will depend upon the manner in which roots are given to the rabbits. Probably no food is so necessary; and if Londoners were to recognize the necessity of buying a bushel or two of carrots, turnips, Swedes, artichokes, and the like occasionally, they might halve their corn bills, and entre nous, double their success. Country fanciers observe this matter better, and thus often keep their rabbitries going at a very nominal cost, reducing their supply of corn, and cutting off the portions that generally go to waste and to feed the rats and mice. Potatoes are included in our list, but they must not be given raw, for reasons that are obvious. Either boiled or baked, and then mashed up, skins and all, with a little bran or meal, they make a first-class food, but are inclined to be a little windy. Corn is the staple dry food for rabbits, of whatever kind it may be.

"Oats are, without doubt, that grand muscle-producing food, and therefore we say, 'Give Oats.' Don't wear the rabbits to death with them, but give oats frequently. The grain may be distributed in many different ways. First, it may be given dry, just as it comes from the thrashing machine; or the grain may have a few tea-leaves mixed with it, or it may be crushed, or

it may be ground. Plans 1 and 2 are both very good, and Nos. 3 and 4 are useful methods for a change and under certain circumstances. Plans Nos. 5 and 6 are open to objection. Crushed oats are very good, but ground oats are doubtful. If you have a small mill of your own, grind the oats occasionally by all means; but if you have to de-

pend on the honour of the miller, grinding is not altogether to be recommended. Soaked oats are certainly
good occasionally, and the corn possesses the most essential properties of rabbit fattening that are possible."

"Good oatmeal is a splendid food, but the really good
qualities are somewhat expensive. Barley meal is another
valuable food under certain conditions, but it is scarcely
suitable for an everyday meal, owing to its heating properties. Buckwheat forms a staple food in Belgium and
the Netherlands, and should not be despised, seeing how
fleshy and nutritious the Ostend rabbit is. Still, it is not
much used in England, and although we have tried it in
many ways we have not found it altogether successful. Beans may be taken
as a good article of diet under certain conditions. They are cheap, and if
given for an occasional treat, act as a tonic and do considerable good. Split
or dried peas make a good cheap food. It is essential to buy them in pretty
large quantities, as a considerable reduction in price is the result. They are
not given dry, but must be soaked all night in cold water. This is strained
off in the morning, the peas given damp. In winter time a little warm milk
and water added makes the dish highly palatable, and causes the food to
'go further.' Oilcake is said to be good fattening food, and to be freely
taken by the rabbits they have been starved into tasting it. We have given it
in different forms: dry and wet, mixed with oats, tea-leaves, meal, milk,
and everything we could think of. In each instance, however, bunny refused pointblank.

"Coming to the articles of food not generally given, we may refer to
the advantage to be derived from the pretty free use of bread in the rabbitry. Where pigs are not kept there is sure to be a quantity of waste bread
about a house, especially in case of a family. If the crusts are hard and
stale, they may be given just as they are, and great fun will be given to
rabbits, especially the old bucks, in eating them. There is another way in
which we have often given bread, and found it a profitable food. Boil the
scraps in as little water as will cover them and mash up with a fork. Then
turn out into a bowl, and add a handful or two of meal, mixing the whole
up in a thick crumbly mash. Let it stand and hour on the hob, and then
give it to the rabbits, and they will give your proof positive that it is exceedingly palatable. A great saving may by this means be effected in the
rabbit expenditure account, and a profit made pretty certain. Rice makes

Various trough feeders from the 1800s.

a palatable food, but is a 'leetle' too dear to be given regularly.

"Many writers of the old school have objected to the use of any kind of mash, chiefly on the ground that it is indigestible, and apt to swell in the stomach. Our readers will see we have taken a different line, and have suggested that it should be given in several forms. In mixing, be not too free with water, and skim milk is a cheap substitute that is good. Where there is a very large rabbitry the mixture can be made sloppy, and then boiled until the surplus moisture has gone off and the whole is reduced to a stiff paste. The rabbits like it best given warm, but there is a great diversity of opinion as to the advisability of so giving it. I have tried both systems, and found that to give the food immediately after mixing, and whilst in a warm state, is the most beneficial and satisfactory. My reasons for saying this are as follows: After the food has become cold I find, as a general rule, the animal does not eat it with half the relish that it does when given warm; also that the swelling process goes on chiefly during the mixing, and what little, if any, which takes place after does not do the slightest injury. And again, I consider that rabbits, when n a confined state, should have at least one warm meal during the day. The other plan we have adopted with great success is to boil the mixture, and then place it in a large basin on the hob or close to the fire. The benefit to be derived from this will be at once seen, when we state that if allowed thus to stand for an hour the mixture will sell at least 20 percent, and it is far better that this should take place outside the rabbit than in its stomach. The rabbits like it far better warm, and it is far better so given, as it makes the coat glossy and is much more fattening."

"The following regime for a week may be of service to a perfect novice:

372

Sunday
- Morning — Roots, dry oats
- Afternoon – Green food and hay
- Evening – Mash of potatoes and meal

Monday
- Morning — Roots, crushed oats and tea-leaves
- Afternoon – Green food and hay
- Evening – Bread and meal mash

Tuesday
- Morning – Soaked oats
- Afternoon – Roots and green stuff
- Evening – Crusts of bread

Wednesday
- Morning – Barley or wheat, dry
- Afternoon – Green stuff and hay
- Evening – Mash of meal and pollard

Thursday
- Morning – Roots, dry oats
- Afternoon – Green stuff and hay
- Evening – Soaked peas or lentils

Friday
- Morning – Hay and roots
- Afternoon – Green stuff
- Evening – Meal and potato mash

Saturday
- Morning – Dry oats and chaff
- Afternoon – Green stuff and roots
- Evening – Bread

"There are two articles of food mentioned in the above dietary not alluded to in our list of suitable food: there are hay and chaff. There is no food that is more generally used than hay, and if green stuff is given in any quantity a better antidote can scarcely be imagined. Hay bought by the load or truss is not really an expensive article, and to the rabbit keeper especially is very good value indeed for money. To chaff, the same remark

Left: Charles E. Kellogg was Director of Animal Husbandry Division of the U.S. Department of Agriculture.

Right: George S. Templeton, Director of the U.S. Rabbit Experiment Station.

is applicable; and the only objection we have ever seen raised to giving it mixed with corn is, that in looking for the latter the chaff is wasted. This is a danger, certainly, but if the troughs are made, it can be avoided."

Now one can easily imagine the time consumed in caring for their rabbits, well over a hundred years ago. Not only were these early fanciers rabbit keepers, but gardeners, cooks and laborers as well. One cannot possibly fathom the time involved in caring for several hundred hutches of bunnies, as it certainly could not have been a one-person operation. Yet this was the norm well into the 1920s, both in the United States and abroad. In the United States when rabbit keeping became a popular business at the turn of the 20th century, the United State government quickly stepped in, with research facilities to study, in depth, the nutritional needs of the domestic rabbit. Several research facilities were established throughout the country, but the most notable one being the U.S. Rabbit Experiment Station in Fontana, California. Through the research efforts of two men in particular, Charles E. Kellogg and George S. Templeton, Americans have been able to gain a vast knowledge of rabbit keeping and the nutritional needs of the same. Through research, rations were developed for the various parts of the country by 1930.

Administration Building at the U.S. Rabbit Experiment Station in Fontana, California, circa 1930.

SUGGESTED RATIONS FOR DRY DOES, HERD BUCKS, AND DEVELOPING DOES AND BUCKS

Ration No. 1 for Northwestern States
Grain and protein: 2 parts whole oats or wheat, 2 parts whole barley, 1 part linseed, soybean, sesame or peanut meal. Roughage: Sweetclover or alfalfa hay. Green feed or root crops. Salt.

Ration No. 2 for Central States
Grain and protein: 2 parts whole oats or barley, 2 parts whole wheat, 1 part soybean or linseed meal. Roughage: Alfalfa, clover or soybean hay. Green fee or root crops. Salt.

Ration No. 3 for Southwestern States
Grain and protein: 2 parts whole barley, wheat or oats, 2 parts whole milo, hegari, feterita or kafir, 1 part soybean, peanut, sesame or linseed meal. Roughage: Alfalfa hay. Green feed or root crops. Salt.

Ration No. 4 For Northeastern States
Grain and protein: 2 parts whole oats or buckwheat, 2 parts whole wheat or barley, 1 part linseed or soybean meal. Roughage: Clover or alfalfa hay. Green fee or root crops. Salt.

RATIONS FOR DRY DOES, HERB BUCKS, AND DEVELOPING BUCKS AND DOES

Ration No. 5 For Central States
Grain and protein: 1-1/2 parts rolled oats, 1-1/2 parts rolled wheat or barley, 1 part corn meal. 1 part soybean or linseed meal. Roughage: Alfalfa, clover or soybean hay. Green feed or root crops. Salt.

Ration No. 6 For Southeastern States
Grain and protein: 1-1/3 parts whole oats, 1-1/3 parts whole wheat, 1-1/3 parts whole milo, sagrain or barley, 1 part peanut, soybean or linseed meal. Roughage: Vetch, lespedeza, kudzu or soybean hay. Green feed or root crops. Salt.

RATIONS FOR DOES AND LITTERS

Ration No. 7 For Northwestern States

Grain and protein: 2 parts whole oats or wheat, 2 parts whole barley, 2 parts linseed, soybean, sesame, or peanut meal. Roughage: Sweetclover or alfalfa hay. Green feed or root crops. Salt.

Ration No. 8 For Central States

Grain and protein: 2 parts whole oats or barley, 2 parts whole wheat, 2 parts soybean or linseed meal. Roughage: Alfalfa, clover or soybean hay. Green feed or root crops. Salt.

Ration No. 9 For Southwestern States

Grain and protein: 2 parts whole barley, wheat or oats, 2 parts whole milo, hegari, feterita or kafir, 2 parts soybean, peanut, sesame or linseed meal. Roughage: Alfalfa hay. Green feed or root crops. Salt.

Ration No. 10 For Northeastern States

Grain and protein: 2 parts whole oats or buckwheat, 2 parts whole wheat or barley, 2 parts linseed or soybean meal. Roughage: Clover or alfalfa hay. Green feed or root crops. Salt.

Ration No. 11 For Central States

Grain and protein: 1-1/2 parts rolled oats, 1-1/2 parts rolled wheat or barley, 1 part corn meal, 2 parts soybean or linseed meal. Roughage: Alfalfa, clover, or soybean hay. Green feed or root crops. Salt.

Ration No. 12 For Southeastern States

Grain and protein: 1-1/3 parts whole oats, 1-1/3 parts whole wheat, 1-1/3 parts whole milo, sagrain or barley, 2 parts peanut, soybean or linseed meal. Roughage: Vetch, lespedeza, kudzu or soybean hay. Green feed or root crops. Salt.

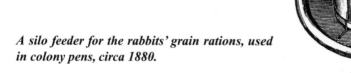

A silo feeder for the rabbits' grain rations, used in colony pens, circa 1880.

Oren Reynolds. *Photo courtesy ARBA's Domestic Rabbits.*

For these rations the recommended feeding for dry does, herd bucks, and developing does and bucks, were to have been fed once a day all of one of the grain and protein mixtures in ration Nos. 1 to 6, that the rabbits would consume within 20 to 30 minutes. Does and nursing litters were to be given all of the grain and protein mixtures Nos. 7 to 12 that they would consume without waste each 24 hours. Green foods were always recommended to be fed sparingly. As we can see, it was a science even then with rabbit feeding, but not an easy procedure to follow.

While discussing the evolution of rabbit feeding with my friend, Oren Reynolds, who at 98 years young is a walking history book himself when it comes to rabbit keeping in America, he shared with me this piece that he wrote:

RABBIT FEED PROGRESSION

"In the late 1930s when I obtained my first rabbits, there were no pelleted rabbit rations on the market that I can recall. Breeders mixed their own whole grain mixture and kept good hay by them at all times. Most added either linseed meal, cotton seed meal or peanut meal for added protein. These came in a small star-shaped, pea-sized cake and were used exclusively until A.E. Staley Manufacturing Co. came out with a soybean pellet that ran approximately 44% protein, and most all breeders switched to its use when available.

"Most breeders used a good grade of third cutting alfalfa, some good clover cut just before it bloomed and others lespedeza, depending upon availability in the area. Many good rabbits were produced with the whole grain and hay feeding formula; however, there was good points and bad points in this feeding program.

"On the downside, some animals scratched out portions of the feed to get to something they liked better in the mixture. Good firm meaty fryers were produced, but it took at least 10 to 12 weeks to produce a four-pound fryer. Feeding hay through a wire hay manger oftentimes became somewhat messy as we had all solid wood floors at the time.

"The first pelleted feed I can recall was an all-grain pellet produced by Dixie Mills which had a plant on the banks of the Mississippi River in East St. Louis, Illinois. Everyone still had to supply hay with the pellet, the same as we did with the grain mixture. Along about this time, or shortly afterwards, another company produced a ground non-pelleted feed; however, it met with little favor and was soon dropped.

"The next advancement was the complete ration pellet, and while it was slow gaining favor, it eventually became the number one favorite of most all breeders. At first, some still held with the all-grain pellet, and the last that I can recall was Rockland Rabbit Ration, owned by Harry Herrlein and manufactured and distributed by Arecady Farms Milling Co. of Chicago, Illinois. This was available, if memory serves me correctly, until sometime in the late 1940s, but gave way to the complete rabbit ration which had shown remarkable improvement with the addition of trace minerals and vitamins, by that time.

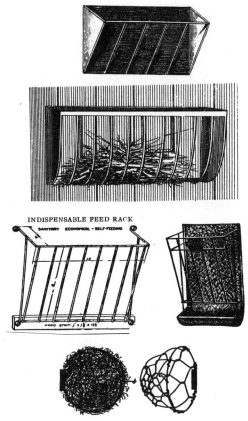

Various hay racks, American made, circa 1920.

"The first complete ration rabbit pellet was a far cry from pellets as we know them today. All were made on a 1/4-inch die and were longer in length than we see today, and this led to considerable waste, especially among young animals just starting to eat solid food. This pellet did, however, lead to the production of four-pound fryers in eight to ten weeks.

"In the 1940s, for some reason of which I am not aware, most all feed companies got the idea that the feed needed more protein. Most went to at least a 21% protein content and some as much as 25%. With the introduction of this, most all breeders found it almost impossible to finish out a rabbit in prime coat, and if they were fortunate enough to do so, it didn't last more than a few days. This idea was dropped about early 1951, and most settled on a 16% or 17% protein content.

"I have often been asked what I believe makes a good rabbit pellet.

The salt spool was manufactured by the hundreds of thousands by Edward H. Stahl's employees in Missouri. It was considered a must-have in the rabbits' diet for better than 50 years.

PURE SALT

SULPHERIZED SALT

MINERAL SALT

Personally, I feel there are several factors that go into the production of a good feed. First, I feel good quality ingredients are a must in a quality pellet. A good pellet is composed of three very important ingredients, namely: energy, protein and fiber, and the proper blending of these are vital in producing a good pellet.

"Too low or too high levels of energy or protein or lack of enough fiber may cause one several problems. These items are really not spelled out on the feed tags, when you get right down to it. Energy is not mentioned on any feed tags I have seen; however, with new rules most ingredients require a posting of the minimum and fiber to post both minimum and maximum.

"If the energy level is too low, does will either not conceive, or they will reabsorb the fetuses. Actual abortion usually doesn't occur from low energy. Low energy will cause loss of body condition, causing animals to become thin in flesh and out of breeding condition.

"Excess energy is actually stored as fat. If a rabbit consumes more energy than is required to meet the caloric requirements, it can bring about softness of flesh, contribute to diarrhea, bring on a quicker molt cycle and cause breeding problems. Too fat an animal becomes harder to breed, and if they breed often they have problems during the littering process. Fat is extremely high in energy. It contains nine calories per gram, while carbohydrate fat, which an

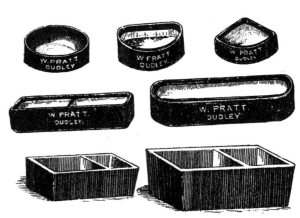

Various Italian rabbit feed and water containers, circa 1900.

379

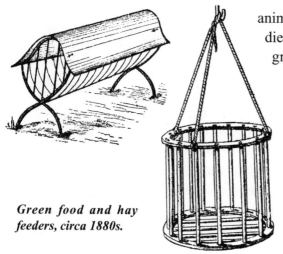

Green food and hay feeders, circa 1880s.

animal produces from a low fat diet, has only four calories per gram.

"The only way to try and hold a prime coat, once it becomes prime, is to feed a diet of low or medium energy level coupled with a higher fiber content. This lessens the chance of diarrhea and seems to produce a firmer fleshed animal and tends to let one hold the coat longer.

"A balanced ration is hard to formulate. When you increase the fiber content, you lower the energy level and vice versa. The most successful way to hold the fiber content and increase the energy level is to add additional fat to the formula.

"The next most important item is producing a good pellet is the actual production of the formula. Pelleting is a form of art and takes experience. Most important is consistency coupled with a good firm pellet with very few fines in every batch.

"If you have the above under control, one can expect to produce a good firm fryer in a shorter period of time and with less feed than in the grain-hay mixture days. We had to figure 4-1/2 to 5-1/2 pounds of feed for each one pound of live weight, with the average about 5 pounds."

Oren Reynolds also reports that the first time he ever saw a 1/8-inch pellet was in 1952, at the Portland, Oregon Convention in the booth of Pillsbury Mills Company, which was 14% protein. He was delighted with this feed, producing many winners in the Normal Fur Class; however, the company stopped producing this feed in the mid-1960s.

Upon investigating the first pelleted rabbit feed, I contacted the corporate headquarters of California Pellet Mill Company, who said they produced the first pelleted rabbit feed in the mid-1930s. They were also the company who manufactured the pelleting machines. It actually turns out that Purina Mills of St. Louis, Missouri produced the first condensed ration of this type. In a full page ad in the *Guide Book and Standard,* 1930, by the American Rabbit and Cavy Breeders Association, Inc., it states, "RABBITS and the New Way of Feeding Them. YOU KNOW what a good feed alfalfa meal is for rabbits ... you know the value of ground oats and wheat middlings ... you know how much better soybean meal and wheat germ meal will make the ration when added ... you know the need for such things as bone meal, salt, calcium carbonate ... all of these ingredients can now be had as one feed. It's Purina Rabbit Chow, made especially for the feeding of rabbits. One ingredient won't do ... not even two or three ... but the ten in Rabbit Chow do the job.

"Rabbit Chow is so easy to feed ... it's now made in little nuggets. It cuts down waste. There's no mixing ... no cooking ... just scoop the nuggets from the bag and feed them.

"Rabbit Chow didn't just happen. It was built ... through years of experimental work in the Purina laboratories and on the Purina Experimental Farm ... until now it has just the right things in the right amounts to do the job of feeding right. Rabbit Chow ... ten ingredients thoroughly mixed and pressed into handy nuggets, is the feed for the job."

Aren't the rabbit fanciers of today the fortunate ones?

History of the "Checkerboard" Design Used by Purina

William H. Danforth founded the Ralston Purina Company in the late 1800s in St. Louis, Missouri. During his childhood, in a small country town in southeastern Missouri, he worked as a clerk in his father's general store and learned many valuable lessons that were to serve him well in his

future business career. Danforth wrote, "The most important thing I learned behind the counter in that country store where we sold everything from linen handkerchiefs to horse collars, was this: I learned the importance of 'dress.' And I learned that lesson from the mother of a large family in our community.

"Among the many articles we handled in our store was 'bolt goods,' mostly old fashioned calicos and sturdy ginghams. Along in the

William H. Danforth, founder of the Ralston Purina Company, circa mid-1930s.

YOU KNOW what a good feed alfalfa meal is for rabbits . . . you know the value of ground oats and wheat middlings . . . you know how much better soybean meal and wheat germ meal will make the ration when added . . . you know the need for such things as bone meal, salt, calcium carbonate . . . all of these ingredients can now be had as one feed. It's Purina Rabbit Chow, made especially for the feeding of rabbits. One ingredient won't do . . . not even two or three . . . but the ten in Rabbit Chow do the job.

Rabbit Chow is so easy to feed . . . it's now made in little nuggets. It cuts down waste. There's no mixing . . . no cooking . . . just scoop the nuggets from the bag and feed them.

Rabbit Chow didn't just happen. It was built . . . through years of experimental work in the Purina laboratories and on the Purina Experimental Farm . . . until now it has just the right things in the right amounts to do the job of feeding right. Rabbit Chow . . . ten ingredients thoroughly mixed and pressed into handy nuggets, is the feed for the job.

First ad for rabbit pellets/nuggets, circa 1930.

spring of the year business picked up in this line of goods. Customers swarmed into the store to buy dress materials. Usually they purchased enough material to outfit the whole family. From the same bolt would be made shirts for the father and all the boys, and dresses and aprons for all the girls. Most of the women who traded with us chose modest patterns and varied them from year to year. But not Mrs. Brown. Mother of a large brood of tow-headed boys and girls of all ages, Mrs. Brown had one invariable choice in spring material. In all the time she traded with us, she never, so long as I remember, swerved from her standard. She always bought a bolt of heavy red-checked gingham. You can imagine the appearance of the Brown family when they came out in their new spring wardrobe.

"Mrs. Brown headed the crew bedecked in her red checkered dress. Mr. Brown supported her with a red checkerboard shirt. And through the whole family the design was repeated — red-checked dresses for the girls, red-checked shirts for the boys.

"You can imagine the appearance the family made. They were conspicuous from afar. Other mothers might temporarily lose sight of a child or two at an ice cream social or a basket dinner. But not Mrs. Brown. She could spot a Brown offspring in any crowd. And so could everyone else.

"Before long the Brown family in that community became indelibly associated with red checkerboard gingham. And from that family I learned that to make a thing stand out you have to dress it to fit the part. And I also learned that dressing alike gives a unity and identification lacking in helter-skelter design."

Years later, when William H. Danforth, fresh out of college, decided to enter the feed manufacturing business, he remembered how a Brown was never mistaken for anyone else in the community. So he decided to dress his products so they would never be confused with other feeds. Thus was born the checkerboard feed bag and the checkered board design we know today, over a hundred years later.

RABBIT IDENTIFICATION SYSTEMS

ince Belgian Hares were the "In Breed" for the United States, which led to the domestic rabbit industry becoming established in this country in the late 19th century, I felt it necessary to write about the early systems of marking rabbits. The National Belgian Hare Club of America was founded in 1897. This organization quickly adopted a system for marking Belgian Hares, and no judge was permitted to place an animal that wasn't properly marked.

The so-called, or better yet, self-proclaimed, expert of the Belgian Hare was a young man by the name of P.E. Crabtree of Denver, Colorado. Crabtree was also the first secretary of the National Belgian Hare Club of America, and wrote on the subject of marking Hares in 1901 in his *The First Belgian Hare Course of Instruction,* "HOW TO MARK AND RECORD."

"THE BEST way to mark Belgian Hares is by punching a notch or half moon in the edges of the ears. This is the national adopted system of marking. A conductor's punch, which may be carried in the vest pocket, is needed. Usually, these punches have two sets of dies, one to punch a circular disk, the other a v-shaped notch, or other device. Anybody who has seen a

Poultry punches were often used for piercing ears, circa 1900.

through ticket at the end of the route will appreciate the variety of devices available to a purchaser of a punch of this description.

"In using the punch, do not cut a hole in the body of the ear, but on the edge. The operation gives little or no pain to the animal, draws no blood, is never outgrown or lost, and does not affect the carriage of the ear.

"Every ear has a thick and thin edge, and always speak of them as thick and thin edges. Never use the terms inner or outer edge in speaking of the ears, for whether the thick edge is the inner or outer depends on the manner in which the ears are carried by the Belgian, or handled by the breeder. The right ear, of course, is on the right side of the head as the Belgian is facing.

"The tip of each ear is numbered 4. The first number on the thick edge of the ear is No. 1. Halfway between No. 4 and the bottom of the ear, on the thick edge, is No. 2. No. 3 is on the thick edge of the ear, halfway between No. 2 and No. 2, just as No. 1 is halfway between No. 2 and the bottom of the ear.

"On the thin edge of the ear, No. 6 is halfway between the tip and the bottom of the ear. No. 7 is halfway between No. 6 and the bottom of the ear, on the thin edge. No. 5 is halfway between No. 6 and No. 4, on the thin edge. Never use No. 1 and No. 2 unless you are short of numbers, because the ear is thick there, and bristly hair is on it there, and the mark is not a pretty one at those two points.

"Sometimes silver wire is used, the ductile, soft-tempered kind which can be easily twisted without breaking. This wire is run through the cartilage of the desired number, and twisted with a pair of pliers, or with the fingers. If wire is used, Nos. 1 and 2 may be employed, the objections mentioned is the case of notching with a punch noted previously not applying.

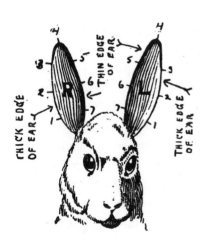

How to mark a Belgian Hare, as proposed by P.E. Crabtree of Colorado, circa 1900.

"In numbering your Belgians, begin at No. 7 on the right ear and exhaust the available numbers on that ear. Proceed next on the left ear from No. 7 and exhaust the available numbers on that ear. Then combine the numbers in this way: R7 and 5, R7 and 4, R7 and

3. Same on the left ear: L7 and 6, L7 and 5, L7 and 4, L7 and 3. Then R7, L7; R7, L5; R7, L4; R7, L3. Next R6, L7; R6, L6; R6, L5; R6,

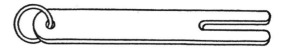

Gauge used in applying the washer to the ear tag, circa 1900.

L4; R6, L3. Suppose your last marking was R4, L3. Then your next Belgian would be marked R3, L7.

"In the rules and regulation of every show should be included the notification to exhibitors that every Belgian should be marked according to the national system. According to the rules of progression, there is practically no limit to the number of variations of which this system is capable."

Crabtree's system was rather short lived, and people demanded to be allowed to use an aluminum tag to identify their animals, which was number, and the same system that the Europeans had employed for some years. Then along came Dr. Burton C. Platt, from Los Angles, California with the simple idea, but a revolutionary one to the rabbit industry of the day, which still stands over one hundred years later, known as tattooing. Crabtree, writing in the Belgian Hare Department of *Field and Stream* magazine in 1901, "An Improved Method for Marking Belgians — A Little Invention of Great Importance":

"Dr. B.C. Platt, with his unbounded energy in all matter relating to the interests of the Belgian bunny, has recently perfected an invention that promises to be the greatest utility to all lovers of that most attractive and popular little animal. This new and improved device enabling each fancier to mark his hares in a manner painless to the animal and yet in a way that cannot be erased or altered.

"Among former devices for this purpose are a system of clipping the edges of the ear, an aluminum tag pressed through the ear with a forceps and clinched in much the same style that lawyers employ to bind together legal documents, or a tag retained in the ear by an aluminum wire. These methods are open to many objections, such as causing the animal considerable pain and being easily removed by dishonest persons either in the rabbitries of breeders and purchasers, with the intent and result of defraud-

Aluminum numbered tag and washer, one of the early methods of identification, circa 1900.

ing buyers and great injury to the reputation of breeders.

"Dr. Pratt's device avoids these and other objections. Like many other little inventions of great utility, it is beautifully simple, and the wonder is that no one ever thought of it before. It consists essentially in tattooing with India ink a device upon the ear of the animal by means of an ingenious little instrument. The plan is capable of infinite variety, so that every breeder may have his own brand, which he may use to the exclusion of all others. And, instead of a deformity, as with the aluminum tag, or clipping the edges, the marking in the ear may be made really ornamental.

"Stars, circles, squares, diamonds, triangles and other designs form the framework of the device and numbers supply the necessary individual characterization. For instance, a breeder may adopt a star and in the center he places the figure 1 for the first hare and may continue the series up to a hundred thousand, if the breeding capacity of his rabbitry supplies the material.

"Some of the advantages of this method are the following:

"First — It is absolutely permanent as a means of identification. The young hare may be marked when taken from his dam and then has a means of identification attached to his person that cannot be removed without cutting off his ear.

"Second — There is no mutilation, no pain. The beauty of the ear lacing in not marred. There is no disfiguring wire or tag. No one likes to torture a pet animal, especially so docile and innocent a creature as the hare. In most localities public sentiment is against cutting off the ears of dogs and the tails of horses, shooting pigeons for sport or running hares with dogs. Although there has been a necessity for marking hares which has undoubtedly justified the somewhat cruel methods theretofore in vogue, yet every sensible and thoughtful person will welcome a method of far great utility and infinitely more humane.

"Third — One may use either numbers, letter or monograms, and the mark employed will constitute a trademark for the owner. With a perfected system of national registration such as is probable in the near future this method will be the best that can be employed. It will enable every progressive breeder to maintain his individuality by advertising and selling the product of his rabbitry under a uniform brand of his own. In California it is a criminal offence to counterfeit or alter the brand of livestock, and laws similar to that of California could be passed in every State.

"Fourth — The cost of this method is only a trifle. Each breeder may

Weston Mfg. & Supply Company of Colorado developed the very popular tattoo clamp in the late 1920s.

illustrate his style of marking on his circulars, stationery and advertising material, and also in his ads in newspapers. It will be a guarantee against frauds in the showroom or between buyers and sellers and will stimulate fanciers in their efforts to breed the best specimens, knowing that the credit cannot be taken from them.

"Dr. Pratt has filed an application for patents upon this device in order to protect both himself and all who may adopt it in practical use. Its simplicity and effectiveness will undoubtedly commend it to every breeder and bring it deserved popularity."

Researching the United States Patent Office records for the years 1901-1904, no patent was issued to Dr. Burton C. Pratt for any type of tattooing device. Perhaps Dr. Pratt realized that the Belgian Hare boom was starting its downward spiral, and there was certainly no need to tattoo a bunch of rabbits slated for the butcher shop, or possibly he sold the idea to another person. An advertisement in 1924, by the Jackson Supply House of York, Pennsylvania, listed an ear punch for 25 cents and an ear marker and out-

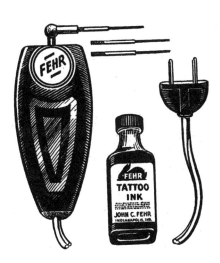

fit for the sum of one dollar. It appears that the Weston's Pet Tattoo Outfit was one of the major distributors for marking rabbits, which started in the late 1920s. Their complete set, which included hand clamp thongs, individual letters and numbers, plus a bottle of ink, sold for $4 to $17, according to the amount of

John C. Fehr is believed to have been the first to invent the electric tattoo, which sold for $3 during the early 1930s.

Fehr's swivel tattoo device, sold for a big 35 cents in the 1930s.

Fehr's retractable tattoo pen was 50 cents.

Fehr's combination fountain pen and tattoo outfit sold for $1.

type necessary for the individual rabbit fancier's operations.

Oddly enough, in the United States rabbits were not required to be tattooed, either for the showroom, or when registered by the national governing body. Serious fanciers usually did tattoo their animals. Rabbit tattooing in America did not become mandatory until 1955. This ruling came about because people were lying about which rabbit was awarded a Grand Champion Certificate. Prior to this, coop numbers were grease-penciled in the rabbit's ear, or written on a piece of paper and placed in the ear canal. Our American system today dictates that breeders place whatever number/letter combination in the right ear, and that the left ear be reserved for the ARBA's registration number, should the breeder wish to follow suit. Through the years, a number of different tattooing devices have been developed: the three needle swivel, a retractable pen like a ball point, various size clamps, which are by far the most popular, battery-operated and the most expensive elec-

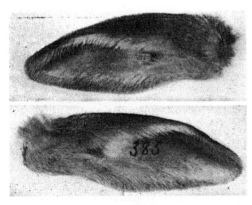

Upper ear marked with a small metal tag; lower tattooed, circa 1920.

A British firm developed a plastic ear tag in the late 1960s which came in assorted colors.

tric tattooing system.

European countries have for years recognized a ear tag system, as late as the 1970s, by employing an aluminum button with a series of numbers, but have since gone to the tattooing of the rabbits. The European manner is to have the rabbit facing you; you read the left ear first. In Holland, for example, if an animal was tattooed 9JC 611, it would trans-

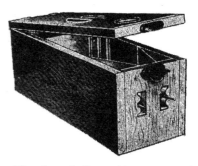

The Owen's Tattoo Box appeared in the early 1940s and sold for $5.

late as: (9) the year, (JC) the local club, (6) the sixth month and (11) the 11th rabbit of the breed tattooed. Belgium requires numbers in just one ear, at the fancier's choice. France has a more precise system, for example: 1F4 BG119, translates to, in the left ear 1F4 would mean, first month, (F) for France, (4) for the year, right ear BG119 is the certificate number issued by the national governing body for the rabbit. In Germany, both ears are also used: 6410 M11 translates, in the left ear (6) the month, (4) 2004, (10) number in register. Right ear (M) is the initial of the state the breeder resides, (11) denotes the member club.

The United Kingdom has been using a ringing system since 1929. These leg bands are made of a light weight metal alloy which does not corrode. They come in 10 different sizes, which are lettered size A to size X. Rings are ordered through the British Rabbit Council and normally first distributed during the Bradford Championship Show in January. Rings are marked with the size letter, the year issued and a series of numbers, for example: BRC 04 E 15437. The BRC stands for the registering body; 04 represents the rabbit's age or year in which the animal is born; E is the ring size. All rabbits must be rung with their correct ring size, according to the breed list. If shown with the incorrect ring size, the animal will be disqualified in the show

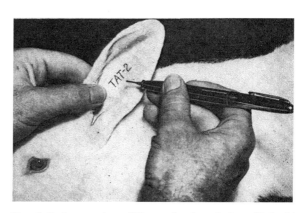

Frank Laboratories of Texas developed the self-feeding tattoo pen in the 1950s.

room. E ring represents the breeds: Angora, Argente Champagne, Deilenaar, Harlequin, New Zealand Red, Perlfee, Rex. Satin, Sussex and Swiss Fox. The 15437 is just a series of numbers, as all rings have different numbers. Depending on the breed, rabbits are typically rung at about eight weeks, and certainly before 12 weeks old. Rings are placed on either hind leg; the leg is pulled straight out and ring slid over the leg and past the hock. Once over the hock, when the leg is back in the normal form, the ring will not come off due to the animal's movement. The British Rabbits Council rules state that all rabbits shown must be rung, except for imported animals which may carry a tattoo number.

AMERICA'S FIRST RABBIT JUDGE?

 hether this is America's first rabbit judge or not, one cannot be certain, but he would certainly have to be considered at the very least as one of the first in the United States and a rather remarkable character, too. Records have been located of a class of 10 rabbits and 9 cavies on display at the California State Fair in Sacramento in 1860. Richard Chenery had come to California from Montague, Massachusetts, to seek his thought to be fortune in gold, during the California gold rush in 1849. At the age of 32 years, this was Chenery's dream, but after just a very short time in his quest for gold, he gave up. Richard Chenery then went to San Francisco and became involved with steamboat mercantile pursuits, as well as the railroad business. This seemingly not only brought him fortune, but fame as well, as he became one of the founding members of the California Steam Navigation Company as a director of the Sacramento Valley Railway Company in 1855.

It was in 1857 that Richard Chenery was sent by the San Francisco voters to represent them at the Sate Assembly, which he was among the first organizers of the Republican Party on the west coast. The governorship entered his mind, but due to the fact that the Democrats were the in thing in California, he lost the possible position.

In 1860, Richard Chenery, was asked to judge the rabbits and cavies that were entered for the first time at the California State Fair. The first place premium at the fair for this type of exhibition was the sum of a $10 gold piece, which Chenery awarded to C.L. Lowell of Sacramento County on a pair of white rabbits. L. Greer of Sacramento would take second place with a spotted rabbit with lopped ears. The winning cavies were also the property of Mr. Greer.

Our likely first rabbit and cavy judge was quite a prominent citizen of his time. When Abraham Lincoln was inaugurated as President of the United States, he was accompanied by a group of personal friends; among them was Richard Chenery. President Lincoln would appoint Chenery as Navy Agent, a position he would hold until 1865, when he was heard of no more.

FATHER OF THE DOMESTIC RABBIT INDUSTRY IN AMERICA

 lthough there have been many great men and a few women as well who have shaped the domestic rabbit industry in the United States over the last 100 years, there is one person who truly stands out, a cut above all the rest, who dedicated no less than 60 years of his life to the advancement and promotion of the domestic rabbit.

Edward Herman Stahl was born on December 14, 1889, on a farm in Wolcottsville, New York, which is some six miles west of Buffalo. He was the youngest of four children and the only boy. His education took him just to the eighth grade, as being the only male child he was expected to stay at home and help his father on the farm. While there was no large livestock to tend to, his father was a crop farmer, as well as the county supervisor.

One September day when Stahl was 20, a neighbor farmer asked Ed's father if the young Stahl could come over and help him gather his crops. His father agreed, and Ed worked a month for the man, who in turn paid him $20 for his services. Edward Stahl went home and said nothing about the money he earned; yet the next morning after finishing breakfast, he walked to the depot in Buffalo and bought a ticket to New York City. Upon his arrival, he made his way to the shipping docks, where he was hired on as a deck hand with a tramp steamer bound for distant cities. Two days into the journey, Ed developed a bad toothache. He received permission

Edward H. Stahl, circa 1925.

to leave ship in New Orleans and to get it pulled, but he had not yet received any wages. With only 50 cents in his pocket, he saw a sign, "Teeth Extracted Upstairs for 50 Cents," and up the stairs he went. Even at this young age, Ed Stahl was a shrewd businessman, because he asked the dentist how much! The dentist told him 50 cents, and Ed replied, "I only got a quarter." The dentist told him to get into the chair. Stahl would tell this story many times over the years, saying, "In all my life, I have never had anything hurt me as much as having that tooth pulled."

The next morning he spent his last quarter for breakfast, then he made his way to the railroad yards and jumped a freighter heading north. There were a number of hitchhikers doing the same and told Ed the train would stop in Kansas City and there could be work available. Once the train arrived, they were spotted by police and whisked off to jail. The next morning appearing before the judge in court, the judge said he would set them free if they promised him they would get out of town, which they did by stealing another ride on a freight train. Ed heard of work in Holmes Park, Missouri, a small town 11 miles outside of Kansas City. He left the train and was hired on at a powder mill factory. Stahl told the foreman that he had no money and was hungry, so the foreman took Ed to a nearby boarding house, fixed him up with a room and meal voucher, which would cost $5 a week and come out of his first pay check.

While working 10-hour days at the mill, then returning to the boarding house, Edward H. Stahl met a local school teacher by the name of Lillian, who also rented a room where Stahl was staying. Love grew and soon Lillian married Ed. The newlyweds purchased two acres and a large seven-room house behind the mill. By 1913 Stahl had been promoted to a foreman at the factory, and at the encouragement of a co-worker, Stahl purchased his first rabbits, four does and one buck, of the ever-popular Belgian Hare, for $15. Not having any cages, he turned the lot loose in an old abandoned wooden corn crib.

The old corn crib, birthplace of America's largest rabbit-raising enterprise.

392

The Belgian Hares, well, bred like rabbits, and soon Stahl had more rabbits than he knew what to do with. He placed a $3 advertisement in the *Kansas City Star,* "Rabbits for sale on Sunday. Young ones 50 cents

Stahl's first Outdoor Enterprise Company in Holmes Park, Missouri. The sign over the buildings reads: "Holmes Park, Mo., Home of the Belgian Hare," circa 1915.

each, old ones $1." Sunday came around and buyers with their horse-drawn buggies filled the yard. Within two hours Ed Stahl was sold out of his

Customers gather to purchase rabbits in Missouri, circa 1930.

surplus, making $85 for his efforts. It didn't take him long to realize that there could be money in rabbits.

Stahl began to breed more rabbits, saving as many of the young for future breeders. If an ad in the local paper could result in this much business, just think what ads in the papers of Chicago, Omaha and St. Louis would produce. He set out right away building hutches during his lunch hour and evenings. Once sales began to roll in, more shipping boxes were being built during lunch, and the rabbits loaded to be carted off to the rail station for shipment. Within one year, Ed was making more from rabbits than being foreman at the mill. Business became so good that Ed was returning to work later and later after shipping the rabbits, so the boss gave him a choice, "Either it's the rabbits or your job," Stahl would later use his answer for the title of one of his many books, *I Chose Rabbits.* The factory closed down just two years later, and Ed's old boss came to work for Stahl's Outdoor Enterprise Company, where he worked for many years.

Soon Stahl rented his first office space on the top floor of a grocery store, then purchased his own printing shop in Kansas City, to accommodate the volumes of printing he was doing to advertise the domestic rabbit. Back in Holmes Park, he rented a 40 x 80-foot building to manufacture salt spools and

A day's shipment ready for the rail station in Missouri, circa 1930.

holders, working two shifts at 10 hours each. These spools sold for five cents each and even with two shifts could not keep up with all the orders.

In the beginning of Stahl's Outdoor Enterprise Company, he was employing 18 full-time employees, with six of these working in the office, including Ed and his wife Lillian. Stahl was drafted into the army during World War I, and at that time his business was already doing some $30,000 per year, just with the sale of Belgian Hares and Flemish Giants. After his discharge, Red and White New Zealands were added to the breeding stock being sold. Then the real moneymaker arrived on the scene, the new fur rabbit from France, the Chinchilla.

The Chinchilla demand was so great that Ed Stahl had a contract with a British shipper in England to supply 500 Chinchillas per month. Most of these rabbits were from the huge rabbitries of Captain W. Brumwell, Lady Victoria Percy and Mr. A.C. Arbuthnot. The rabbits were, of course, sent via ship, then transferred to railroad cars in New York, bound for Kansas City. Stahl would recall, "When I opened the shipping crates, two out of every six arrived dead in the crate," but the demand was greater than he could supply. At Stahl's own operation, he maintained a

Ed Stahl in his Missouri office, circa 1930.

394

row of 40 Chinchilla herd bucks alone and at the time operated 600 holes.

There was many days that he hated to see the mail arrive, as he knew he could not possibly fill all the orders for breeding stock. All business operation were done through the mail, and through the years he was only contacted by the postal inspectors twice, due to dissatisfied customers.

Meanwhile he had been made aware of the National Pet Stock Association which had been formed as a national rabbit governing body in Detroit, Michigan in 1910. Ed was displeased with the workings of this group and disassociated himself with them, along with most of his large following of

Captain W. Brumwell, circa 1928.

rabbit friends he had made. Ed became friends with another rabbit pioneer, John C. Fehr of Indiana, who was a member. By 1917 the national changed their name to National Breeders and Fanciers Association, but trouble brewed within the organization and there were two, with the new national, going by the same name, being organized in 1919. Ed Stahl was a member of the new one, and his now not-so-good friend, John C. Fehr, in the old one. Stahl's organization was growing strong, and the old group began to wane. To make a very long story short, it was at the encouragement of Edward Stahl that the two bickering factions united into one strong national body. This was at the Kansas City Convention in 1923. At the Lima, Ohio Convention in 1924, thus was born the American Rabbit and Cavy Breeders Association.

Through Stahl's promotion of the domestic rabbit, by the mid-twenties he was now grossing an im-

Stahl's Outdoor Enterprise Company, showing the rabbit buildings in Missouri, circa 1930.

pressive $350,000 a year and oversaw 65 employees. Business was booming for the Stahls. So how much was Stahl charging for the rabbits at this time in history, one would ask. Jeffery "Ted" Wengert of Illinois purchased a trio of Standard Chinchillas from Stahl in 1931. The two does cost 35 cents each and the buck was 25 cents, which to me is unbelievable. Wengert became a very popular judge, and continued raising Chinchillas until he died in 1981.

Jeffery "Ted" Wengert.

In 1932, Ed Stahl branched off to the east, taking over the extensive operations of the Chinchilla Breeders of America at New City, New York. This operation stayed until 1940, when he purchased a large tract of land at Pearl River, New York, and moved the eastern facilities there. In 1946, Edward H. Stahl retired from his extensive live rabbit sales business and moved back to Holmes Park, Missouri in 1950, to the fine house on the hill that he fondly called, "The house that rabbits built."

John C. Fehr, circa 1925.

Although Ed no longer raised rabbits, he kept busy promoting them, writing and took over as chairman of the America Rabbit Breeders Association Advertising Department. It was through Stahl's urging that this committee was founded which would prove extremely beneficial to the growth of the ARBA. Small ads were placed in some of the leading publications of

One of five buildings at the New York City, New York operations, circa 1932.

the time, offering a small booklet called *A Practical Beginning to Successful Rabbit Raising.* Between 1948 and 1966, no less than 375,000 were mailed to interested parties, which resulted in a mini-

A shipment about to leave New York, circa 1932.

Early ad designed by Stahl for the ARBA appeared in many large publications, circa 1960.

mum of 1,000 new members to the ARBA annually.

The two rabbits on the ARBA emblem were actually real rabbits, Stahl's Chin Champ was Best Standard Chinchilla at the 1924 Lima, Ohio Convention, winning over many Chinchillas, brought in from England, just to try to beat Stahl. The other rabbit was Stahl's White Champ, a New Zealand White buck that took Best of Breed at the 1932 Pittsburgh, Pennsylvania Convention. Edward H. Stahl designed the emblem, with the rabbits looking to the right, to represent "Looking to the Future," and coined the terms, Food, Fancy and Fur.

During the early 1990s, the association's emblem would become more modernized, and

Modernized emblem.

the words Food, Fancy and Fur were removed. This was at a time when animal rights activists were really stirring things up. People who did not eat rabbit were against the word "Food," and heaven forbid the word "Fur." Although Stahl's two rabbits remain as part of the logo, I personally believe that they would be better suited to include the words, "Fancy, Food, Fun," because

Chin Champ and White Champ Look to the Future.

let's face the facts, rabbit meat is the highest protein meat, next to fish, and had it not been for rabbit meat, many a person world-wide would have gone hungry during both World Wars.

Remarkable as it may seem, Ed Stahl, by the time he had retired, had started more people into the hobby and business of raising rabbits than any single individual past or present, and was responsible for securing more members for the ARBA than anyone

Official ARBA emblem designed by Stahl in 1953.

else ever, and continues to hold that title still to this day. Amazingly, many of the people Stahl started in rabbits kept them for 40, 50 and 60 years, and became legends with rabbits in their own right.

This author never was able to meet the man, but one February day in 1971, arrived a letter from him, congratulating me on winning ARBA Rabbit King, and that he had heard good things about me from his friend, ARBA Secretary Jim Blyth. He wrote, "The ARBA needs more youth like you, for the future of our organization and industry, I hope you stay with us."

The last published picture of Edward H. Stahl, circa 1967.

The late John C. Fehr, who in 1919-1920 battled Ed Stahl and the newly formed National Breeders and Fanciers Association of America bitterly, realized years later that Stahl only cared about the organization's future. He wrote and said many times, "I never had a brother, but if I had one I hoped he would be like Ed Stahl!" That is about the best tribute one man can ever give to his fellow man.

Edward H. Stahl was active until the end, when he was taken to the hospital and passed away May 22, 1978. A legend was now gone, but certainly will not be forgotten.

OUR AMERICAN MEAT CLASSES

In the mid-1800s, most domestic rabbits were of a mixed lot; homesteads might have a few hutches for a change of meat for the dinner table, but typically rabbits would be kept as a child's pet. Rabbit meat was a seasonal meat. When the weather turned cool, the men would go into the countryside and shoot a rabbit or two for a hot bowl of stew that evening. There were few purebred rabbits in America at this time, other than English Lops and Angoras. This would soon change in 1888, when Mr. E.M. Hughes of Albany, New York imported the first Belgian Hares from England. Hughes, along with two other men, promoted the Hares throughout the country at various small stock shows. By 1898 the Belgian Hare Boom was starting; hundreds of animals were crossing the Atlantic and changing hands at unbelievable prices for the day. That boom would go bust by the early 1900s when the market was flooded with Hares, particularly from the Midwest to Pacific Coast. Many fortunes were made, but many would be lost as well. Though the Belgian Hare was touted to be a supreme meat animal, "with a delicate tasting flesh," they were by no means a quality fur animal. Breeds that quickly fitted both bills were the American Blues, Flemish Giants and New Zealand Reds.

Everything would soon change when a British fellow traveled by ship from England in 1919 to exhibit a new breed of rabbit at the New York State Fair. The Chinchilla breed had hit the American shore. Once the exhibition ended, all of his Chinchillas were offered for sale and a new "Boom" had just begun. By 1925, there would be no less than three breeds of Chinchilla, and the meat and fur industry was in full swing.

It was on January 10, 1910, that the National Pet Stock Association was founded, which is the forerunner of our ARBA. The new national body established a registration, judging and show system

Early posing of rabbits hardly showed the fullness of the hindquarters, as they were posed stretched out, circa 1930s.

RABBIT MEAT

wholesome
appetizing
nutritious

FRIED RABBIT

BAKED RABBIT

¶Domestic rabbit meat
is delicious, tender and
fine flavored
¶It is firm and white,
like the breast of
chicken
¶Far superior to wild
rabbit and always in
season
¶Rich in protein and
economical

For further information on rabbits write to
BIOLOGICAL SURVEY
U.S. DEPARTMENT OF AGRICULTURE
WASHINGTON, D.C.

A poster issued in full color by the Department of Agriculture, Bureau of Biological Survey, Washington, D.C. It measured 16 x 25 inches, and was posted in many butcher shops throughout the nation, circa 1930.

right away. Breed standards were in place, and showing had become common place throughout the U.S. While the early standards called for full shoulders, loins and well-developed hindquarters for many of the early breeds, rabbits were stretched flat as a flitter on the show bench. This was hardly any way to show the true depth of the so-called "in meat breeds" of the day. The national organization always spoke of the great value of rabbit meat to its membership and worked closely with U.S. governmental agencies to promote it; it seemingly had no place in the showroom.

To further promote rabbit meat, the national body on Friday, August 29, 1919, in Cleveland, Ohio at the Third Annual Convention put forth Resolution No. 17. "Whereas, it is desirable to establish some suitable, uniform name descriptive of the flesh of the domestic rabbit to be used by the trade and consuming public; and, Whereas, Webster has defined 'venison' as the 'flesh of any wild beast of the chase.' and, Whereas, the rabbit was originally a 'wild beast of the chase' which has now been domesticated, and, Whereas, the name 'domestic venison' accurately describes the flesh of the domestic rabbit, is attractive, and will be easily and readily adopted by the public. Now, therefore be it resolved, that the National Breeders' and Fanciers' Association of America shall and does adopt the name DOMESTIC VENISON as and for the flesh of the domestic rabbit, and recommends that all its members use such name at all times in marketing domestic rabbit meat." Carried.

400

Judge John C. Fehr of Indianapolis, Indiana, one of the early pioneers of the industry, rallied for assorted meat classes, circa 1925.

Oh, deer … well, we all know that resolution didn't fly in this country with its members or general public. After many years of hard persuasion and encouragement, the late John C. Fehr was able to get many of the National Specialty Clubs to recognize pre-junior, as well as fryer-fur classes in their breed standards. Mr. Fehr, one of the great rabbit pioneers of the time, was also able to get an assortment of meat classes accepted within the ARBA's Standard beginning in 1938. The Standards would state: "These classes are to be judged primarily for meat qualities only, fur quality to be considered only in case of a tie, where a decision cannot otherwise be reached."

TYPES — Offspring of standard breeds, regardless of color or fur structure. Small Types, maturing under 7 lbs., Medium Types, maturing at about 10 lbs., and Large Types, maturing at 12 lbs and up.

BROILERS — would be a pen of 3 animals, age limit of 8 weeks and would also be recognized in Small, weight limit 3 lbs., Medium, 4 lbs., and Large at a 5 lb limit.

FRYERS — would be a pen of 3 animals, age limit 3 months and would be again recognized in Small, weight limit 4 lbs., Medium, 5 lbs., and Large at a 6 lb limit.

BAKERS — would be a class of 1 animal, age limit 6 months and would be recognized in Small, weight limit 7 lbs., Medium, 9 lbs., and Large at a 12 lb. limit.

Now if you are laughing at these, just wait until you read this!

"GENERAL DISQUALIFICATIONS NOT TO APPLY, but disqualify for any diseased condition. Only such breeds as are recognized by the A.R. & C.B.A., Inc., are eligible to compete." "Not to compete in sweepstake points."

My, how times have changed, but I never could figure out what a broken tooth or toenail had to do with the quality of flesh in the rabbit. I guess that's why we call that book, the Standard of PERFECTION.

Well, all this was fine and dandy. John Fehr had been able to realize his dream of meat classes, but for some reason all hell would break loose when the standards book was published, as the organization quickly issued a revised supplemental standard for all Commercial Classes to become effective July 1, 1940. These were the only showroom classes which had no point scale recognized at the time.

BROILERS — Pen of 3, age limit 8 weeks, weight limit 3-1/2 lbs. each.

FRYERS — Pen of three (3). Age limit three (3) months. Weight limit five (5) pounds each.

BAKERS OR ROASTERS — One (1) to class, age limit six (6) months. Weight limit twelve (12) pounds.

REQUIREMENTS — Very plump and full over and around hips, with firm meaty saddle, carried as full and meaty as possible to nape of neck and down on sides over ribs and shoulders. With as little offal as possible. To be in good healthy condition. Cut severely for excessive dewlap or loose, flabby skin or waste fat over shoulders. General disqualifications not to apply, but disqualify for any diseased condition. Only such breeds as are recognized by the American Rabbit and Cavy Breeders Association, Inc. are eligible to compete. However, fryer pens may consist of two or three different breeds. But preference shall at all times be given to pens of same breed and color, other points being equal. Try for uniform size and weight in fryer pens. Correct meat type and condition of flesh to be given preference over size and weight.

By 1950, John Fehr wrote: "Although we have three separate classes for fryers — small, medium and large, and also for Roasters and Stewers, the medium breeds have been most popular and especially in the fryer class,

Jeffery "Ted" Wengert.

age limit 3 months, weight limit 6 pounds." (Note an increase by 1 pound.)

The first time meat classes were judged live, then butchered and judged again, was in 1951 at the ARBA Convention in Springfield, Illinois, and were judged by the late Ted Wengert of Rockford, Illinois. Oren Reynolds would have the honor of being the last judge to do this at the Colorado Springs, Colorado Convention in 1983. From the actually show records of 1983, points were given for live placing (first 20, second 18, third 16, etc.), then points were allowed for dressed placing at a 55% of carcass placing and at a 45% of carcass. The winning pen was Californians, total live weight 224 oz., dressed weight 128-1/4 oz., carcass 57.3%. Though this pen placed first in live, it was second in dressed. The second place pen of New Zealand Whites placed second in live weighed more at 231 oz. and first in dressed, but was 4.2% lower in dress-out, therefore was awarded second place.

Now that is some pretty accurate judging skills. It doesn't hurt to mention here that the judge came by his skills honestly, having being a butcher by trade for 42 years. Butchering of rabbits was last written in the 1991-1995 Standards. Meat Classes were never very popular with the adults after the mid-1960s; however, during the 1940s to early 1960s it was pretty commonplace to see anywhere from 20 to 35 meat pens exhibited at a one-day open show. Now you're lucky to see even three to five exhibits at a table show today.

Meat pen classes were a tremendous boom to our youth members, namely those in 4-H and FFA programs throughout the U.S. Meat pens are commonplace at nearly all fair shows in our country, with usually the top 10 pens selling at very lively auctions. Lots of amazing dollar figures have been awarded to the youngsters over the years for just three small rabbits. The all-time record EVER paid for a meat pen was at the Indiana State Fair

Miss Courtney Dickerson of Morgan County, Indiana, breaks a world record with her meat pen of New Zealand Whites, when they sold for $15,000 in 2000 at the Indiana State Fair.

on August 15, 2000, when a young 12-year-old little lady by the name of Courtney Dickerson, of Morgan County, Indiana, walked away with a check totaling a mere $15,000. The buyers were "Friends and Supporters of Courtney Dickerson and Farm Bureau Insurance Company." I trust those people savored the flavor in every last morsel.

CASTRATION

 astration or to caponize a male rabbit was a fairly common practice during later 19th and early 20th centuries, in order to produce a much larger carcass for the table, or when keeping rabbits in a colony environment, especially Angoras, for the production of wool. A knife was normally the chosen tool of choice, although a tight string placed around the testicles was also employed, as illustrated in this Italian illustration from *Giornale degli Allevatori,* 1906.

From P. E. Crabtree's, *The First Belgian Hare Course of Instruction,* 1901, on the subject of "HOW TO CAPONIZE," I quote, "Male hares when caponized at the age of three months or thereabouts, when the testicles are developed, grow to an extra large size, weighing 10 or 12 pounds,

Italian illustration of holding the rabbit and placing the cord. This method replaces the use of a knife, circa 1915.

and their meat is better flavored. A large number can be kept in a single hutch without their fighting; therefore by caponizing, the breeder will economize his space. People prefer fat caponized hare to eat as they prefer fat caponized chicken.

"Do not caponize an ailing Belgian. Be sure he is sound and healthy.

"Before performing the operation, take the hare to a place out of sight and hearing of the other hares, and make as little fuss about it as possible.

"Use a razor, or a very sharp knife. The knife is better. Make certain that it is chemically clean

The castration knot and how to tie, Italy, circa 1915.

by dipping it in a disinfecting solution, or by passing it through the flame of an alcohol lamp. Of course, do not heat the blade enough to draw the temper.

"It is best to have an assistant when performing the operation. Let him hold the Belgian in his lap, turning its back towards him and its rump towards you, and holding one front and one hind foot in each hand, spreading the legs apart, thus exposing the parts to be operated upon.

"Your assistant should have good nerves, and should grasp the hare firmly, but not too tightly. If you decide to begin the operation, be sure and carry it through at once to a successful finish.

"Seize with the thumb and first two fingers of the left hand one of the testicles, which the animal will endeavor to draw up into his body. When you have succeeded in grasping it, divide the skin of the outer pouch, or scrotum, with a single stroke of the knife. It is necessary to cut deep enough to make a good-sized opening in the scrotum, and in doing this the testicle will be laid open more or less. With the left hand take the testicle from the scrotum, drawing it out about two inches. With the knife separate the artery and the spermatic cord, cutting upward, and leaving a little pea-shaped bulb and the testicle, allowing the cord to drop and return to the scrotum.

"Next, commence about two inches from the testicle to scrape on the sides of the artery downwards with the edge of the knife, making a light and slow drawing stroke, touching the artery a little lower or nearer to the scrotum with

Carcasses of brothers, both one year old; the one on the left was castrated, circa 1920.

each stroke. Perhaps a dozen or twenty of these little fine cuts will be necessary to wear down before severing the artery, which should be done well down, close to the scrotum. In this way, but little blood would be lost, while if the artery is cut square off, much blood would be lost, and the hare might die. Repeat above operation with the second testicle. The testicle on the left side should be taken out first.

"Apply a little hogs' lard or Vaseline to the wound. If it is summer time, apply a little pine tar to keep the flies from doing injury. Do not put any water on the wound. The wound ought to heal, and usually does, in four or five days. The percentage of loss by caponizing is very small. Be gentle, but firm and quick, in performing this operation. The sooner it is over, the better for the Belgian."

The castration of rabbits is little used today in the meat production industry; however, it is quite common of the huge Angora wool farms of China and other rabbit wool producing countries, as once castrated the bucks will not fight one another.

FUR INDUSTRY

he rabbit fur industry was big business which started to really take off in the 1900s and would remain a viable market until about 1950. Those early breeds were, of course, the Belgian Hare, Flemish Giant and New Zealand Red. The market would soar with the arrival of the Chinchilla rabbit, closely followed by the Rex breed. Two distinct groups, rabbits and the wild hares, were being marketed. Extensive breeding operations could be found not only in the United States, but in Belgium, England, France and Germany. Typically, the wild hares gave a larger pelt than the rabbit. However, the pelts were weak, and the rather long hair was brittle, therefore not as durable as the rabbit. Millions of pelts were being exported

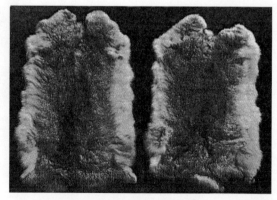

Dressed Chinchilla pelts ready for market, circa 1925.

406

from Australia and New Zealand, since those countries were so heavily plagued by the introduction of the European Wild Rabbit. Pelts would be sheared, plucked, and then dyed to imitate the more costly and rarer furs so often in demand, but out of reach for the normal person. The scientific treatments used by the fur-dyeing houses of the time were so advanced

The largest rabbit fur collection house in America was located at 447 South Hewitt Street, Los Angeles, California, with a 15,000-square-feet floor space, circa 1930.

that it was rather difficult to tell the rabbit pelts from the real thing, when made into various garments.

Rather exotic names were given to the dyed, sheared and plucked pelts, both in rabbits and hares. In June of 1938, the U.S. Federal Trade Commission ruled that these names were no longer permissible, as they were misleading the consumers. The following is a sizable list of those exotic fur names of yesteryear. You will obviously notice after reviewing the list of names and varieties, that the brown shades were by far the color of choice in those days, but justly so, as who didn't want to own a true Seal, Mink, Beaver, or even a Nutria Rat coat.

- Artic Seal — Seal, dyed rabbit
- Australian Coney — Rabbits from Australia
- Australian Rabbit — Rabbits from Australia
- Australian Seal — Sheared and Seal, dyed Australian Rabbit
- Baffin Seal — Seal, dyed Rabbit
- Baltic Black Fox — Black, dyed Rabbit

Evening cloak of pulled Chinchilla made by the Fur Board of England for Lady Evelyn Guinness, circa 1925.

407

The real Lady Evelyn Guinness with her Chinchilla coat, circa 1925.

- Baltic Brown Fox — Brown, dyed Rabbit
- Baltic Leopard — Australian Rabbit dyed and marked like a Leopard
- Baltic Lion — Natural Agouti of Australian Rabbit
- Baltic Red Fox — Natural Red Australian Rabbit
- Baltic Seal — Seal, dyed Rabbit
- Baltic Tiger — Australian Rabbit dyed and marked to resemble a Tiger
- Baltic White Fox — Natural White Rabbit or Hare
- Bay Seal — Seal, dyed Rabbit
- Beaverette — Beaver, dyed Rabbit
- Belgian Beaver — Beaver, dyed Rabbit
- Black Hare — Black, dyed Hare
- Bluerette — Blue, dyed rabbit
- Buck Seal — Seal, dyed Cony (Rabbit)
- Buckskin Seal — Seal, dyed Rabbit
- Castorette — Beaver, dyed Rabbit
- Chapchillas — Sheared and Chinchilla, Dyed White Hare
- Chinchilla Rabbit — The Actual Chinchilla Rabbit Breeds
- Chinchillette — Chinchilla, dyed Rabbit
- Chipped Seal — Seal, dyed Rabbit
- Coast Seal — Sheared and Seal, dyed Rabbit
- Cocoalette — Cocoa, dyed Rabbit
- Cony — An old name for the Rabbit, but particularly those from Europe
- Cony Beaver — Beaver, dyed Rabbit
- Cony Kit — Small Rabbit
- Cony Leopard — Rabbit dyed and patterned to imitate Leopard
- Cony Mole — Seal, dyed Rabbit
- Electric Mole — Mole, dyed Rabbit
- Electric Seal — Seal, dyed Rabbit
- Ermiline — White Rabbit

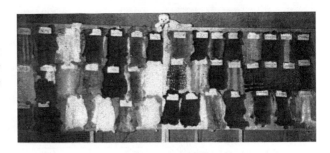

A display of 46 plucked, clipped and dyed rabbit pelts, all different, circa 1930.

- Ermine — White Rabbit
- Erminette — White Rabbit
- Fox Hair — Fox, dyed Hare
- French Beaver — Beaver, dyed Rabbit
- French Chinchilla — Chinchilla, dyed Hare
- French Cony — Sheared White Rabbit
- French Leopard — Hare dyed and patterned to resemble a Leopard
- French Sable — Sable, dyed Rabbit
- French Seal — Sheared and Seal, dyed Rabbit
- Galland Squirrel — Squirrel, dyed Cony
- Geller Seal — Seal, dyed Rabbit
- Hair Fox — Fox, dyed Hare
- Hair Sable — Sable, dyed Hare
- Hudson Bay Seal — Seal, dyed Rabbit
- Imitation Ermine — White Rabbit
- Jap Rabbit — Domestic Rabbit from Japan
- Kit Cony — Name for a young Rabbit
- Lapin — French word for Rabbit
- Laskin Seal — Seal, dyed Rabbit
- Le Meuse Seal — Seal, dyed Rabbit
- Leopard Cony — Leopard, dyed Rabbit
- Mar—Konie — Marmot, dyed Rabbit
- Marmotine — Marmot, dyed Cony
- Mendoza Beaver — Sheared and Beaver, dyed Rabbit
- Meskin Beaver — Sheared and Beaver, dyed Rabbit
- Meskin Ermine — White Rabbit
- Meskin Moline — Mole, dyed Rabbit
- Meskin Seal — Sheared and Seal, dyed Rabbit
- Minkony — Mink, dyed Rabbit
- Molin — Mole, dyed Rabbit and then sheared

- Moline — Mole, dyed Rabbit
- Muskratine — Sheared and Seal, dyed Rabbit
- Near Seal — Sheared and seal, dyed Rabbit
- New Zealand Seal — Sheared and Seal, dyed Rabbit
- Northern Seal — Sheared and Seal, dyed Rabbit
- Nu—Nutria — Dyed Giant White Rabbit from Japan
- Nutriette — Sheared and dyed to resemble the Nutria Rat
- Polar Seal — Seal, dyed Rabbit
- Polo Seal — Seal, dyed Rabbit
- Red River Seal — Seal, dyed Rabbit
- Roman Seal — Seal, dyed Rabbit
- Russian Leopard — Rabbit dyed and patterned to resemble the Leopard
- Russian Lynx — Often used improperly for Lynx, dyed Hare
- Russian Taupe Fox — Taupe, dyed Rabbit
- Sable Hair — Sable, dyed Hare
- Seal Musquash — Seal, dyed Rabbit
- Sealette — Seal, dyed Rabbit
- Sealine — Sheared and Seal, dyed Australian Rabbit
- Southern Seal — Seal, dyed Cony
- Squirreled — Squirrel, dyed Rabbit
- Squirreling — Squirrel, dyed Rabbit
- Twin Beaver — Dyed in alternating brown and white stripes from Rabbit
- Visonette — Mink, dyed Rabbit

Typically, most rabbit breeders of the early years did not own operations with thousands of animals, which is what most fur buyers wanted. Buyers usually preferred to purchase in lots from 25,000 to 100,000 pelts, but some would settle

Rabbit pelts being graded and sorted, circa 1925.

for a few hundred skins. This greatly hampered the average breeder, so they usually settled for whatever price they could get. The Sears & Roebuck Company ran many ads during the 1920s, to ship your skins to them for the best possible market price. Various store

Bales of rabbit pelts ready for the daily shipments to all parts of the U.S., Canada and Europe, circa 1925.

houses, particularly on the eastern coast, would buy small lots of your dried pelts, which would be graded accordingly, then railed to the raw-fur receiving houses.

Fur Buyers would usually grade the raw rabbit skins as first, seconds and thirds. The First and seconds are further divided into five classifications, based on color; white, blue, Chinchilla, red and mixed. Some buyers would go another step, sectioning out the first and second as small, medium and large. The white, blue, red and Chinchilla pelts would always be separated out, packed in color groups, and shipped. All other colors are just put together in bundles.

Prior to World War I, there were no less that 100,000,000 rabbits pelts being utilized annually in the United States. From those numbers, about 55,000,000 pelts were dressed, sheared and dyed to be used in the making of garments and trims. The remainder of these pelts, which would be the least grade, were chiefly used as linings for gloves and

Typical six-skin stole by the Fur Board of England from the fashionable Chinchilla rabbit, circa 1925.

in the manufacturing of felt, mostly for making hats. In the felt-making process, the skins would be cut into fine shreds, and once the hair was removed, the skins shreds would be used to manufacture glue. Remember, the glue on the back of postage stamps, well, guess what, that was made from rabbits.

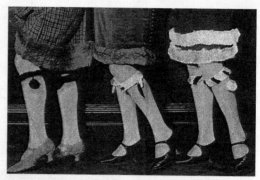

Rabbit fur was not only used for coats and trimmings of garments, but during the roaring 1920s, even for fine garters, circa 1927.

Those millions of rabbit pelts required by the American consumer and valued at some $25,000,000 would be almost totally imported, chiefly from Australia, New Zealand, Belgium, Germany and France. The United States production of rabbit pelts amounted to less than 2 percent of those millions used.

Many rabbit breeders chose not to sell their pelts, but instead dress, tan, and make items to wear themselves. The rural housewife and her children were usually given these chores, and a number of recipes were available for tanning and preserving the skins. Two of the most commonly used processes were the Salt-Acid and the Salt-Alum.

Salt-Acid Process for Tanning

The formula for the salt-acid process is a solution made up of 1 pound of common table salt and 1/2 ounce of concentrated sulphuric acid to each gallon of water used. First, dissolve the salt and then carefully pour in the sulphuric acid while stirring. The tanning solution should never be used in metal containers of any kind, but instead glass, earthenware or wooden containers. Gloves should be worn, and care must be taken to keep the strong acid solution off skin and clothing, not to go unmentioned, avoid inhaling the strong fumes when pouring in the acid. After the solution has cooled, it is ready to use.

Place the cleaned and softened pelts into the solution so

Wire stretcher to spread skins vertically, circa 1930.

that they are covered entirely. After one, but up to three days in the solution, and having been stirred frequently during this time, the skins are removed and rinsed in clean and cool water. Each skin should be worked for about

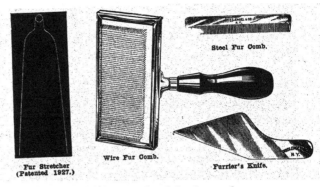

Steel Fur Comb.

Wire Fur Comb.

Fur Stretcher
(Patented 1927.)

Furrier's Knife.

Various tools of the fur trade.

10 minutes in a solution of one ounce borax to a gallon of water. Rinse again in clean water and squeeze to make the pelt as dry as possible, but not wring. Work the skin for a few minutes in your hands by pulling and rubbing; then it should be tack out flat on a board, with the flesh side up. At this time apply a tin coating of grease or oil to the flesh side and let it dry. Olive oil or fresh butter are ideal for this purpose.

Once the pelt is nearly dry but still slightly damp, begin to work it with your hands, stretching and pulling in all directions. Ideally, working the flesh side over a board in a shoe-shine fashion is perfect. Should the skin be rough, it may be smoothed further by working it over with a sandpaper block, which greatly helps to making the skin soft and pliable. The success in producing a soft pelt depends upon the repeated working of the skin, which must be done while the pelt is drying out and not after it has become completely dry.

Should the skin not be soft enough when completely dry, it should be dampened and worked again as before. If the skin is still greasy, it may be given a quick bath in gasoline, with the final cleaning by working it in a warmed, dry box of hardwood sawdust. This final process will give a beautiful luster to the finished pelt.

Salt-Alum Process for Tanning

The formula for the salt-alum process is 1 pound of ammonia alum (ammonium aluminum sulphate) or potash alum (potassium aluminum sulphate), which is then dissolved in 1 gallon of water. To this add 4 ounces of washing soda (crystallized sodium carbonate) and 8 ounces of your common table salt dissolved together with 1/2 gallon of water. Once dissolved, pour the soda-salt solution very slowly into the alum solution

Lillian Stahl, wife of the Father of the Domestic Rabbit Industry in America, models a Chinchilla coat, circa 1925.

while stirring vigorously. Then mix the combined solution with sufficient flour to make a thin paste; however, first mix the flour with a bit of water to prevent lumps.

Then take the pelt, which has been cleaned and softened as described in the previous process, and tack the pelt smoothly to a board, with the flesh side out. Then coat the pelt with your tanning solution, applying about an eighth of an inch thick and cover with paper, or better yet sacking, so that the paper does not come into contact with the paste. The next day, you scrape off most of the paste, and repeat the process. Thick skins, say from mature bucks, will usually take three applications, all at one-day intervals. Regardless, your last coating of paste should be left on the pelt for three to four days. The final process is to scrape off the paste and work the pelt in borax water solution, rinse, squeeze dry, and then do the back-and-forth process over a board in the same manner as described in the previous process.

The salt-alum process is more widely used than the salt-acid process; however, when tanning with alum, there is much more work required to make the pelts soft and supple. It is also advised to use a less than desirable skin in the beginning, until you learn the process fully and perfect your technique of tanning.

Beginning in 2002, rabbit fur, especially the Rex breed, has been drawing the attention of the fashion designers, because color has become the in thing. Rex breeders have so greatly improved the quality of the breed's coat, that even designers who don't normally work with furs are taking the lead in this renewed interest in rabbits. To sum it up, rabbit fur seems to be the "hip" thing in trendy fashion today.

414

COOKERY OF THE RABBIT

 aving been a collector of antique gas parlor and wood cook stoves for a number of years, and the fact that I do love the various ways that rabbits can be cooked, this book could not be complete without touching upon rabbit recipes from yesteryear. Excluding the first two recipes, each have been cooked on a wood stove by this author. The fragrant smells of oak, pecan or hickory wood cooking the meat and the marriage of the blending of herbs and vegetables is a delight to everyone's senses. The finished product can only be called, "Simply Delicious."

Rabbit has been a popular meat for hundreds upon hundreds of years. The Romans relished the taste of the unborn and newly born kits since the very earliest times. It was Pope Gregory the Great who issued the Papal Edict in 600 A.D., that rabbit was not considered meat and could be consumed during Lent, which was a great relief for the monks, who have been credited with the domestication of the species shortly thereafter. I personally don't care to know just how this dish of the young kits was prepared. Europeans have always had a deep appreciation for the tasty all-white meat of the rabbit.

It is interesting to note the demand for rabbit in both Europe and England. In Germany, where they have been raised for centuries, breeders consume most of their product in their own homes. In 1911, Bavaria alone produced 415,000 rabbits. Before World War I, approximately 100,000,000 rabbits were marketed annually in France, with some 2,200,000 being raised in Belgium in 1898 for home consumption and for export. The value of rabbits which were exported annually from Ostend to England easily exceeded one million dollars. In England, the country men were producing from 30,000,00 to 40,000,000 rabbits. In 1911, the consumption of rabbits in London alone amounted to 500,000 pounds daily, and in Paris to 200,000 pounds.

Little post-war data is available,

2,500 pounds of rabbits leaving Ontario, California, for the Los Angeles market, circa 1925.

but earlier records show that in 1910 from Belgium alone nearly 24 tons of dressed rabbit were shipped to the London markets, and the total imports of fresh and frozen rabbits from other countries for the same year was a staggering 332 tons, with a large portion of this coming from Australia and New Zealand. The value of the rabbit meat imported in 1910 for the last two destinations amounted to $4,500,000.

The Americans were a bit slow on the rabbit meat idea, as the domesticated rabbit was pretty much kept for pets, and shooting wild rabbit was a seasonal past time. Dr. T.S. Palmer, in a Report on the Rabbits of the United States, as published by the U.S. Department of Agriculture, *Bulletin No. 8,* 1896, "Many persons have a prejudice against eating rabbits because at certain seasons they are infested with parasites, or because the flesh is supposed to be 'strong.' This prejudice, however, is entirely unfounded. The parasites of the rabbit are not injurious to man; furthermore, the ticks and warbles occur at a season when the rabbit should not be killed for game, while the tape-worm can only develop in certain of the lower animals, as, for example, in the dog."

This all took a change in the minds of the American people with the introduction of a rabbit called the Belgian Hare in the late 19th century. Rabbit would become a mealtime favorite, and especially so during both World Wars when meat was extremely scarce, especially for the city dwellers.

At a grand feast given at the installation of the youngest brother of "the Kingmaker" as Archbishop of York in 1467, no

Canned rabbit meat, circa 1925.

less than 4,000 rabbits appeared on the bill of fare. Archer, in his *Highways of Letters,* describing ordinary dinners in the time of Chaucer, begins with a pottage called "backend," made of fowl or rabbit, cut up fine and stewed, as was the fashion then, with a diabolical variety of spices. The rabbit seems only to have lost caste with the

Illustration from the cover of "The Kitchen Companion," a cookbook which was published in Philadelphia, 1844.

change of the dynasty upon the demise of Queen Anne; for the 'rabbit tart' was a standing dish on the table of Her Majesty, who was noted as a voracious eater. In The *Noble Boke of Cookry for a Houseolde or Any Other Estately Houseolde,* which was written about the same time as the great Neville banquet, rabbits were always served during the cooler months of the year. Curiously enough, they seem generally to have been placed upon a spit, but in order to make them tolerably succulent, the carcass must be heavily basted to prevent drying out, since rabbit has little to no fat. There was no practicable way to baste four thousand rabbits simultaneously. Here are a couple of those venerable recipes which have a historic, rather than a gastronomic value.

Cony Rost (1400s)

A Conye tak and drawe him and parboile him rost him and lard him then raise his leggs and hys winges and sauce him with vinegar and powder of ginger and serue it.

Rabettes Rost (1400s)

To rost rabettes tak and slay them draw them and rost them and let their heddes be in first parboile them or ye rost them and serue them. Smyt them in small pieces and sethe them in good brothe put them to minced onions and grece and drawe a liour of brown bred and blod and seison it with venygar and cast in pouder and salt and serve it.

Rabbit Fricassee

Although rabbit might have been considered by most Americans of the late 1700s as a frontier food, the third President of the United States, Thomas Jefferson, delighted in this Rabbit Fricassee, which was served many times at his beloved Monticello estate.

Cut rabbit into serving pieces and dust with flour. Heat butter is a skillet with a tight-fitting lid, add rabbit pieces, and sprinkle with salt and pepper. Fry until nicely browned on all sides. Now stir in one medium finely chopped onion and cook for a few minutes. Next, pour in a glass and half of red wine. Tie a quarter of a lemon rind, chopped parsley, two stalks chopped celery, and one bay leaf in a little cheesecloth bag and drop into the skillet. Cover and simmer gently until meat is tender — takes about one hour. Lift rabbit pieces to a hot serving platter. Discard seasoning bag. Work flour and butter together until well blended, then add to liquid, and cook, stirring constantly, until sauce bubbles. Pour over rabbit and sprinkle top with chopped parsley.

Roast Rabbit — A Genuine Warren Recipe (1850s)

Make a force-meat of bread-crumbs, minced beef-suet, lemon-peel, nutmeg, pepper and salt, and a little lemon-thyme, if sweet herbs are approved. Beat up two eggs, and mix with them, the whole into paste. Put this force-meat inside the rabbit, and sew it up, and skewer it into the proper form. Rub the outside of the rabbit over with butter, flour it a little, and stick on very thin

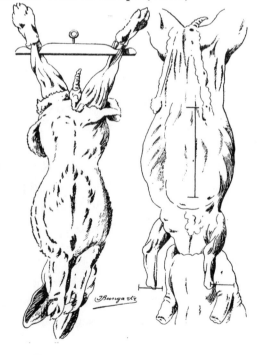

German illustration showing how to hang and dress rabbit, circa 1917.

slices of bacon by means of small skewers of iron wire. A French cook would lard them with a larding-needle. These slices of bacon will roast up till they become quite crisp and dry; the fat which oozes from them will keep the rabbit moist and juicy. Still, it ought to be well basted while roasting. Make a gravy with a small piece of beef (or livers of rabbits, if they are not roasted inside), a whole onion put in without peeling it, some whole peppercorns, a blade of mace, and a clove or two, with a small crust of bread toasted very dry and brown, but not burnt. When the gravy is boiled enough, strain it, add a little catsup and flour well braided together. Make the gravy just boil up (not for a minute or two), before serving with the roast rabbit, in a separate tureen by itself. Some add a glass of port wine to the gravy.

Boiled Rabbit, Smothered with Onion Sauce (1850s)

They must be skewered and trussed, so as to come to table in a crouching posture. Dust it with flour, as you would a boiled chicken, to make it come out the whiter. Tie it in a cloth; if young, put it into boiling-hot water; if old, into cold water. The time of boiling must be entirely regulated by the apparent age and tenderness of the rabbit. Tomato instead of onion sauce is a much approved variation of this dish.

While the rabbit is boiling, prepare your onion sauce thus: Peel your onions, halve and quarter them, put them on in a sauce-pan in cold water, boil till perfectly soft, strain them from the water, and then braid them through a colander. To the pulp thus made, add a lump of butter and some thick cream, with a little pepper and salt. Then make it just boil up, being careful that it does not burn, and pour it over the rabbit as it lies on its dish. Serve at the same time a piece of boiled white bacon to eat with it, and a tureen of melted butter.

Stewed Rabbit — An English Staple (1850s)

Cut the rabbits into joints. Half fry them into butter, and lay them into a stew-pan. Fry some sliced onions, and put them over the rabbit in the stew-pan, with a little powdered mace, pepper and salt. Pour sufficient water over them to cover them, allowing for the waste by evaporation during cooking. The stew must be done very slowly, only being allowed just to simmer. It will take two hours to do it properly; when enough, take out each piece of rabbit and lay it on the dish on which it is to be served; with the gravy which remains in the stew-pan mix a pickled walnut finely and smoothly braided, with a good tablespoonful of catsup and a dust of flour.

Set it over the fire, and pour it over your rabbit directly that it shows symptoms of boiling up.

Italian illustration showing a well-nourished rabbit and dressed carcass, circa 1930.

Rabbit Pie (1850s)

Cut the rabbits into joints, and simply stew them with water, pepper, salt and pounded mace, till they are half done. Proceed then as for pigeon pie, putting veal or pork, or both, instead of beef. Cover with paste, and bake till enough.

To Curry Rabbits (1850s)

Take a young rabbit or two, skin and cut them into conveniently-sized pieces to serve, put them into a frying-pan with some butter, and fry them to a nice light brown color; then place them at the bottom of your stew-pan.

Slice and fry six or eight large onions; place them over the rabbit in the stew-pan. Then mix four tablespoonsful of best curry-powder and some good stock gravy (which is a great point in insuring success), with salt, Cayenne pepper, nutmeg, three or four slices of lemon with the peel on, small quantity of chopped pickles of all kinds that are at hand, and a glass of sherry.

Boil well, and pour it over the rabbit and onions in the stew-pan; let all simmer together for three hours; serve it up in a dish encircled with rice that has been boiled in the following manner: put the rice in cold water, and when it boils let it boil exactly sixteen minutes afterwards. The seventeenth minute would spoil it utterly. It is as with the charmed bullets of Zamial, "The six(-teenth) shall achieve, the seven(-teenth) deceive."

FRENCH WAYS OF COOKING RABBIT (1850s)

Marinade of Rabbit

The French have a habit of steeping or pickling many viands, especially white meats and fresh-water fish, in what they call marinade, or pickle, of various compositions.

If you are going to make use of a tame rabbit, hulk it as soon as it is killed, and stuff the inside with thyme, bay-leaves, sage, basil, pepper and salt. Roast it till it is half done, and let it get cold. Cut it into joints, and put them into a marinade composed of white wine or (cider), lemon-juice, and parsley, shallots, thyme, bay-leaves, and a clove of garlic, all chopped up fine together. After they have soaked an hour, dip them in butter, and fry them in oil or butter which is not too hot. Fry them to a bright clear brown, and serve them dry, garnished with fried parsley.

Italian illustration showing a malnourished rabbit and the dressed carcass, circa 1930.

Gibbelotte

This is the name of a particular mode of stew or fricassee, in which various meats and poultry may be served. Gibbelotte of rabbit (which is the original gibbelotte) is thus made: Cut a rabbit into joints. Put a lump of butter into a stew-pan, and some lean bacon cut into slices. When they are browned, take them out and put your rabbit in. As soon as it has had a toss or two, add a spoonful or flour, a glass of white wine, and a glass of good broth, a little pepper and nutmeg, a dozen small onions, a few button mushrooms, or instead of them a dessert spoonful of mushroom catsup, and a bunch of sweet herbs. When the rabbit is done enough, take the fat off the gravy; thicken it if required, so that it be neither too thick nor too thin; pour it over the rabbit, and serve garnished, either with pieces of toast or of fried bread round the dish.

It is not an uncommon practice with French cooks to add an eel or two cut into short pieces, when this and similar dishes are half cooked, and then to serve the whole together.

Civet

Civet is the French name appropriated to a dish of stewed hare, but rabbits are commonly dressed in the same way, when hares are out of season.

Civet of Rabbit is made by cutting it into joints, putting it into a stew-pan, and giving it two or three turns on the fire. Then add a dusting of

421

flour, a liberal allowance of red-wine, salt, pepper, and a few slices of bacon. Throw in some small onions that have fried whole in butter, with a bouquet of sweet herbs. Make it boil up and skim off the fat. As soon as it is done enough, take away the bouquet, and serve hot. But a small quantity of gravy should come to table.

Rabbit Pate

A very useful standing dish may be made of any size, the larger the better. Have ready your rabbits; cut them up into joints; have, also, an earthen or stoneware pate-dish with a close-fitting cover. This kind of pate is made without any crust. At the bottom of the dish lay slices of bacon, and over that a layer of minced meat, or any kind you happen to have at hand, mixed with chopped parsley, chives, a large clove of garlic, mushrooms and pepper. Upon this bed lay the whole of your rabbits, as closely as you can pack the pieces, and then the remainder of your mince-meat, and some more slices of bacon to cover the whole. Shake it well together. Throw in a glass or two of white wine, put the cover on the dish, and set it in the oven till it is done enough. It must not be touched to be eaten until it is cold.

En Papillottes or In Curl-Papers

Here is a favorite French way of serving small portions of meat, such as joints of poultry and game, chops, cutlets, &c. For rabbits in curl-papers, cut them into quarters if they are very young, and into joints if they are full grown; marinade, or pickle them, several hours in a mixture of oil, salt, pepper, catsup, and chopped parsley and chives, well mingled together. Have ready some oiled or buttered white writing paper, prepared exactly as for cutlets en papillotes; do up each piece of rabbit with a little of the seasoning and a thin slice of bacon enclosed in the paper; grill then on a gridiron over a very slow fire, and when they are thoroughly done, serve them smoking hot in the paper, just as they are.

Considering the Belgian Hare was considered the ideal meat breed at

Special rabbit meat packaging began in the late 1930s. A cellophane window allowed the customer to view the product, and rabbit recipes were printed on the bottom of the carton. These cartons, oddly enough, were issued by the Federation of American Angora Breeders of East Haven, Connecticut.

the beginning of the last century, I should not fail to included a trio of recipes printed over 100 years ago. Of course, any rabbit will do, instead of the beautiful and stately Belgian Hare.

Jugged Hare

Bone a hare and cut in small pieces. Cut also an equal weight of fat and lean ham, put in a stew-pan with a little butter. One cup of stock, pepper, salt, allspice and mace. Let it draw for an hour over a slow fire, then add a pint of port wine and boil very gently until the liquor is reduced to a glaze. Pound the meat tender in a mortar till very smooth. Add seasoning if required. Pack closely in small porcelain pots. Pour a tablespoonful of clarified butter into each, and place in a slow oven for half an hour. When cold, fill up the pots with clarified butter. This will keep a month in a cool place.

Hare a la Créme

Clean and cut up the hare. Melt two tablespoonfuls of butter, fry it with a small onion, minced, then fry the hare until light brown. When well colored, remove the hare and add to the butter an equal measure of corn starch. Stir until smooth, then add milk to make a thin sauce. Place the hare in a baking pan. Pour over it the sauce, strain and bake in the oven until thoroughly done.

Raised Hare Pie

Cut hare in small pieces and season to taste with salt, pepper and nutmeg. Cut half a pound of bacon to dice, and when the raised crust is made, place in dish with the meat and intersperse yolks of three or four eggs. Pour over the top tomato sauce or some good gravy. Cover with pastry, brush with egg, and ornament if you wish. Bake in moderate oven until a skewer may be thrust through to the bottom — about an hour and a half. Serve either hot or cold.

Advertisement by the American Rabbit and Cavy Breeders Association, Inc. to promote domestic rabbit meat. This is rabbit fried in cracker crumbs, circa 1927.

423

NATIONAL GOVERNING ORGANIZATIONS

AMERICAN RABBIT BREEDERS ASSOCIATION

 ecords will show that purebred rabbits were to be found in the United States during the early 1840s, namely Angoras and English Lops, but the earliest record of a rabbit club being formed was not until shortly after 1888, when the American Belgian Hare Association was founded. This organization was rather short lived, due to the scattering of members. Another attempt was made in 1897, when the National Belgian Hare Club of America was founded in 1897, which was also about the same time that the American Flemish Giant Club was organized. Both organizations flourished, especially the Belgian Hare Club, as it was the breed of the rabbit boom period in America. Within three years, nearly half of the states of the Union and the major cities had established Belgian Hare Clubs as well. During the flurry of importations from Europe and particularly England during the years 1898 through 1901, other breeds were making their appearance on American shores. Yet there was no national rabbit governing body which catered to all breeds of rabbits.

From the lengthy diary of the late Oscar M. Sennewald, who was born April 7, 1898 in a log cabin on a poultry farm in Roseville, Michigan, we are able to learn much of the early history. I quote, "1900, Dad Sennewald cut this article out of the Roseville newspaper. Detroit Pet Stock Association, a rabbit club organized by Charles S. Gibson, 1045 West Warren Avenue, Detroit, Michigan. Officers; President - Al Funke, Vice-President - Ben Gibson, Secretary-Treasurer - Charles S. Gibson, Board Members - Fred Miller and John Wiggins. This is the first rabbit association in the state of Michigan." It was at this time the Sennewalds moved to Detroit, where the family purchased a bakery.

Oscar received a pair of rabbits for Easter Sunday, 1901, but after many scratches, they became dinner. In 1902 for his fourth birthday, he received another pair of rabbits, called White Silk Hares, doe weighed 5 pounds and the buck was 4-1/2 pounds, very cobby in shape and the fur shined like

Oscar Sennewald, last charter member of the National Pet Stock Association.

424

Left: Artist's rendering of the Gibson home where the forerunner of the American Rabbit Breeders Association was founded on January 10, 1910. Below: Photo of the back of the Gibson home where a store front had been installed.

silk. Now to avoid a multitude of pages on this history, I must simply say that Oscar was an eager beaver with his rabbits, adding Belgian Hares in 1904, and in 1907 was invited to join the Detroit Pet Stock Association, trading a young Belgian Hare buck to Charles Gibson for his $2 membership fee.

The big day would come on January 10, 1910, as written in Oscar's diary, "A VERY SPECIAL MEETING, All members of the Detroit Pet Stock Association waiting for this special meeting January 10, 1910, at Charles S. Gibson's home, 1045 West Warren Avenue, Detroit, Michigan at 8 a.m. Charles S. Gibson called the meeting to order with 13 rabbit breeders present, 4 out of state and 9 local members present.

"Charles Gibson explained his plans to organize the First National Rabbit Association in the United State. After his plans were explained, questions were asked and he answered same. Then Mr. George Eckert made a motion to organize and officers were elected.

"Mr. Al Funke nominated Mr. William Lyons for president, voted on and carried. Ben Gibson nominated Mr. George Eckert

Charles S. Gibson, Founder of the National Pet Stock Association, Secretary-Treasurer, 1910-1920.

Early rabbit pioneers, left to right: William Lyons, C.R. Deardorf, H. Simon, John C. Fehr, Edward H. Foullois and Roy Knill. William Lyons was the first President of the National Pet Stock Association from 1910-1912. Roy Knill was President from 1913-1915.

for vice-president voted on and carried. Mr. Lyons nominated Mr. Charles Gibson for secretary/treasurer voted on and carried. Mr. Fred Miller nominated Mr. George Eckert, Ben Gibson and Al Funke for directors, voted on and carried.

"John Wiggins moved all members joining, be chartered members, voted on and carried.

"Name of association 'The National Pet Stock Association' voted on and carried.

"Moved by Fred Miller that we leave drafting of the constitution and by-laws and etc. up to present officers. Voted on and carried.

"Mr. Al Funke moved we adjourn meeting. Meeting closed and all members very happy to have a national rabbit breeders association.

"Charles Gibson's mother served a very lovely lunch of rabbit sandwiches, wonderful cake and coffee. For which the new national association thanked Mrs. Gibson with a rising vote 'Thank you, Mrs. Gibson Dearly."

Early rabbit pioneers, back row, left to right: believed to be Ben Gibson; Al Funke, Charles S. Gibson, George C. Eckert and John Coil. The identify of the front row is not known. George C. Eckert became Secretary-Treasurer of the Old National.

The 13 chartered members were; Charles Chambers, Jack Coil, Al Funke, Ben Gibson, Charles Gibson, Fred Miller, Otto Peans, John Wiggins, and Oscar Sennewald, all from Michigan; plus George Eckert of Chicago, Illinois, William Lyons of Waukegan, Illinois,

M.S. Stanton and M. Milligan of Fort Wayne, Indiana. It should be noted here that Oscar Sennewald was just 11 years old at this meeting, and would become the last surviving member, passing away in 1991, after a remarkable membership that spanned 81 years.

It was a rather rough year keeping the organization going, but ended up with 183 members. A new president was chosen by the name of Roy Knill in 1913, and the growth of the association improved. The first club to charter with the national was the Pikes Peak Rabbit and Pet Association in September of 1914. Lewis S.J. Griffin became president in 1916.

Lewis S.J. Griffin, President 1916-1917, Secretary 1943-1945.

The National Pet Stock Association issued a very simple standard in 1914, which included the following breeds: Angora, Belgian Hare, Dutch, English (Spot), Flemish Giant, New Zealand Red Hare, Checkered Giant, Giant rabbits (?), German, Havana, Himalayan, Imperial, Japanese, Polish, Tan and Lops (both English and French).

It was in 1917 that a major turn for the betterment of the organization took place; the name was changed to the National Breeders and Fanciers Association of America. The first real set of show rules, Constitution and By-laws and Standard of Perfection were written. The standards were started by a Dr. W.F. Roth in early 1911, but he died on September 3, 1911, before completing the work. C.R. Deardorff, along with Charles T. Cornman, finished the first real Standard of Perfection. The first official emblem was designed and produced by the George Lauterer Company of Chicago, Illinois. You may find it a bit unusual, but this organization not only catered to rabbits and cavies, but instead just about every type of small stock possible; mice, rats, muskrats and foxes, to name just a few.

In 1918, William H. Ashton, of Dayton, Ohio, was elected president, with Charles Gibson remaining as the secretary-treasurer. While the organization was growing and produced their first guide book, problems developed between Ashton and Gibson, or the inner circle of leaders, so to speak. Ashton appears to have quit, and Gibson

First emblem designed by George Lauterer Co. of Chicago, Illinois.

Dr. W.F. Roth (left) began the first breed standards, which were completed by C.T. Cornman (center) and C.R. Deardorff (right).

installed Lewis Salisbury of American Blue fame from Pasadena, California as president. The organization split apart, with a new National Breeders and Fanciers Association of America forming in 1919. Joseph Blank of Mt. Vernon, New York became the president, and Charles Gibson, moved into the secretary-treasurer position with the new group. Yes, there were two national governing bodies going by the same name; yet to stop confusion, they were known as the "Old National" and the "New National." Gibson set up headquarters at Mt. Vernon, New York. The Old National president remained William Ashton, and the secretary-treasurer became George C. Eckert, who set up offices in rented room numbers 424 and 425, at 3166 Lincoln Avenue, Chicago, Illinois.

Two well-known rabbit men of the day: John C. Fehr of Indiana belonged to the Old National, and Edward H. Stahl from Missouri was associated with the New National. On January 29, 1920, the New National incorporated. Oddly enough, though the Old National began to lose strength, they even advertised in the New National's Guide Book for members. A new president by the name of Henry M. Adolph, of Cleveland, Ohio, was elected to the New National in 1920. In 1921, Ellis L. DeLancey, of York, Pennsylvania, was elected president and a new secretary-treasurer by the name Raymond L. Pike of Crawfordsville, Indiana. Charles Gibson was not the best-liked official, and because he was a railroad conductor, was able to travel extensively by rail free of charge, so he was given the posi-

William H. Ashton, President, 1918.

tion of a field-man and organizer to boost memberships and establish affiliate clubs on a set salary. Well, this did not work out; Gibson was never paid. He, of course, became angry with the association, quit and moved to California, where he would spend the rest of his years. He is buried at the Veterans cemetery in West Los Angeles. Raymond Pike came into the office like a house on fire, the nation was flooded with circulars, and the national magazines boosted him.

In the fall of 1922, word began to circulate that the association finances were just about depleted by Raymond Pike's fancy promotional literature. At the Chicago Convention that same year, the board discovered bills amounting to over $500 that could not be covered. The board quickly took action by replacing Pike with Arthur Weygandt of Chicago, Illinois, to become effective on January 1, 1923. The national headquarters were moved to Weygandt's home at 7408 Normal Avenue. Two rooms of his house were converted to offices, and

Lewis H. Salisbury, President, 1918.

Joseph Blank, President, 1919.

the basement was used for storage. It was also at this time that the secretary-treasurer office was split, with Miss N.M. Flaherty of Chicago, Illinois becoming the treasurer and the first woman officer. Within three years, Weygandt had paid off all the debts, produced two yearbooks with another in the making, issued sev-

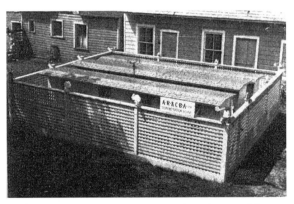

Rabbit display established behind the home of Secretary Weygandt, which thousands of people viewed yearly, circa late 1920s.

Note: No pictures have been located of Henry M. Adolph, President of the New National in 1920, or of Raymond Pike, Secretary-Treasurer of the New National in 1920-1922.

429

eral bulletins, a booklet for beginners, a pocket standard, had $500 set aside to fight the high express rates, plus showed a surplus of over $2,000 on the treasurer's books. Weygandt even established a rabbit display plant behind his home, where thousands of visitors, especially school children, viewed a number of different breeds each year. Arthur Weygandt had saved the association and would remain in office for no less than 20 years, until he suffered a paralyzing stoke on February 1, 1943.

Arthur Weygandt, Secretary, 1923-1943.

During the 1923 Convention held in Kansas City, Missouri, at the urging of Edward H. Stahl, the two brewing factions became united into one strong governing body. Well, actually the Old National had just about totally died out. In 1924 at the Lima, Ohio National Convention, the name was again changed to the American Rabbit and Cavy Breeders Association and incorporated at the same time under the laws of Illinois.

Trouble again surfaced in 1926, and Ellis Delancey, the president, resigned. Edward H. Stahl, acting vice-president, became the president for the

Ellis L. DeLancy, President, 1921-1925 (resigned).

Miss N.M. Flaherty of Illinois (left) became the first female officer, soon followed by Mrs. Etta Powers of California (right) as a Director.

Edward H. Stahl,
President, 1925.

remainder of the term, until J.S. Bales of Springfield, Illinois was elected president on January 1, 1927. Bales would serve through 1936, when Oscar F. Schultze of Norwalk, Connecticut was elected for the years 1937 and 1938, followed by John C. Fehr as president in 1939 to 1943, when Schultze was again elected president in 1944.

J.S. Bales,
President, 1927-1936.

By 1927 there were six national specialty clubs chartered: National Belgian Hare Club of America, Federation of Flemish Giant Breeders, American Federation of New Zealand Breeders, American Chinchilla Rabbit Breeders Association, American Checkered Giant Club and Havana Club.

During John Fehr's presidency, he would appoint Lewis S.J. Griffin, of Colorado Springs, Colorado, as the new secretary in 1943, with the headquarters moving to 812 East Costella, Colorado Springs. The membership was right at 1,600 members, 100 affiliates, and by 1946 it had grown to just over 9,000, 320 affiliates, 300 registrars and over 100 judges. During the election for 1946, James Blyth of Pittsburgh, Pennsylvania ran against Lewis Griffin for secretary. Griffin received 736 votes, and Blyth garnered just 360 votes; yet James

Offices of the American Rabbit and Cavy Breeders Association, Inc. in Secretary Weygandt's home, circa 1929.

Oscar F. Schultze,
President,
1937-1938, 1944-1953.

John C. Fehr
President, 1939-1943.

James Blyth,
Secretary, 1946-1972.

Blyth became the new secretary. Griffin had encouraged Blyth to run for the position, so when Blyth was defeated, Griffin resigned, paving the way for this outstanding man to serve the organization for the next 27 years. The headquarters were moved to 5941 Baum Boulevard, Pittsburgh, to rental space on the third floor of an office building, without the use of an elevator. The landlord soon started raising the rent until it was cost prohibitive. The entire board met in Pittsburgh in 1948 and decided to purchase the association's first national headquarters at 4323 Murray Avenue in Pittsburgh for $15,500. This building was a former Jewish Synagogue, but with some remodeling would serve the association well for the next 25 years. Blyth and his family lived upstairs, with the offices on the main floor, and the basement acted as storage facilities. Let it be known that the money to purchase the headquarters was made possible through the generous donations of the members and affiliated clubs of the national governing body. Jim Blyth would serve under no less than six presidents, longer than any other secretary. He retired in 1972 under the presidency of Oren Reynolds.

James Blyth would prove a great benefit to the association. Membership stood at 12,000 in 1948; he brought the office up to date with equipment, especially to assist with mailings. He streamlined things: license renewals for judges and registrars became due on January 1st each year, as were club renewals, a news bulletin was started, the Standards were printed as a separate book for the first time

beginning in 1950, which led to the first Yearbook issued in 1955. The *Practical Beginner Booklet* had been published by Blyth in 1949, selling for 10 cents, and it sold by the tens of thousands. James Blyth would see the next major change in the organization, when the board of directors, in 1952, dropped the word "cavy" from the association's name. The logic being it was the rabbit, for meat and fur, and this is what the organization had become based upon. Of course, it was just a name change, and cavies continue to remain within the working structure, as they do so today. It was under Blyth that the

First National Headquarters, which was owned by the American Rabbit & Cavy Breeders Association, Inc., Pittsburgh, Pennsylvania, 1948-1972.

red, white and blue merit system for registration began.

Although a youth program was begun in 1949, little headway was achieved. It was not until 1958 that a Youth Division was established as a specialty club, so to speak, with youth officers and an adult advisor as overseer. This youth club had its own show rules, sweepstakes, constitution and by-laws. The youth department would see a dramatic change take place

Interior view of main office with Secretary Blyth and long-time assistant, Miss Cil Tully, circa mid-1960s.

when Oren Reynolds of Illinois was elected president of the ARBA in 1971. At the first board meeting, Oren laid out his plans for the youth having all the rights and privileges of adults, except the right to vote. They would be members of the ARBA at a reduced rate and receive all the same benefits. This was dubbed the "Reynolds Plan" and was given a six-month trial period. At the time of the Reynolds Plan, there were approximately 700 youth members, and within a year the youth membership more than doubled. So successful was Oren's idea, that in 1996 the ARBA boasted no less than 14,000 youth memberships.

James Blyth retires.

James Blyth retired on December 31, 1972, and Oren Reynolds appointed Ed Peifer, Jr. of Bloomington, Illinois as the new secretary. Once again, the national headquarters were moved, this time, of course, to Bloomington, to a rental at 1006 Morrisey Drive. Within six months, it was realized that a larger space was needed, so another rental was secured at 2401 West Oakland Avenue, where the offices would remain until November 1976. Meanwhile, the Pittsburgh headquarters was sold for $27,000, which became the seed money to purchase the ARBA's next national headquarters at 1925 South Main for $125,000.

Edward Peifer, Jr. would also prove to have been an excellent choice, as he brought the ARBA into a new era; within 10 years the membership had grown from 11,000 to over 33,000 members. He introduced the association to the computer age, modern office equipment, established an in-house printing shop, modern mailing facility, camera and darkroom, which saved the organization many thousands of dollars. The ARBA's net worth jumped a staggering $70,000 to well over $900,000. It was also at the beginning of Peifer's tenure that the *Domestic Rabbits* magazine started. The cover of that first issue produced for January-February 1973 stated "ARBA enters new era," and no truer statement could have ever been made. Oren Reynolds has been the editor of the magazine

Ed Peifer, Jr., Secretary, 1973-1984.

Oren Reynolds, President, 1971-1974.

for no less than 32 years and, I might add, never missed a deadline.

Glen Carr of Columbus, Ohio was appointed the new ARBA secretary in 1985, after Ed Peifer, Jr. announced his retirement. Instead of

Second National Headquarters which was owned by the American Rabbit Breeders Association, Inc., Bloomington, Illinois, 1976-1996.

Glen moving the national headquarters to Ohio, he moved to Bloomington. Under Carr's guidance, the registration system was computerized, many new brochures were written, the Standard of Perfection had all the breeds shown in color at the front of the book, color breed poster, additional cooping

Glen C. Carr, Secretary, 1985-current.

Partial view of the ARBA's Hall of Fame Library, showing some of the many publications, old trophies and Hall of Fame inductees.

Present National Headquarters, owned by the American Rabbit Breeders Association, Inc., purchased February 1996, Bloomington, Illinois.

had been purchased to now accommodate 20,000 animals at the national conventions. Overall, business runs approximately $700,000 per year, and the association's net worth is over $1,000,000.

Glen Carr looked for some time to find better facilities for the headquarters, and in February 1996 the offices were moved to a 10,000-square-foot, near maintenance-free building, at 8 Westport Court, which was purchased for $375,000. The other building was sold for a good profit of $135,000. In November 2003, the title of secretary was dropped and replaced with "Executive Director," which far better suits this day and age.

One of the greatest achievements for the ARBA in recent times, at least in this author's opinion, was the dedication of the American Rabbit Breeders Association Hall of Fame Library, which is housed at the national headquarters in Bloomington. Dedicated October 5, 2002, this beautifully furnished 20 x 30 foot room houses the most complete English language collection of rabbit and cavy material in the world. There are thousands of books, publications, photos, and other memorabilia that trace not only rabbit raising in America back to the mid-1800s, but also the fancy of the United Kingdom through the same time span.

The American Rabbit Breeders Association, Inc. through its 94-year history, has certainly become one of the world leaders in the rabbit industry. Their registration system cannot be topped by any other rabbit governing body, and there is little doubt that they offer their membership more benefits for their yearly dues than any other organization.

American Rabbit Breeders Association, Inc.
P.O. Box 426, Bloomington, Illinois 61702 USA
Phone: 309-664-7500
Email: ARBAPOST@aol.com
Web Site: http://www.arba.net

THE REMAINING PRESIDENTS WHO HAVE LED THE AMERICAN RABBIT BREEDERS ASSOCIATION, INC.

Charles A. Pine,
President,
1954, died in office.

Pete M. Leeuwenburg,
President,
1955-1956.

Dick F. Parker,
President,
1957-1965.

Rev. R. Wayne
Willmann,
President, 1966-1970.

Don Reid,
President,
1975-1980.

Glessner Arthur
(G.A.) Burke,
President, 1979-1980.

Dennis L. Holcomb,
President,
1981-1982.

Dr. Terry E. Reed,
President,
1983-1988.

Cindy Wickizer,
President,
1989-1994, 1997-1998.

Gary Michaud,
President,
1995-1996.

Dr. Chris Hayhow,
President,
1999-2004.

Show room of the National Convention in Colorado Springs, Colorado, in 1925.

Early National Rabbit Conventions in America

While our national rabbit conventions of the past have been well recorded, particularly starting in 1924, I thought it might be interesting to give some of the information of the early shows, which date back to 1917.

Talk had been going on by President Lewis Griffin and Secretary Charles Gibbons, along with the rest of the board members, that it was time to hold a national convention for the National Breeders and Fanciers Association of America. The membership was steadily growing strong, and there were 42 chartered clubs which had become affiliated with the national. It was therefore decided to hold a feeler convention in the spring of 1917. This show was sponsored by the Great Lakes Rabbit and Pet Stock Association and held in Grand Rapids, Michigan. Those in attendance for the meeting were: President Griffin, Vice-President George Echart, Secretary/Treasurer Charles Gibson, along with Al Funke, Gale Johnson, John Fehr, Joseph Blank, Mrs. Alfred Guggenheim, Edward Lacey, Henry Adolph, Marcel Meek, Fred Miller, John Wiggins, Otto Peans, Charles Champers and Oscar Sennewald. It was reported this convention was a great success, represented by ten states and over 600 rabbits entered.

In a report written by Secretary Charles Gibson and published in August, 1917, it stated, "Bids are now open for THE FIRST REAL NATIONAL CONVENTION. The members seem to be ready for conventions and the good old National with its nearly 3,000 members certainly can support a convention each year."

438

The following month in September, under the heading, "NATIONAL CONVENTION," Mr. J.D. Lane, president of the Mid-West Pet Stock Association, wrote, "At our monthly table show a resolution that the Mid-West Pet Stock Association make a bid for the first convention was unanimously carried."

In November of 1917, a national vote was taken on behalf of the various cities which had bid for the convention, which appeared under the heading "NATIONAL CONVENTION RESULTS." Kansas City-87, St. Louis-80, and Chicago-69.

The First Annual Convention of the National Breeders and Fanciers Association of America was held in Kansas City, Missouri on January 14-19, 1918. That same year, on December 3-8, 1918, in Chicago, Illinois, a convention was held and reported as the Second National Convention. Cleveland, Ohio, in August 25-30, 1919, held the Third National Convention. The Fourth National Convention was held in Syracuse, New York on September 13-18, 1920.

It has been long believed that the next three convention dates had been lost, but with a bit of detective work, I was able to locate all three dates. The Fifth National Convention was held in Omaha, Nebraska on December 2-7, 1921. The Sixth National Convention was again Chicago, Illinois on December 11-15, 1922. The Seventh National Convention went back to Kansas City, Missouri on November 18-25, 1923. *(Note, this was the longest of any convention at seven days.)*

The Eighth National Convention was in Lima, Ohio on November 24-30, 1924, where the organization was renamed the American Rabbit and Cavy Breeders Association, and would no longer cater to all the other various small stock other than rabbits and cavies.

The national conventions have become huge functions; thousands of fanciers come together each fall, where they can visit hundreds of vendor booths, attend various meetings, lectures, sightsee and, of course, show their animals. The largest convention on record was in 2000, at the 77th ARBA Convention held in Columbus, Ohio, with no less than 21,794 animals entered. Our founding forefathers would have been proud.

AMERICAN LIVESTOCK BREEDS CONSERVANCY

The American Livestock Breeds Conservancy was founded in 1977, by a group of historians of agriculture who were concerned with the disappearance of old breeds of America. This organization is dedicated to the conservation and promotion of over 100 breeds of livestock and poultry. They promote these endangered breeds to their membership and the general public. They are constantly studying the genetic diversity, the status of breed populations, and support the breeders who make the effort of keeping these animals from extinction.

This author has been working with the ALBC for the last year in an effort for this organization to add the last breed of domestic livestock, which, of course, is rabbits, into their scope of operations, as America is faced with a number of endangered breeds of rabbits. The ABLC, having met on a couple of occasions on this issue, will make their final decision during their executive meeting in November 2004.

American Livestock Breeds Conservancy
P.O. Box 477, Pittsboro, North Carolina 27312
Phone: 919-542-5704
Email: albc@albc-usa.org
Web site: http://www.albc-usa.org

BELGIUM RACE RABBIT SPECIALTY

This is a rather unique organization which was founded on February 8, 1996, in Sint-Gillis-Waas, Belgium, for the promotion of all rabbit breeds which were developed in Belgium. They offer exhibitions, member gatherings, publications for their members, as well as dedicating themselves to keeping a few of the very critically endangered breeds alive. Currently they recognize 12 breeds, of which one is already believed to be extinct. The organization proper is called "Het Belgisch Raskonijn vzw," and I can only admire their efforts, especially for saving such breeds as the Blue of Ham, St. Nicholas Blue and the Stone rabbit.

440

Het Belgisch Raskonijn vzw
Mr. Reginald Deyaert, Secretary
Kattestraat 19, 9170 Sint-Gillis-Waas, Belgium
Phone 32 (o)3 770 65 13
Email: info@raskonijn.be
Web site: http://www.raskonijn.be

BRITISH RABBIT COUNCIL

England is, of course, the birthplace of the exhibition rabbit, having started with the first rabbit club in 1840, which was for the "Fancy rabbit" or Lop. On May 29th, 1918, in Birmingham, England, 17 people met to form a new organization, which was called "The Beveren Club." It was founded "in an endeavor to raise the dignity and status of rabbit breeding, and with the object of promoting the development and production of the best fur breeds." It was from this early beginning that began the British Rabbit Council.

Now it must be remembered that at this time there were very few fur breeds to be found in England. The Rex were yet still unknown, as were the Satins. The fact is, the only breeds which were granted standards in this organization and in the next year were the Beverens and Havanas. The third standard which was adopted was that of the Chinchilla, which was not until 1921.

As new breeds were developed or imported, the Beveren Club would adopt new standards for them. By the end of 1924, a number of breeds were being catered for by the Beveren Club, and it was at this time a proposal was issued to alter the name of the organization. This was done in early 1925, when the club became known as "The British Fur Rabbit Society," which incorporated the Beveren Club. While the first part of the name was fitting of the organization, the latter part was a bit cumbersome, which was later dropped. Further still, when the organization began recognizing all breeds, the word "Fur" was also removed.

The membership strengthened, and by 1928 standards were issued for 13 breeds, including Bleu Argente, Crème Argente, Champagne Argente, the Sables, both Marten and Siamese, Lilac, Beaver, and the New Zealand Red, along with those which the Beveren Club had already recognized.

Over 25 local and agricultural societies were affiliated by this time, as well as 21 specialty clubs. Championships, prefixes (stud names) and trade-

441

marks were being issued, along with trophies and other types of show support. The national governing body was making steady headway.

On November 26, 1927, a meeting was called by the Animal Breeding Research Department of Edinburgh University at the Freeman Hotel in Leicester. Dr. J.N. Pickard, who would later become secretary of the British Rabbit Council for many years, was working under the famous geneticist, Professor F.A.A. Crewe, at Edinburgh.

At this meeting some 40 people attended who were particularly interested in the formation of a Wool Test for Angoras. There was a great deal of interest in Angoras at this particular time, and people wanted to know more about the wool yield as controlled in part by the inheritance of the rabbit. It was hoped that a center could be established to set up and test the inherited qualities of the various strains of Angoras, which would greatly improve the yield of the breed. At this time the Animal Breeding Department of Edinburgh University was working on the inheritance of wool yield, among other tests conducted on rabbits.

There was a fairly good response to the idea of establishing the wool test center. Of the 96 breeders polled, 84 were in favor and four undecided. Of the 84 in favor, 53 had promised to enter their rabbits if a test was established. A number of meetings were called of the Wool Test Committee; however, for some reason or the other, no test were actually carried out. The Wool Test Committee called together an open meeting on March 15, 1928, in Birmingham.

Fur and Feather, the next week, stated, "The event will rank as historic in the annals of the rabbit, cavy, mouse and rat fanciers and industries." It would be right on the target.

The idea was to establish a national authority to cater to all small fur breeders. There was a great deal of discussion at this meeting, and a Formation Committee was formed to study and design the entire functions of the governing body. The Formation Committee consisted of ten people, who met in June of 1928. An open conference was called, which was held at the famous Bradford Championship Show the following January, when it was decided that the National Rabbit Council should be formed. Articles of Constitution were adopted at this time, and the second parent body of the British Rabbit Council was well on its way to becoming reality. Now it should be noted that the National Rabbit Council was not actually known by that name, but instead, the actual title was "National Rabbit Council of Great Britain and the Dominions." Many committees were recognized, such as: Commercial Wool Production, Commercial Meat Production, various scientific sub-committees, etc.

As with any national organization, much work is involved, and a great number of debates took place, as opinions greatly differed on various issues at hand. Arguments flared between the two national factions. One of the biggest opponents of the National Rabbit Council was Mr. E. C. Richardson, who would later do so much work for the British Rabbit Council. Years of strife existed between the two organization, and many attempts were made to fuse the organizations into one strong national governing body, which did not happen until October 1934. Representatives of the two organizations agreed unanimously to urge a merger at a joint meeting held in November 1934.

The merger meeting was successful, and thus was born the British Rabbit Council. It was then left to a conference between the newly elected representatives and the officers of the British Rabbit Council, along with delegates from all the national specialty clubs, to give the final approval to the entire idea. The response was overwhelming, as only three people voted against the new organization.

The ringing scheme of rabbits, as a method of identification, has always had a close association with the national bodies. The original authority that issued rings was the National Rabbit Marking Council, Ltd. This organization was composed of members elected during a meeting held in 1929. The meeting had been organized by the British Fur Rabbit Society, for the purpose of inaugurating a ringing scheme, and each member of it represented one or more of the national specialty clubs. There had been a great deal of discussion as to a unified system under one national governing body during the years just prior to World War I, yet no success was achieved. It was then agreed that as of September 1938, the British Rabbit Council should have its own ringing system, with *Fur & Feather* acting as agents for the distribution of the rings. In later years, the ringing scheme and its administration reverted to the British Rabbit Council in its entirety and remains so to this day.

The British Rabbit Council would see its greatest growth during the war years. At the end of 1939, the organization showed a membership of just 313 members and 72 affiliated societies. Because of the war, rabbit keeping became very popular as a food source, and the council would record a membership of 1,620 and 120 affiliates by the end of 1941. By the end of 1942, the membership totaled 5,570 persons and 679 affiliated clubs, and the peak year for memberships was reached in 1944 with 900 affiliates and 8,700 members. By the end of the war, the British Rabbit Council had grown to 28 times its pre-war size. It was only natural that there would be a drop in membership at the end of the war, and by 1947 the numbers were 4,100 members and 780 affiliated clubs. A peak again occurred in 1951, with 6,730 members and 840 clubs, and a decline in 1956 showed 3,830 members and 567 clubs.

During 1951, major changes in the British Rabbit Council would occur. Youth members were allowed at a reduced rate, and reduced membership fees for adults over 65. Persons who had reached the age of 70, with 10 years of continuous membership, did not have to pay.

Membership in the British Rabbit Council as of 2000 shows 3,509 individual members and 355 affiliated organization. Permanent headquarters for this national organization are:

British Rabbit Council
Purefoy House, 7 Kirkgate
Newark, Notts NG24 1AD ENGLAND
Phone 01636 676042
Email: info@thebrc.org
Wed site: http://www.thebrc.org

The official voice of the British Rabbit Council is *Fur & Feather* magazine, first published on Thursday, June 7, 1888, by Mr. J.E. Watmough.

An Illustrated Weekly Journal for Town and Country.

No. 583. Vol. XXIII. (OLD SERIES No. 683 Vol. XXIII)   THURSDAY, JULY 18, 1901.   (Post Free, 3/3 Half-yearly.)   ONE PENNY.

Founding Fathers of the British Rabbit Council

Left: James Read served as the first P,resident, a position he held longer than any other individual, 1935-1946.

Right: Thomas Leaver was the first Vice-President, serving longer than any other person, from the years 1935-1943. Leaver also developed the Opossum Rex in the late 1930s.

Left: F.C. Woodgate was one of the driving forces behind a national rabbit governing body for the United Kingdom, served many positions and authored several books.

Right: John C. Sandford served as Secretary of the BRC longer than any single individual, from 1950-1965, and authored a number of books.

Right: George Scott, celebrating the 100th anniversary of the UK Dutch Rabbit Club, was responsible for introducing a number of breeds in England, and one of the founding members of the Rare Varieties Club.

All photos courtesy of the archives of Fur & Feather.

445

Mr. and Mrs. J.E. Watmough, who founded Fur & Feather, circa 1930.

The publication was first issued in a newspaper form as a weekly, later to become a bi-weekly publication. Today *Fur & Feather* is a high-gloss color magazine, published monthly, which incorporates another publication called simply *Rabbits.*

Fur & Feather
Elder House, Chattisham
Ipswich, Suffolk IP8 3QE ENGLAND
Phone: 01473 652789 or 01473 652354
Email: furandfeather@btinternet.com
Web site: http://www.furandfeather.co.uk

FRENCH FEDERATION OF CUNICULICULTURE

The French Federation of Rabbit Breeding was founded in 1961 and is dedicated to all facets of rabbit keeping in France. This is a national governing body, with many regional, local and specialty clubs being affiliated. They maintain their own breed standards.

French Federation of Cuniculiculture
28 Street of the Rock, 75008, Paris, France
Web site: http://www.ffc.asso.fr

HOUSE RABBIT SOCIETY

The House Rabbit Society was founded in California in 1988, and today have over 8,000 members with numerous chapters throughout the United States, Canada, United Kingdom and Asia. This is a worthwhile organization which has adopted out some 10,000 rabbits since its founding. They have a rabbit rescue program, and spay or neuter each animal before it is adopted.

House Rabbit Society
148 Broadway, Richmond, California 94804
Phone: 510-970-7575 — Web site: http://www.rabbit.org

RABBIT COUNCIL OF NEW ZEALAND

For many years rabbits were outlawed in New Zealand, just as in Australia, due to the destruction which the European wild rabbit had caused for many years. It was only in 1979 that a total of six breeds were made legal in New Zealand on a commercial basis: Angora, Flemish Giants, New Zealand Whites, Standard Chinchilla, Rex and Californians which were all imported from America. In 1980 the Rabbit Council of New Zealand, Inc. was formed with 12 affiliated clubs. The government approved the importation of some fancy breeds in the mid-1980s from England, namely Tan, Silver Fox (Silver Martens), Dutch and Netherland Dwarfs. Then a huge interest began to develop by commercial rabbit farmers in the fiber trade, so imports of German and French Angoras were brought in from France and Germany. Further imports were approved in the early 1990s for Lop in the Miniature, Dwarf, Cashmere and French breeds, as well as Mini Rex, Satins and Harlequins, once again coming from the United Kingdom. When the Enderby Island rabbits were liberated from the sub Antarctic island of Enderby and made available to the general public, these too were recognized.

Since New Zealand is divided with a north and south island, the Rabbit Council of New Zealand holds two national conventions each year. They maintain their own standard, and their system of judging is based on the British System.

Rabbit Council of New Zealand
P.O. Box 56-285, Dominion Road
MT Eden, Auckland, New Zealand

447

SCANDINAVIAN COUNTRIES

Denmark, Finland, Norway and Sweden all have national rabbit organizations. One standard is pretty much recognized by all four countries, and judges are free to judge in any of these countries.

Denmark

Denmark's national rabbit association is called Kaninavierforening and was founded on March 6, 1895.

Web site: http://www.kaniner.dk

Finland

Web site: http://www.kaniyhdistys.com

Norway

Norges Kaninavisforbund is the national rabbit association of Norway, founded on November 6, 1897, in Kristiania. Their first show was at Drammen in 1901, and at the time there were already 4,500 members. It is reported that in 1929 at their national show, no less than 200,179 rabbits were entered. Note, I have not been able to substantiate these figures, which certainly seem extremely high, to say the least.

Web site: http://www.kanin-nkf.net

Sweden

Swedish national body is called Sveriges Kaninavelsforeningars Riksforbund and was founded February 23, 1919, in Stockholm. However, the first rabbit club in that country was founded in Malmo in 1908.

Web site: http://hem.passagen.se/kaninforbund/main.htm

This is but a very small sampling of all the national rabbit governing bodies of the world, but because of space it is just not possible to include them all. Countries such as Italy, Switzerland, Germany, Croatia, Belgium, Austria, Czechoslovakia, Holland and even Malta are just a few which have developed their own breed standards and promote rabbit keeping in their own countries. I find it amazing just how far reaching the domestic rabbit and all of its breeds have come in nearly 200 years for us all to enjoy, whether it is a single pet rabbit kept in an outside hutch, a playful companion in the form of a house bunny, or a barn full of rabbits. Rabbits have given man much pleasure and will continue long after into the future generations.

SOME LITTLE KNOWN FACTS ABOUT RABBITS

- First domesticated by monks.
- First considered as a food source by man in Asia, 3,000 years ago.
- Have been marketed in Europe for over 1,000 years.
- The country Spain translates to "Rabbit Coast."
- Eaten by the inhabitants of all the continents.
- Pope Gregory the Great ruled in 600 A.D. that rabbit could be eaten during Lent.
- Rabbits were the last type of livestock domesticated by man.
- Raised all over the world for meat, fur, fun, fancy and wool.
- Queen Elizabeth I kept rabbits.
- U.S. Government has spent large sums of money experimenting with rabbits.
- Raised in all 50 states and territories.
- In trying to produce a better meat rabbit, seven breeds were developed in U.S.
- Edward H. Stahl is the only person to make more than a million dollars from the sale of breeding stock in the 1920s to 1940s.
- Only 600 head of producing animals will provide full-time employment.
- Carl Linnaeus, the Father of Taxonomy, would describe the European Wild Rabbit, *Oryctolagus cuniculus,* in 1758, which is the species from which all breeds of domestic breeds evolved.
- Rabbit can be prepared more different ways than chicken and pork can be.
- Over 6,000 Belgian Hares were shipped to America from England in 1900 alone.
- The first picture of an Angora rabbit dates to 1757.
- The oldest living active rabbit judge ever is Oren Reynolds, at 98 years young.
- Youngest rabbit judge ever licensed is Debbie Corkum at 17 years old.
- Only American Judge to judge in all 50 States is Glen Carr.
- Longest continuous membership in America was Oscar Sennewald at 81 years.
- First woman to develop a breed: Mabel Illingworth, began in 1896 in England.
- There are two breeds of domestic rabbits that are not known as a rabbit, the Belgian Hare and the Miniature Hare (British Polish) of Europe.

- The most rabbits ever registered for a single breed was the Chinchilla with 17,328 during November 1928–November 1929.
- First pelletized rabbit feed appeared in 1930.
- The largest single litter produced by a rabbit on record was 26 with 24 living.
- Largest rabbit book ever written was in Berlin, Germany in 1942 at 660 pages.
- The most valuable book totally written about the domestic rabbits is from England by Kempster W. Knight, called the *Book of the Rabbit,* 1881, at $800.
- The longest time a person kept a single breed was 80 years, by a Mr. Mason from England with English Lops.
- Longest time for one person to keep rabbits was Walter Grunnet at 87 years.
- A one-eared rabbit was being bred in England in the late 16th century.
- World's ugliest breed of rabbit is the Furless.
- The earliest picture of a white rabbit dates to the 1300s by Gaston Phebus III, Count de Foix (1331-1391).
- The first Black & White rabbits were depicted in a German painting in 15th century.
- Strabo (19-64 A.D.) mentions shiploads of meat rabbits coming from Spain to the Roman markets.
- The Boy Scout Rabbit Merit Badge was adopted in November 1943.
- The largest rabbit ever registered in the USA was in April,1933, a White Flemish Giant doe named Rhodes' Gilroy Queen, weight 23-1/4 lbs at 10-1/2 months.
- The smallest rabbit ever registered has been five: four Netherland Dwarfs and one Britannia Petite, all weighing 1 pound each.
- There are more breeds of Lop eared rabbits than any other type known.
- World's longest eared rabbit, an American bred English Lop measuring 31.25 inches.
- The Himalayan rabbit has been known by more names than any other breed.
- Oldest continuous rabbit club in America is for the Flemish Giant, founded 1916.
- Oldest rabbit club in the world, United Kingdom Dutch Rabbit Club, began 1879.
- Longest continuous rabbit publication, *Fur & Feather,* founded June 7, 1888.

- Wool of the rabbit is lighter and warmer than any other wool.
- 93% of the rabbit can be used.
- 3,000,000 lbs. of rabbit meat was processed in San Diego Co., CA in 1970.
- One of the highest nutritional meats available.
- Rabbit meat is 20.8 % protein, 10.2% fat, 27.9 moisture, and 795 calories per lb., which beat chicken, veal, turkey, beef, lamb and pork.
- Only 7 to 8% of domestic rabbit is bone.
- Domestic rabbits have no communicable disease injurious to man.
- The glue used on the back of postage stamps is made from rabbit.
- Most felt hats are made from rabbit fur.
- Domestic rabbit is ALL white meat.
- The purest breed of rabbit genetically is the Enderby Island Rabbit.
- Rabbit feet have been omens of gook luck for hundreds of years.
- Rabbit manure is one of the world's best — high in nitrogen and will not burn.
- Rabbits were deemed the most dependable as a pregnancy test.
- The only animal that will produce 10 times its own weight in a year.
- May be eaten year round and are non-heat flushing.
- Have never been known to carry Tularemia or Rabies.
- They are the cleanest vegetarians.
- Rabbits can be bred all year round.
- A good Angora can produce over a kilo (2-1/4 lb) of wool per year.
- Angora rabbit wool is the highest selling of the typical wool breeds.
- The heaviest rabbit on record is a Flemish Giant bought in Holland, at 16 kg or 35.274 lbs.
- Highest price ever paid for a single rabbit was $5,000.
- Highest price ever paid for a meat pen of three rabbits to be eaten was $15,000.
- There are 45 recognized breeds in America and over 180 world-wide.
- There are over 60 extinct breeds of rabbits.
- The first Rabbit Club ever founded was in England for Lops in 1840.
- The world's largest collection of publications dealing with rabbits in the English language is owned by the American Rabbit Breeders Association Hall of Fame Library in Bloomington, Illinois.
- A national governing body for all breeds of rabbits was founded on January 10, 1910 in the U.S .and is now known as the American Rabbit Breeders Association with 31,000 plus membership.

COLOR PHOTO ACKNOWLEDGEMENTS

The author would like the thank the following organizations and people for allowing me to use their photographs for this book:

AMERICAN RABBIT BREEDERS ASSOCIATION, USA — American, Lops; American Fuzzy, English, French, Holland, Mini, Angora; English, French, Giant, Satin, Beveren, Britannia Petite, Californian, D'Argent; Champagne, Crème, Checkered Giant, Chinchilla; American, Giant, Standard, Cinnamon, Dutch, Dwarf Hotot, Florida White, Harlequin Magpie, Havana, Jersey Wooly, Lilac, New Zealand, Palomino, Polish, Rex, Mini Rex, Rhinelander, Satin, Silver, Silver Fox, Silver Marten, Tan.

BRITISH RABBIT COUNCIL, UK — Alaska, Argente Brun, Belgian Hare (Red), Deilenaar, English Spot, Harlequin Japanese, Himalayan, Lop; Cashmere, German, Meissener, Miniature Cashmere, Harlequin Dutch, British Flemish Giant, Golden Glavcot, Netherland Dwarf, Pointed Beveren, Sallander, Siberian, Smoke Pearl, Squirrel, Thrianta, Thuringer, Vienna, Vienna White, Wheaten, Astrex, and Opossum Rex.

Het BELGISCH RASKONIJN VZW and members, Belgium — Flemish Giant, Reginald Deyaert - Belgium Silver, Johan Van Hyfte - Ham Blue, David Muyldermans - Pearl Grey of Halle, Willy Kreydt - Stone, Marc Vancayzeele - White Termonde.

KANINUPPFODAREN, Sweden — Kanel.

SCHWEIZERISCHER RASSEKANANINCHENZUCHT VERBAND, Switzerland — Czeck Spot, Petit Papillon Tricolor, Perlfee, and Swiss Fox.

ZENTRALVERBAND DEUTSCHER RASSEKANINCHENZUECHER, Germany — Hermelin, Jamora, Mecklenburger Scheck, Rhoen, Sachengold, Schwarzgrannen, Kathleen Blair, USA - Brazilian, Yolanda Bortels, Belgium - Dwarf Angora, Loretta Bowman, USA - Micro Rex, Jacques Czsechan, France - Lutterbach, John Daniels, England - Sussex, Reinhard Danninger, Austria - Giant Papillon, Mike Dettmann, USA - Mini Satin, Warren Hill, Australia - Mini Satin Rex, Lenka Kadeoabkova, Czechoslovakia - Moravien Blue, Czech Albin, Dr. Steven Lukefahr, USA - Altex, Furless, Sofie Lundhus, Denmark - Vit Land, Ruth Morris, England - British Giant, Jean Claude and Pierre Periquet, France - Argente Saint Hubert, Blanc de Hotot,Blanc de Vendee, Bourbonnais Grey, Brown Chestnut of Lorraine, Chinchilla Giganta, Dwarf Rex, Dwarf Lop Rex, Fauve de Bourgogne, Fee de Marbourg, Giant Blanc du Bouscat, Large Himalayan, Normand, Michael Ratajczak, Germany - Little Silver Bright, Large Silver, Sitereh Schouten, New Zealand - Enderby Island, Carl Aage Sorensen, Denmark - Lutino, Dr. Zsolt Szendro, Hungary - Pannon, Pauline Taylor, New Zealand - Mini English Angora, Tom Twining, USA - Lionhead, Franz-Josef Wissing, Germany - Little Silver, Nacera Zerrouki, Algeria - Kabyle.

HISTORIC RABBIT ART REPRODUCTIONS

The author has made available all illustrations in this book for those individuals who may already or would like to start collecting rabbit art. These prints are reproduced on quality card stock in full color or, if the print is black and white, these are reproduced in archival (sepia) tones. Each print measures 8 x 11 inches, ready for your favorite frame. These prints are beautiful for any room of the house or office and make wonderful gifts or show awards.

The Ernest George Wippell collection has a total of 15 prints in gorgeous full color.

All prints should be ordered by page number and title.

Pricing:
    1 to 10 prints, $7.00 each
    11 to 20 prints, $6.00 each
    Over 20 prints, $5.00 each

Shipping & Handling: 1 to 10 prints, $3.00 US or $6.00 International
                          11 to 20 prints, $6.00 US or $12.00 International
                          Over 20 prints, $12.00 US or $20.00 International

All sales are in U.S. funds only. Make check or money order payable to:
Bob Whitman
2355 Rusk St.
Beaumont, Texas 77702-2454 USA
http://www.rarebitsandpieces.com
rarebits@ev1.net

Visa and MasterCard are also accepted through my PayPal account at:
    www.paypal.com   (account = **rarebits@ev1.net**)

ADD A LITTLE MORE RABBIT HISTORY TO YOUR HOME TODAY!

BREED INDEX

THE END